A Computer Approach to
Introductory College Mathematics

A
Computer
Approach to
Introductory College Mathematics

Frank Scalzo

Queensborough Community College
City University of New York

Rowland Hughes

Fordham University, Lincoln Center
New York City

PETROCELLI / CHARTER

NEW YORK 1977

First Printing

Printed in the United States of America

Library of Congress Cataloging in Publication Data

Scalzo, Frank, 1941–
    A computer approach to introductory college mathematics.

    Includes index.
    1. Mathematics—1961–   2. Mathematics—
Data processing.   I. Hughes, Rowland, 1935–
joint author.   II. Title.
QA39.2.S287   512.9'0028'54   77-486
ISBN 0-88405-434-9

For Anne and Madeline

Contents

3

Systems of Linear Equations and Inequalities

4

Introduction to the Foundations of Mathematics

5

Sophisticated Counting, Probability, and Related Prepackaged Computer Programs

6

Descriptive Statistics and Related Computer Programs

Appendices

Prepackaged Computer Programs

Preface

This textbook is designed to offer a practical alternative to undergraduate courses in introductory college mathematics. It is easily read and uses an intuitive approach to the solving of practical problems.

The authors have presented flowcharting, the BASIC programming language, and the use of time-sharing computer terminals to students who have completed intermediate algebra. Furthermore, they have endeavored to guide the student in writing original BASIC programs to solve practical elementary mathematics problems. Prepackaged computer programs with detailed flowcharts are presented as tools to solve more advanced problems.

This textbook covers the BASIC programming language; the use of computer terminals; topics from elementary, intermediate, and advanced algebra; an introduction to matrix algebra and linear programming; symbolic logic; Boolean algebra, and switching algebra; sophisticated counting and probability; and selected topics from elementary statistics.

The student will find in the Appendices a set of advanced programming projects with wide applicability; explanations of additional BASIC programming statements and functions; and comprehensive lists of common BASIC programming statements, commands, predefined functions, and error messages.

The authors have chosen to place exercises at the end of each important concept so that students can gradually build their competence through solving applicable problems.

Frank Scalzo
Rowland Hughes

Acknowledgments

The authors gratefully acknowledge permission from the following companies for the photographs used in this book:

Teletype Corporation, Skokie, Illinois, for photographs of a computer terminal, its keyboard, and its paper tape unit;

Anderson Jacobson, Inc., Sunnyvale, California, for the photograph of an acoustic coupler.

The authors wish to thank Professor Michael Brozinsky of Queensborough Community College, City University of New York, for his careful reading of the text, many helpful suggestions, and for the use of his prepackaged ECHELON and SIMPLEX programs; and Dr. Anne Hughes of St. John's University, Jamaica, New York, for her constructive criticism.

Our appreciation and gratitude are extended also to Muriel Smith for her assistance in typing, and to Lori Ann Reinhard for her work with the computer programs.

Especially, we thank Malcolm Mills, whose expertise in typing, suggestions concerning format and text clarity, and patience proved invaluable.

Suggestions to the Instructor

During the past two decades we have become a computer-oriented society. In the 1950s colleges and universities used the computer primarily for research and administrative purposes, but the computer was soon to be assimilated into education as a tool of instruction. Within the relatively short span of twenty years, nearly all institutions of higher learning have come to provide computing services for both classroom instruction and research.

Computers are now being used by educators in the instruction of mathematics, physics, chemistry, biology, medicine, business, environmental health, electrical technology, mechanical technology, and social science. The close relationship of computer science and mathematics suggests that an introductory course in college mathematics would be made more relevant if the use of computers were an integral part of the course.

The purpose of this text is to integrate the use of computers with the standard topics presented in an introductory college mathematics course. More specifically, the authors have attempted (1) to introduce students to the BASIC programming language; (2) to guide students in the use of BASIC for writing original programs; (3) to illustrate the use of prepackaged computer programs as a practical tool in the solution of comprehensive mathematical problems; and (4) to provide a greater understanding of the development and use of the foundations of mathematics.

In Chapter 1 the authors illustrate five steps in the development of original computer programs: flowcharting, coding, inputting, processing programs, and debugging. They further suggest that the instructor stress the use of flowcharting throughout the course as a useful tool in the development of mathematical procedures.

For example, after discussing how to decide whether a natural number is prime by illustrating a number of examples in class, the students might construct the following flowchart:

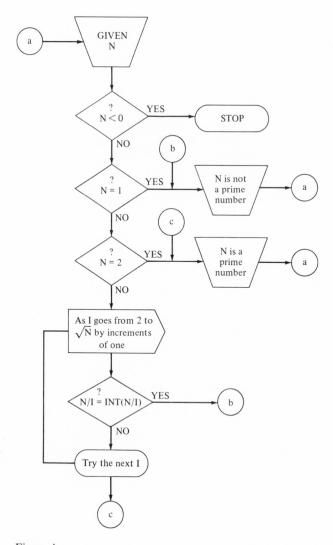

Figure A

The instructor could now guide the students in coding this flowchart in BASIC and running the program to test larger values of N.

Many of the mathematical topics in this text may be presented in the following order: (1) doing manual calculations, (2) writing an original BASIC program, (3) using a prepackaged computer program. For example, after evaluating functions manually, the instructor could direct students to write a BASIC program, such as the following one:

```
10 PRINT "T","T↑3-4*T"
20 FOR T=-3 TO 3 STEP0.5
30    PRINT T,T↑3-4*T
40 NEXT T
50 END

RUN
T                  T↑3-4*T
-3                 -15
-2.5               -5.625
-2                 0
-1.5               2.625
-1                 3
-.5                1.875
0                  0
.5                 -1.875
1                  -3
1.5                -2.625
2                  0
2.5                5.625
3                  15

*READY
```

Later the students can use the prepackaged program in Chapter 2 which searches for maximum and minimum values of a function defined on an interval.

In Chapter 3 the students can write original BASIC programs to solve any two by two system of linear equations or any three by three system via determinants. They can then use the prepackaged program ECHELON to solve an *m* by *n* system of linear equations, or employ the prepackaged program SIMPLEX to solve linear programming problems.

Each prepackaged program consists of an instruction sheet, a flowchart, and coding in the BASIC programming language. The instruction sheet gives the program name, a brief description of purpose, and a sample run of the prepackaged program. To use a prepackaged computer program the student simply must load the program into his user's space (by program name); enter the data to solve a specific problem; command the computer to run the program with the given data; and interpret the computer output. It is important that the student fully understands the mathematical procedure before he uses a prepackaged computer program. The student must be able to read a mathematical problem, extract the given data from the problem, decide which prepackaged program to use, and follow the instructions for using the program.

This text contains eleven prepackaged programs used as practical tools in the solution of mathematical problems related to the study of functions, metrication, systems of linear equations, linear programming, probability, and elementary statistics.

Chapter 4 includes presentations of symbolic logic, set theory, and switching (computer) algebra. The relationship of the rules of symbolic logic and set theory, as well as that of set theory and switching algebra, is used to give a practical application of symbolic logic. Too often throughout an introductory college mathematics course students wonder what is the purpose of studying symbolic logic.

In Chapter 5 the instructor will find that the relationship of set theory and probability is explained informally. A number of prepackaged programs are used to facilitate the study of probability and combinatorial mathematics.

An introduction to descriptive statistics is offered in Chapter 6. Prepackaged computer programs are used to solve problems in descriptive statistics, as well as those involving standard normal curve approximations.

While the completion of Chapters 1 through 6 is desirable, it is not always feasible in a one-semester introductory college mathematics course. Some practical course guidelines are offered as follows:

1) *Business Majors*: Chapters 1, 2 (2.6–2.11), 4, 5 (5.1–5.11), 6 (6.1–6.5)

2) *Liberal Arts Majors*: Chapters 1, 2 (2.1–2.8), 4, 5, 6

3) *Technical (Electrical, Mechanical) Majors*: Chapters 1, 2 (2.6–2.11), 3 (3.1–3.7), 5, 6, 7, Appendices (A, D, E, F)

4) *Social Science Majors*: Chapters 1, 2 (2.6–2.11), 3, 4, 6.

1

Understanding the Use of Computers

1.1

Introduction

During the past two decades we have become a computer-oriented society. The introduction of programming languages such as FORTRAN and BASIC has made the computer more readily adaptable to the work of education, economics, finance, and medicine, as well as mathematics and science. The use of the computer has opened the door for ready accomplishment of complicated statistical studies not previously feasible. Programming instructions are presented throughout this text in the BASIC language because it is easily learned and conveniently used in time sharing on computer terminals.

1.2

Steps in Computer Problem Solving

How does a person use a computer to solve problems? The answer to this question need not remain a mystery to the general public. The computer is not a genius; it is an idiot waiting to be told what to do. Let us look at the five steps one should follow in order to use a computer to solve problems.

1. *Flowcharting*: After the problem has been clearly defined, the programmer should construct a flowchart. A flowchart is a diagram of the step-by-step procedure the computer must follow to solve the problem. That is, what do you want the computer to do first, second, . . . , last?

1

2. *Coding*: The second step is to translate this flowchart into a machine language or a compiler language program—a series of statements which instructs or directs the computer to perform a specific task. The only language the computer can understand is the binary (machine) language. In the binary language, all numbers, instructions, and commands must be written using only two symbols, 0 and 1. Writing in the binary language requires the utmost precision. Other programming languages such as BASIC, FORTRAN, and COBOL are constructed to resemble and adapt to the languages used in certain sciences or professions. For example, the computer language used throughout this text is BASIC (Beginner's All-Purpose Symbolic Instruction Code), which is easily learned and applied to the solution of problems in mathematics and the physical sciences. Any programming language other than the binary language is called a "compiler" language. When we feed our BASIC language program to the computer, a binary language program (the compiler), which is stored in the computer's memory, will translate our BASIC language program into a binary language program. Then the computer can execute our program.

3. *Inputting*: The third step is to put our program on some device so as to feed it to the machine. These devices will be discussed when computer terminals are introduced later in this chapter.

4. *Running*: The fourth step is to have the computer run through the steps of our program and (we hope) give us the results we are looking for.

5. *Debugging*: Very few original programs will run smoothly the first time. Therefore, the fifth and final step is to find the errors, and run the program again. A person should not get discouraged when a program does not run. It should be a challenge to find and correct the errors.

1.3

Flowcharting

There are many standard symbols used in flowcharting, but only a few are necessary for the topics covered in this textbook. This article describes those we will use.

INPUT

In order to show that we want the computer to accept some numerical or alphabetic data, we use the following symbol:

Suppose we wanted to show that the computer must read a value for A, B, and C. This is illustrated in your flowchart as

ORDER OF STEPS

The arrow used in the symbol represents the flow of the program. That is, in the illustration above, if we want to know what the computer must do next after reading values for A, B, and C, we follow the arrow.

ARITHMETIC STATEMENTS

In order to show that we want to compute the value of some variable (on the left side of the equation), given the computer already knows the values of any variables on the right side of the equation, we will use the following symbol:

Suppose, after reading values for A, B, and C, we want the machine to compute $3A + 2B$ and store it in a place called X, then compute $3X + A^2$ and store it in a place called Y, then compute $A + Y$ and store it in the place reserved for A. This sequence is illustrated in Figure 1.1.

Figure 1.1

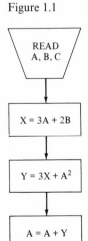

Note: An arithmetic statement like $A = A + Y$ may appear in a flowchart. Moreover, this may appear when $Y \neq 0$. Use of such a statement leads us to the discussion of the $=$ sign in computer programming. When the computer knows the value of A and B, and we tell it to compute $X = 3A + 2B$, it will store the value of $3A + 2B$ in a place called X. However, if the computer has the value of 2 stored in a place called A and the value of 3 stored in a place called Y, and we tell it to compute $A = A + Y$, the $=$ sign means "is replaced by." That is, the old $A = 2$ is replaced by the new $A = 2 + 3 = 5$. Therefore, the 2 stored in a place called A is erased and replaced with 5.

The memory of a computer might be compared with the work of a tape recorder. What happens if a song is recorded on a certain length of tape and you play it back at a later date? The song is repeated. Now, what happens if you record another song on the same length of tape? As you know, the first song is erased and the new song takes its place.

DECISIONS

In order to show that we want the computer to make a decision or test the value of some arithmetic expression, we use the following symbol:

For example, consider the previous illustration in which we want the machine to read values of A, B, and C, then compute values for $X = 3A + 2B$, $Y = 3X + A^2$, and replace A with $A + Y$. Now suppose what we do next depends on whether A is less than zero. Our flowchart is illustrated in Figure 1.2. As you can see, this diamond-shaped symbol allows you to express a desire to branch to two different locations in your program after testing to find whether A is less than zero.

OUTPUT

The symbol for showing that we want specific results given to us is the same as the symbol for input. If we want the computer to print out the values stored in A, B, C, X, and Y, we write:

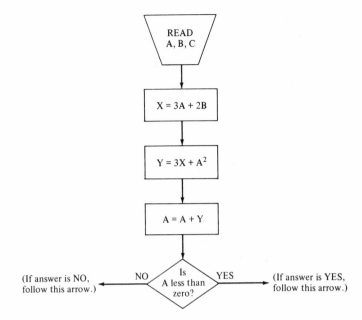

Figure 1.2

UNCONDITIONAL BRANCH (CONNECTOR)

If the programmer desires to break the natural order of steps in a flowchart, he will use the symbol

where "a" is *any letter of the alphabet.* This symbol will also appear elsewhere in the flowchart to express a desire to branch unconditionally ahead to another step in the program or to return unconditionally to a previous step in the program. See Figure 1.3.

TERMINAL

In order to show that we want the computer to stop executing our program, we write

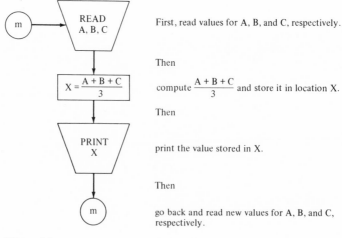

First, read values for A, B, and C, respectively.

Then

compute $\dfrac{A+B+C}{3}$ and store it in location X.

Then

print the value stored in X.

Then

go back and read new values for A, B, and C, respectively.

Figure 1.3

Figure 1.4

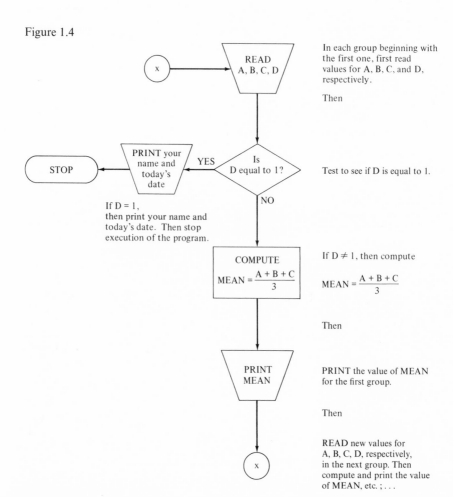

In each group beginning with the first one, first read values for A, B, C, and D, respectively.

Then

Test to see if D is equal to 1.

If D = 1, then print your name and today's date. Then stop execution of the program.

If D ≠ 1, then compute

$$MEAN = \dfrac{A+B+C}{3}$$

Then

PRINT the value of MEAN for the first group.

Then

READ new values for A, B, C, D, respectively, in the next group. Then compute and print the value of MEAN, etc. ; . . .

6

1.4

Sample Flowcharts

Given: A,B,C,D,; A,B,C,D,; . . . , a collection of groups of four numbers, one group of four at a time, where all D are zero except the last (D=1). For example, suppose we have 95,52,27,0; 77,82,51,0; 75,83,91,0; 0,0,0,1.

Wanted: A flowchart (Figure 1.4) that will process four numbers at a time and either

1. compute and print out MEAN = (A+B+C)/3 if D=0, or
2. print out your name and today's date if D=1. That is, the value of D will tell the computer whether to compute the *mean* of A, B, and C, *or* stop executing the program.

Now construct a flowchart (Figure 1.5) to compute and print out SUM = $1+3+5+7+ \cdots +10001$. That is, have the machine compute and print out the sum of these odd counting numbers.

Figure 1.5

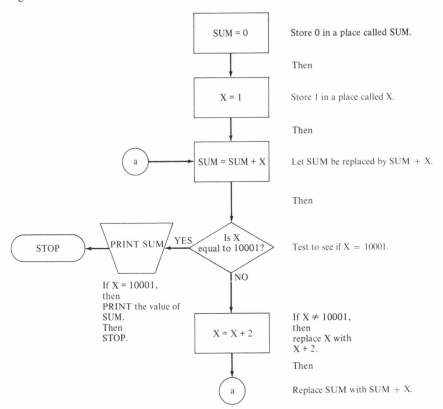

The computer will generate the final sum as follows

SUM	X
0	1
1	3
$1+3$	5
$(1+3)+5$	7
$\vdots$	$\vdots$
$(1+3+5+\cdots+9997)+9999$	10001
$(1+3+5+\cdots+9999)+10001$	

It is very important to note that flowcharts may be constructed in more than one way to solve the same problem. To illustrate this possibility, consider the alternate flowchart (Figure 1.6) for this same example, $\text{SUM}=1+3+5+\cdots+10001$.

In Figure 1.5, the computer tested for $X=10001$ to decide when to print the SUM, since the incrementing of X by 2 is done *after* the testing. Therefore, when the computer tests X and finds it equal to 10001, it has already been added to the SUM.

In Figure 1.6 the computer tested for $X=10003$ to decide when to print the SUM, since the incrementing of X by 2 was done *before* the testing. Therefore, when the computer tests X and finds it equal to 10001, it has not yet been added to the SUM.

Figure 1.6

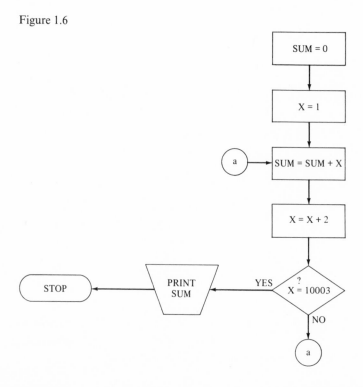

Problem Set 1.1

1. Construct a flowchart that can be used to write a program to print out a table of values for X and X^2, where X = 1,2,3,...,10.

2. *Given*: NAME, AGE, NAME, AGE, NAME, AGE, ..., NAME, AGE.
   Wanted: A flowchart that can be used to write a program to read each NAME and AGE, and print out a list of names and ages for people younger than 30.

3. Revise the flowchart in Problem 2 so as to print out a list of names and ages for people older than 50 and for people between the ages of 30 and 50.

4. Construct a flowchart that can be used to write a program to compute and print out

   $$SUM = \frac{2+4+ \cdots +782}{97}$$

5. Construct a flowchart to compare two numbers and print them out in numerical order. That is,
   Given: A,B,A,B, ..., A,B
   Wanted: A flowchart that will take each A and B in the order given, compare them, and then print out the numbers from smallest to largest.
       For example, given 3,6,4,1,2,1,4,4,−9,−8,−62,−100.

   Desired Output

3	6
1	4
1	2
4	4
−9	−8
−100	−62

1.5

Coding in the BASIC Language

The following table contains some of the symbols for operations and relations in BASIC:

Symbol	Example	Meaning
+	R+T	The sum of R and T
−	R−T	Subtract T from R
*	R*T	Multiply R by T
/	R/T	Divide R by T
↑	T↑3	Raise T to the third power
=	R=T	R is equal to T
>	R>T	R is greater than T
<	R<T	R is less than T
>=	R>=T	R is greater than or equal to T
<=	R<=T	R is less than or equal to T
<>	R<>T	R is not equal to T

Internal Functions

An internal function is one whose meaning has been incorporated in the BASIC compiler. The following expressions are some internal functions that can be evaluated, given the proper argument R. The argument R is the value you place in the parentheses and which the computer is to use when applying the function's rule.

Function	Meaning	Example
SIN(R)	Find the sine of R radians	SIN(0.5321)
COS(R)	Find the cosine of R radians	COS(0.8104)
TAN(R)	Find the tangent of R radians	TAN(0.7110)
ABS(R)	Find the absolute value of R	ABS(-3)
ATN(R)	Find the arctangent of R	ATN(1)
SQR(R)	Find the square root of R	SQR(57.23)
INT(R)	Find the largest integer less than or equal to R	INT(27.2)
LOG(R)	Find the natural log of R	LOG(23.3)
EXP(R)	Find the natural exponent of R(e^R)	EXP(3)
SGN(R)	Assumes the value	$\begin{cases} +1 \text{ if } R>0 \\ 0 \text{ if } R=0 \\ -1 \text{ if } R<0 \end{cases}$

Simple Variables

In BASIC a simple variable is named by a single letter or a single letter followed by a single digit. For example:

Acceptable variables: T, A, X3, B6
Unacceptable variables: SUM, X97, TAVERAGE

Numerical Constants

In most BASIC compilers numerical constants may contain from one to seven significant digits.

Example	Written in BASIC
-55.34	-55.34
32.333333	32.33333
0.000000237	$2.37E-7=(2.37)(10^{-7})$
295,000,000	$2.95E+8=(2.95)(10^8)$

Suppose we had a number that consisted of more than seven significant digits, such as

123.45674   or   123.45678

Some computers would truncate (chop off) the extra digits, while other computers would round off to the nearest significant digit. For example:

Number	Truncate to 7 Sig. Digits	Round Off to 7 Sig. Digits
123.45674	123.4567	123.4567
123.45678	123.4567	123.4568

Rounding Off Errors

In the manual calculation of $(3/7) \cdot 14$, we get an exact answer of 6. If a computer allows for six-digit accuracy, the internal calculation of $(3/7)*14$ will be executed as follows: $(3/7)*14 = 0.428571*14 = 5.99999$. We cannot therefore expect the computer to print out exact answers for every internal calculation.

Natural Order of Steps

When a program is run on a computer, the computer will execute the first executable statement first, the second executable statement second, and so on until the last executable statement is executed, unless one of the statements is a command to branch out from this sequence. In a BASIC program, each statement must be numbered. The statements must be numbered in ascending order, from smallest to largest. When the programmer numbers the statements, he usually does not number the steps of the program consecutively because in many instances he may have inadvertently omitted required steps in the program. The nonconsecutiveness of the numbering of the steps will allow him, if necessary, to type in the omitted steps at the end of the program.

THE END STATEMENT

The last statement in any BASIC programming must be the END statement.

General Form: Line number END; for example, 100 END. One way to have the computer stop executing a program is to direct it to execute the END statement.

THE STOP STATEMENT

Most BASIC compilers will not accept more than one END statement. If you want the computer to stop executing a program before it reaches the END, or last statement in the program, you can use the STOP statement.

General Form: Line number STOP (for example, 75 STOP).

OUTPUT

In BASIC we use the PRINT statement to obtain numerical values stored in the computer's memory or to direct the computer to print out symbols contained on its keyboard.

General Form	Example
Line number PRINT expression, expression, . . .	5 PRINT A,B2,X
Line number PRINT "symbols," "symbols," . . .	27 PRINT "HELLO IT'S ME"
Line number PRINT "symbols," "expressions," . . .	52 PRINT "T = ",T

Let us consider the following BASIC programs.

	BASIC Program	Output	Comments
(a)	2 PRINT "HELLO" 4 END	HELLO	The computer will print out the symbols within the quotation marks.
(b)	5 PRINT 2+3, 3−5 10 END	5 −2	The computer will perform calculations in the PRINT statement. If we use a comma between different desired outputs, the computer will skip a definite number of spaces, dependent on the BASIC compiler used. Many BASIC compilers will skip 15 spaces if a comma is used.

BASIC Program	Output	Comments
(c) 5 PRINT $2+3$; $3-5$ 8 END	5 -2	The computer will skip a definite number of spaces between different output if a semicolon is used. Many BASIC compilers will skip 7 spaces if a semicolon is used.

(d) 5 PRINT $2+3$
     10 PRINT $3-5$
     15 END
	5
	-2
		The computer will return the carriage before printing when it executes another PRINT statement.

(e) 11 PRINT "SUM1=$\,$"; $2+3$ 13 PRINT "SUM2=$\,$"; $3-5$	SUM1=5 SUM2=-2	Symbols and numerical values can be outputted using the same PRINT statement.

(f) 15 PRINT "SUM1=$\,$"$2+3$; "SUM2=$\,$"$3-5$
     20 END
     OUTPUT: SUM1=5   SUM2=-2

It is important to note that 5 PRINT "T" commands the computer to print out the *symbol* T, while 5 PRINT T commands the computer to print out the *numerical value* stored in a location called T.

Problem Set 1.2

1. Write a BASIC program to print out your name and today's date on the same line.

2. Write a BASIC program to print out your name and today's date on separate lines.

3. Write a BASIC program to print out your name, date of birth, and age on separate lines.

THE LET STATEMENT

In BASIC we use the LET statement to represent an arithmetic statement, which allows us to compute and store the numerical value of some variable.

General Form: Line number LET variable = arithmetic expression. Before we consider some examples, remember that the algebraic expressions

$$x + y, x - y, xy, \frac{x}{y}, x^3$$

are written

$$X+Y, X-Y, X*Y, X/Y, X\uparrow 3$$

in the BASIC language.

Arithmetic Statement	Written in BASIC
$a = 3 + 2$	5 LET A = 3 + 2
$c = 2 - \dfrac{5}{x}$	8 LET C = 2 − 5/X
$z = 5 + 7 - 9^4$	29 LET Z = 5 + 7 − 9↑4
$x = 3a + 2c$	91 LET X = 3*A + 2*C
$y = 3x^2 - 5x + 7$	21 LET Y = 3*X↑2 − 5*X + 7
$Average = (T + R + S)/3$	88 LET A = (T + R + S)/3
$t_2 = \sqrt{957.22}$	11 LET T2 = SQR(957.22)
$t_3 = \sin x$	13 LET T3 = SIN(X)

Note: There is only one variable to the left of the equals sign. Do not use a LET statement in a program unless all the variables on the right side of the equation have been previously defined. Also, the following hierarchy of five algebraic operations must be adhered to when writing your LET statement.

1. All work inside parentheses.

2. Raising to a power.

3. One-term operation (take the negative of an expression $-(+2) = -2$, $-(-2) = 2$).

4. Multiplication or division.

5. Addition or subtraction.

Now let us consider the following BASIC programs:

BASIC Program	Output	Comments
(a) 2 LET T = 5 4 LET R = 7 6 LET S = 9 8 LET A = T + R + S/3 10 PRINT A 12 END	15	The computer first divided the value of S by 3, and then added the values of T and R.
(b) 2 LET T = 5 4 LET R = 7 6 LET S = 9 8 LET A = (T + R + S)/3 10 PRINT A 12 END	7	The computer first added the values of T, R, and S, and then divided by 3.

Problem Set 1.3

Write LET statements for each of the following:

(a) $x = 5 - 2^3$

(b) $y = 2 - 17^3 + \dfrac{27}{101}$

(c) $T = \dfrac{8 + 7^2}{21}$

(d) $SUM = A + B - 3C^2$

(e) $AVERAGE = \dfrac{T1 + T2 + T3 + T4}{4}$

(f) $Y = \sqrt{57.321}$

(g) $CURVE = \sin x + 3 \cos y$

(h) $FUNCTION = 2\sqrt{x^2 - 1} + 2x - 7$

(i) $SNOOPY = 2 + 7 - 3^3 + \sqrt{94}$

(j) $HOBO = 1^2 + 3^2 + 5^2 + 7^2 + 9^2$

2. Write a BASIC program to compute and print out the variables T, Y, SNOOPY, and HOBO defined in Problem 1.

Input

In BASIC we have two different statements which allow us to send data into the computer's memory. One statement is the READ statement, which requires an additional DATA statement. The other statement is the INPUT statement, which does not require another statement.

GENERAL FORMS

Line number READ variable, variable . . . ;
Line number INPUT variable, variable, ...

Examples:

    5   READ A,B,C2
  29 INPUT X,Y3

Note: Every READ statement requires a DATA statement.

GENERAL FORM

Line number DATA number, number, ...

Example:

  77 DATA 5,2,3, − 7,14.51,27.1

Note: The DATA statement may appear anywhere in a BASIC program except that it cannot be the last statement in any program (END statement must be the last statement) and it cannot be the first statement in some programs (programs requiring a DIM statement). The DATA statement is a nonexecutable statement; that is, it does not command the computer to perform any internal operation. The DATA statement is used primarily as a place to store numbers.

Example:

Output
———

```
 5   READ A,B,C2
10   LET Y = A + B + C2
15   PRINT "SUM = "Y        SUM = 8
20   DATA 1,3,4
25   END
```

The INPUT statement does not require a DATA statement. When the computer executes the INPUT statement in a BASIC program, it will ask the programmer to type in a numerical value for each of the variables in the INPUT statement. Sample programs using the INPUT statement will be illustrated later.

The GO TO Statement

In BASIC we use the GO TO statement for an *unconditional branch* to a certain line in the program.

GENERAL FORM

Line number GO TO line number.

Example:

```
15   GO TO 97
```

When the computer executes line 15, it will branch to and execute line 97 next.

The IF-THEN Statement

In BASIC we use the IF-THEN statement for a *conditional branch* to a certain line number in the program.

GENERAL FORM

Line number IF expression relation expression THEN line number.

Examples:

1. 5   IF X=999 THEN 27; that is, if X=999, the computer will execute line 27 next. If X≠999, the computer will next execute the line immediately following line 5.

2. 12   IF T+R<=A+27 THEN 100; that is, if T+R is less than or equal to A+27, the computer will execute line 100 next. If T+R is greater than A+27, the computer will next execute the line immediately following line 12.

SAMPLE PROBLEM

Wanted: a BASIC program (Figure 1.7) to print out the even integers from 2 to 12 and their squares.

Solution

		Output	
10	LET X=2		
12	PRINT X; X↑2	2	4
14	LET X=X+2	4	16
16	IF X<=12 THEN 12	6	36
18	END	8	64
		10	100
		12	144

Figure 1.7

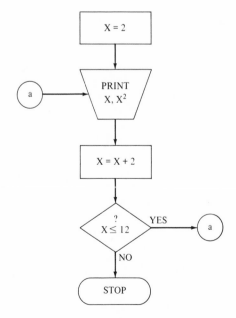

The FOR and NEXT Statements

Any BASIC program that involves initializing a variable at some numerical value and incrementing the variable by some set number until it reaches some maximum value can make use of the FOR and NEXT statements.

GENERAL FORM

Line number FOR j=m to n STEP r (j is a simple variable; m,n,r are constants, variables, or expressions), where m is the initial value for j, n is the maximal value for j, and r is the increment.

Example:

5   FOR X=2 TO 12 STEP 2

Note: Every FOR statement requires a NEXT statement.

GENERAL FORM

Line number NEXT variable; j is a simple variable.

Example:

20   NEXT X

Consider the following general program:

```
 5   FOR j=m to n STEP r
10   ········
15   ········
20   ········
25   NEXT j
```

where 10, 15, 20 are any executable statements.

The computer would execute statements 10, 15, 20 with j=m; then execute statements 10, 15, 20 with j=m+r; then execute statements 10, 15, 20 with j=m+2r, etc., until it executes statements 10, 15, 20 with j=n; then and only then will the computer execute the next statement after line 25. This procedure, by which the computer executes the same sequence of steps more than once in the same program, is called *looping*.

For example, let us consider the program in the sample problem for the IF-THEN statement.

		Output	
10	LET X=2	2	4
12	PRINT X; X$\uparrow$2	4	16
14	LET X=X+2	6	36
16	IF X<=12 THEN 12	8	64
18	END	10	100
		12	144

This could be rewritten, using FOR and NEXT statements, as follows:

		Output	
5	FOR X=2 TO 12 STEP 2	2	4
10	PRINT X; X↑2	4	16
15	NEXT X	6	36
20	END	8	64
		10	100
		12	144

Note: If the variable used in the FOR and NEXT statements is incremented each time by 1, it is not necessary to include the STEP in the FOR statement. For example,

		Output	
10	FOR X=1 TO 5	1	1
20	PRINT X; X↑2	2	4
30	NEXT X	3	9
40	END	4	16
		5	25

We have already seen that every READ statement requires a DATA statement. If the same computation is to be computed more than once, a GO TO statement is required. Consider the following BASIC program:

		Output
10	READ A,B	
15	LET T=A+B	8
20	PRINT T	
25	DATA 3,5,−2,7,4,9	
30	END	

Only one value of T is computed and printed out because after the computer read 3 and 5 for A and B, and then computed and printed out T, it executed the next executable statement, the END statement, which tells the machine to stop executing the program.

Now let us add a GO TO statement after the PRINT statement:

		Output
10	READ A,B	8
15	LET T=A+B	5
20	PRINT T	13
22	GO TO 10	
25	DATA 3,5,−2,7,4,9	OUT OF DATA LINE 10
30	END	

After the computer reads the initial values for A and B and computes the initial value of T, it then prints the initial value of T. Statement 22 (22 GO TO 10) commands the computer to execute statement 10 again so as to read two other values for A and B. Then the computer will compute the new value of T and print the new value of T, and so on, until there are no more data in the DATA statement. This procedure is another example of *looping* in computer programming.

The computer will read the first two numbers in the DATA statement, then the next two numbers in the DATA statement, and so on until there are no more data. Then the computer will tell you it is out of data and stop executing your program, even though it never executes the END statement.

The preceding program could be rewritten so as to have the computer stop executing the program by reaching the END statement. Consider the following revised program:

	Output
10 READ A,B,C	8
12 IF C=1 THEN 27	5
15 LET T=A+B	13
20 PRINT T	END OF PROGRAM
22 GO TO 10	
25 DATA 3,5,0, – 2,7,0,4,9,0,0,0,1	
27 PRINT "END OF PROGRAM"	
30 END	

In this revised program the computer will execute the statement 27 if C=1 and then reach the END statement to stop executing the program. This alteration is unnecessary unless a comment is required upon completion of the program.

Now, if we change line 20 in the program above, we could have our answers printed out in various different forms.

	Line 20	Output		
(a)	20 PRINT T,	8	5	13
		END OF PROGRAM		

By placing a comma after T, we can have the machine print on the same line and skip 15 spaces between the different values of T.

	Line 20	Output		
(b)	20 PRINT T;	8	5	13
		END OF PROGRAM		

By placing a semicolon after T, we can have the machine print on the same line and skip 7 spaces between the different values of T.

	Line 20	Output
(c)	20 PRINT "T="T	T = 8
		T = 5
		T = 13
		END OF PROGRAM

	Line 20	Output
(d)	20 PRINT "T="T;	T = 8 T = 5 T = 13
		END OF PROGRAM

The REM (Remark) Statement

The REM statement is used to place important remarks in a BASIC program. Any number of remarks may be inserted in a BASIC program to explain the nature of the program; to give directions for general usage of the program; to identify important parts of the program; or to explain the user's input and/or the computer output of data. This statement is a nonexecutable statement.

GENERAL FORM

Line number REM remark.

Example:

```
10   REM THIS PROGRAM PRINTS A TABLE OF
15   REM SQUARES AND SQUARE ROOTS FOR
20   REM THE COUNTING NUMBERS FROM 1 TO 100
25   PRINT "N↑2", "SQR(N)"
30   FOR I=1 TO 100
40   PRINT I↑2, SQR(I)
50   NEXT I
60   END
```

The TAB Function

We have seen that the use of a comma in a PRINT statement allows us to skip about 15 spaces, and the use of a semicolon in a PRINT statement allows us to skip about 7 spaces. The TAB function allows us to move to a desired position in a line.

GENERAL FORM

TAB(X), where X is any positive real number, commands the machine to move to position X if X=0,1,2,3, ... On most computer terminal printers the spaces are numbers 0,1,2, ... , 71. If you exceed 71 spaces on a line, the computer will start at the zero position on the next line.

Example:

		Output
5	FOR X=0 TO 5	F.S.
10	PRINT "F."; TAB(X+2); "S."	F. S.
15	NEXT X	F. S.
20	END	F. S.
		F. S.
		F. S.

Note: If line 10 were printed as 10 PRINT "F.", "S.", then the computer would skip about 15 spaces between F. and S. But if line 10 were printed as shown here, the TAB(X+2) function commands the machine to skip X spaces between F. and S.

Problem Set 1.4

1. Code the sample flowchart in Figure 1.4. Use the following:

DATA 1,3,5,0,97,88,21,0,999,275,87,0,0,0,0,1

2. Code the sample flowchart in Figure 1.5
(a) without using FOR and NEXT statements, and then
(b) using FOR and NEXT statements.

3. Give the computer output for the following programs:

(a)   5   LET A=1
     10   LET B=A+4
     15   LET C=2*B+A+5
     20   LET D=2*(B+A)+5
     25   PRINT A,B,C,2*D
     30   END

(b) 10   LET E=1
     20   LET E=3↑2
     25   LET F=(E+2)↑3+1
     35   PRINT E,F,SQR(E),F/9
     40   END

(c) 10   READ A,B,C,D
     20   LET X=A+B−D
     30   LET Y=A−B+C
     32   PRINT X,Y
     36   DATA 1,2,3,4,5,6,7,8,9
     40   END

(d) Program (c) with the following additional line:
     34   GO TO 10

(e) 10 READ A,B
    20 LET M=(A+B)/2
    30 IF M> =95 THEN 50
    40 GO TO 10
    50 PRINT A,B, "MEAN="M
    60 STOP
    70 DATA 52,96,81,95,94,100
    80 END

(f) 10 REM AFTER COMPLETING SECTION 1.6 OF THIS TEXT
    20 REM YOU CAN RUN ANY OF THE PROGRAMS
    30 REM IN THIS EXERCISE TO CHECK YOUR ANSWERS
    40 PRINT "X", "X↑2", "X↑3"
    50 FOR X=1 TO 6
    60   PRINT X, X↑2, X↑3
    70 NEXT X
    80 END

4. Code the Figure 1.8 flowchart in the BASIC language.

Figure 1.8

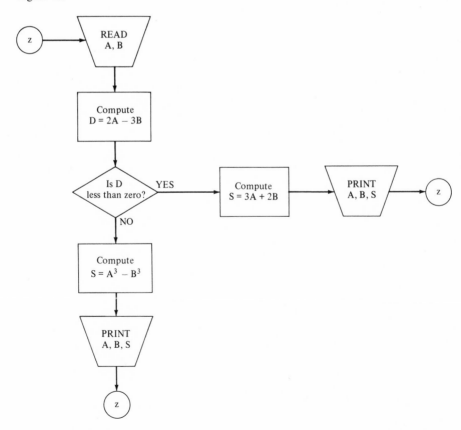

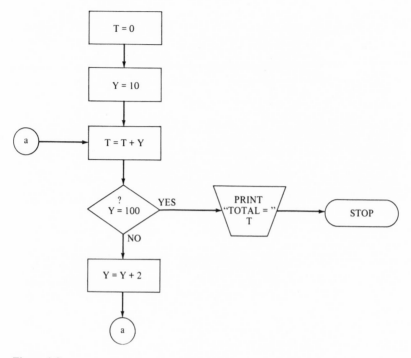

Figure 1.9

5. Code the Figure 1.9 flowchart in the BASIC language.

6. Give the computer output for the following program:

```
 7   PRINT "USING THE TAB FUNCTION"
 9   LET X=5
11   PRINT X; TAB(6); X↑2
13   PRINT 2∗X; TAB(8); (2∗X)↑2
15   END
```

1.6

Operating a Computer Terminal

A computer terminal (Figure 1.10) is an alternative to operating a computer directly. Basically, a computer terminal is a Teletype machine that communicates with a computer by means of a telephone line. Therefore, the computer may be located miles from a computer terminal. This allows many people to share the cost of one large computer. There are three integral parts to a computer terminal: the keyboard, the paper-tape unit, and the acoustic coupler.

Figure 1.10 Computer terminal

THE KEYBOARD

The keyboard (Figure 1.11) can be used to type a program directly to the computer once a telephone connection has been made, or to prepunch a program on paper tape and then contact the computer and have it read the paper tape. The latter procedure is preferred because it will reduce the costly computer time used.

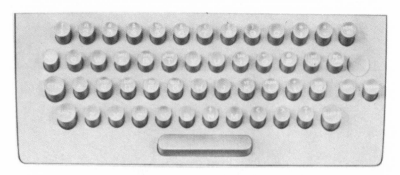

Figure 1.11 Computer keyboard

Figure 1.12 Paper-tape unit

THE PAPER-TAPE UNIT

The paper-tape unit (Figure 1.12) can be used in the following ways:

1. *Off line* to prepunch a program on paper tape.

2. *On line* to have the computer read the program on paper tape.

3. *On line* to have the computer place a program from its memory onto paper tape.

THE ACOUSTIC COUPLER

The acoustic coupler (Figure 1.13) is the device that allows us to transmit information to a computer and receive information from a computer by means of a telephone line.

Procedure for Running a Program on a Terminal

1. Prepunch the coded program on paper tape.

2. Contact the computer by telephone.

3. Have the computer read the paper tape.

4. Have the computer run the program.

5. Debugging or receiving results.

6. Sign-off procedure.

Figure 1.13 Acoustic coupler

Procedure for Punching a Paper Tape

1. Turn switch on right of machine to LOCAL.

2. Turn tape unit ON.

3. Press HERE IS on the keyboard. This will allow for some space on the tape for threading.

4. Punch each line in your program exactly the way it appears on your coded sheet. Punch one line at a time. Press RETURN and then LINE FEED on the keyboard at the end of each line.

5. After punching the last statement in the program, punch HERE IS on the keyboard again.

6. Shut off the machine and the tape unit.

Note: If you are to punch a statement such as

5   READ A,B,C

and you make an error such as

5   READ AB

(you forget to punch the comma between A and B), there are two ways to correct your error:

(a) Press RETURN and LINE FEED on the keyboard and retype the complete statement again. (When the computer reads the tape, it will erase the first line 5 and replace it with the corrected line 5.)

(b) Press the symbol $\overleftarrow{0}$ in upper shift on the keyboard. The symbol ← will command the computer to erase one character to the left of it. Therefore, in the sample error given above, we would punch 5 READ AB←,B,C. If we were supposed to punch

10   LET X = 3*A + 2*B↑2

but we punched

10   LET X = 3*B + 2

and then noticed our error, we could correct by erasing more than one character:

10   LET X = 3*B + 2←←←A + 2*B↑2

Procedure for Contacting Machine

1. Turn switch on right of machine to LINE.

2. Turn acoustic coupler ON and set the duplex switch on FULL.

3. Dial a system phone number. The system will answer with a high-pitched sound.

4. Place the phone in the acoustic coupler.

5. The computer will ask for your identification number. Type in your ID number and press RETURN.

6. The computer will print out some information such as the system's name, date, time, and any news. Then the computer will type READY. At this time you can punch a program directly to the computer or have the computer read a program from a paper tape.

Procedure for Running a Punched Paper-Tape Program

1. Follow the procedure for contacting the computer.

2. Place the tape-reader switch in the FREE position.

3. Place your paper tape in the tape reader.

4. Type in TAPE on the keyboard.

5. Move the tape-reader switch to the START position. (The computer will read the paper tape and store the program in its memory.)

6. Type in LIST on the keyboard. This commands the computer to list the program with any corrections that might have been made while punching on tape.

7. Type in RUN on the keyboard. This commands the computer to execute the steps in your program. It will either print out your results or tell you that you have an error.

   Example: If the computer read a paper tape as follows,

   ```
   5 READ AB←,B,C,←
   10 LET X = 3*B+2←←←A+2*B↑2-C
   15 PRINT A;B;C,"X="X
   20 DATA 1,1,1,1,2,3
   ```

type in LIST and press RETURN on the keyboard. The computer will print

   ```
   5 READ A,B,C
   10 LET X = 3*A+2*B↑2-C
   15 PRINT A;B;C,"X="X
   20 DATA 1,1,1,1,2,3
   ```

Type in RUN and press RETURN on the keyboard. Some computers will print

   ERROR

Press RETURN and the computer will print END STATEMENT NOT THE LAST STATEMENT IN PROGRAM (or some equivalent message).

You can correct this error by typing: 25 END (return). Then line 25 will be added to your program in the computer's memory. Summarizing this procedure:

Type	Press	Computer's Response
LIST	RETURN	5 READ A,B,C 10 LET X = 3*A+2*B↑2-C 15 PRINT A;B;C,"X="X 20 DATA 1,1,1,1,2,3 25 END
RUN	RETURN	1 1 1 X= 4

*READY

Note: This program does not have a language error, but it does have an error in logic. The DATA statement contains another set of values for A,B, and C. If the computer is to read them, we need to add statement 17 GO TO 5.

Type	Press	Computer's Response
17 GO TO 5 LIST	RETURN RETURN	5 READ A,B,C 10 LET X = 3*A+2*B↑2-C 15 PRINT A;B;C,"X="X 17 GO TO 5 20 DATA 1,1,1,1,2,3 25 END
RUN	RETURN	1 1 1 X= 4 1 2 3 X= 8

OUT OF DATA IN LINE 5

At this time you can either sign off by typing in some command such as BYE and pressing the RETURN button, or you can allow another person to use the computer by typing in some command, such as SCRATCH or NEW, and pressing the RETURN button (a command such as SCRATCH or NEW erases the previous program from the computer's memory).

Type	Press	Computer Response
SCR TAPE	RETURN RETURN	The computer will read a new tape if it has been placed in the tape reader. Assume it reads the following tape:

Type	Press	Computer Response

```
5 INPUT A
10 IF A = 9999 THEN 35
15 FOR X = 1 TO 3*A
20     PRINT X;X↑2
25 NEXT A
30 GO TO 5
35 PRINT "JOB DONE BY SNOOPY"
40 END
```

Type	Press	Computer Response
RUN	RETURN	ERROR
	RETURN	UNDECIPHERABLE OPERAND
		LINE 25
		(should be NEXT X)

25   NEXT X RETURN

Type	Press	Computer Response
RUN	RETURN	? (You must now enter a numerical value for A. Let's assume you type 3.)
3	RETURN	1 1
		2 4
		3 9
		? (You must now enter the next value for A. Let's assume you type 7.)
7	RETURN	1 1
		2 4
		3 9
		4 16
		5 25
		6 36
		7 49
		? (Let's assume you type 9999.)
9999	RETURN	JOB DONE BY SNOOPY
BYE	RETURN	OFF AT (time)
		_____ minutes of computer time

At this time you will lose your telephone connection to the computer.

Note: A partial listing of possible BASIC compiler error messages is included in Appendix B.

Problem Set 1.5

1. Punch the following program on paper tape:

```
10   READ X,Y,Z
15   LET W = 3*X + Y↑2
```

```
20  LET T=Z+Y+X/2
23  PRINT X,Y,Z
30  PRINT "W="W; "T="T
40  DATA 2,4,6,12,0,1,18,-7,-3
45  END
```

2. Contact the computer by telephone and have it read the tape for Problem 1 and ask it to RUN the program.

3. Add statement 35 GO TO 10 to the program and ask the computer to LIST the program and RUN the program.

4. Have the computer SCRATCH (erase) the program for Problem 1 from its memory.

5. Type in the following program ON LINE to the computer:

```
2   INPUT A,B,C,D
4   IF D=0 THEN 10
6   PRINT "AVERAGE="(A+B+C)/3
8   GO TO 2
10  END
```

Use the following data:

A	B	C	D
5	3	9	1
22	99	88	1
67	27	92	1
0	0	0	0

6. Each of the following programs contains statements that have errors in the BASIC language. If you can find them, correct them. In either case, type each of them (separately) into the computer. If you have made the proper correction, the computer will execute the program; if not, the computer will tell you which statements contain errors. Then try to correct the errors.

```
(a) 10  PRINT FIND THE ERRORS
    20  READ A,B
    30  LET S=(A+B↑2)
    40  PRINT, "ERRORS", A,B,S
    55  IF A=B THEN 80
    60  PRINT SUM
    65  GO TO 20
    75  DATA 2,5,7,8,9,3
    80  END
```

```
(b)  5  READ A,B
     7  LET Y=3*A-7*B+2
    10  GO TO 5
    15  DATA 1,2,7,9,8,27
```

```
(c) 10   READ A,B
    20   PRINT A↑2; TAB(10); B↑2
    30   GO TO 5
    35   DATA 3,4,5,6,7,8
    40   END
```

1.7

Subscripted Variables

In BASIC a simple variable can be named by a single letter or a single letter followed by a single digit. Therefore, given a group of scores, we could define them by X0,X1,X2, . . . ,X9. What if we had more than ten scores? We could use subscripted variables by placing the subscripts in parentheses. That is, X(0),X(1),X(2), . . . ,X(10),X(11), ... When using subscripted variables in BASIC, you as the programmer must reserve space for them in the computer's memory. This is done by means of a *dimension* statement.

GENERAL FORM

Line number DIM variable (*r*), variable (*s*), . . . , where *r* is the number of spaces reserved for a single row of scores for the first subscripted variable, and *s* is the number of spaces reserved for a single row of scores for the second subscripted variable. For example: 2 DIM X(5), Y(12).
 • The DIM statement *must be* the first statement in a BASIC program.
 • It is *acceptable to overdimension* (reserving more places than necessary) for a subscripted variable.
 • It is *not acceptable to underdimension* (not reserving enough places) for a subscripted variable. For example, suppose we wanted to write one program that could be used to compute the average score on a statistics exam for each class section in your school. If the number of students in each section varied from 15 students in the smallest section to 36 students in the largest section, we would have to DIM variable (36) if the program were to handle all sections.

Note: It is possible to have double-subscripted variables, such as A(1,2), X(3,6). These are used in matrix algebra, a topic that will be discussed in Chapter 3.

There are other advantages in using subscripted variables.

SAMPLE PROBLEM

Given: N, X(1), X(2), . . . , X(N), where N ≤ 30.

Sample Data: DATA 5,75,82,71,52,91
              DATA 10,52,75,76,74,81,82,87,94,51,81

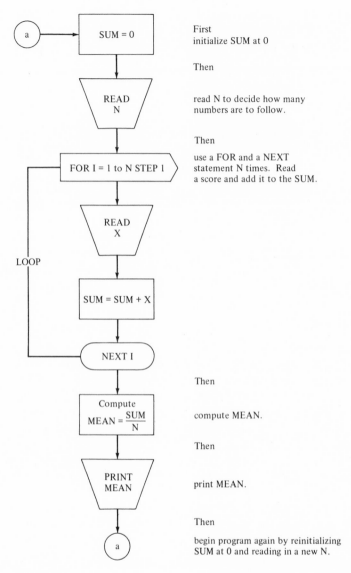

Figure 1.14

Wanted: A flowchart (Figure 1.14) and a BASIC program to compute and print out the arithmetic mean (average) of *N* given numbers.

Note: The first number in each DATA statement tells how many scores are to follow. This program could be written with or without subscripted variables, as shown in the following comparison of two printouts of Figure 1.14.

Without Subscripted Variables

```
 5 LET S=0
10 READ N
15 FOR I = 1 TO N
20     READ X
25     LET S=S+X
30 NEXT I
35 LET M=S/N
40 PRINT "MEAN="M
45 GO TO 5
50 DATA 5,75,82,71,52,91
55 DATA 10,52,75,76,74,81,
   82,87,94,51,80
60 END
```

With Subscripted Variables

```
  2 DIM X(30)
  5 LET S = 0
 10 READ N
 15 FOR I = 1 TO N
 20     READ X(I)
 25     LET S = S+X(I)
 30 NEXT I
 35 LET M = S/N
 40 PRINT "MEAN="M
 45 GO TO 5
100 DATA 5,75,82,71,52,91
105 DATA 10,52,75,76,74,81,82,87,94,51,80
200 END
```

In the program with subscripted variables, each of the N scores has been saved in the computer's memory. In the program without subscripted variables, the only score saved is the last one read. However, both programs would produce the following output:

```
MEAN= 74.2
MEAN= 75.2

OUT OF DATA IN LINE 10
```

SAMPLE PROBLEM

Now consider the following change in the preceding program:

Given: I,X(1),X(2), . . . ,X(I); assume I ≤ 30.

Wanted: A BASIC program to compute the arithmetic mean of I numbers and then subtract the mean from each of the scores. (That is, find out how much and in what direction, positive or negative, each score deviates from the mean.)

If we were given

DATA 5,75,82,71,52,91

the desired output would be as follows:

I	X(I)	X(I) – MEAN
MEAN = 74.2		
1	75	0.8
2	82	7.8
3	71	– 3.2
4	52	– 22.2
5	91	16.8

However, the program with the subscripted variables could be modified as follows to obtain the desired results:

```
5   DIM X(30),D(30)
10  REM    THIS PROGRAM COMPUTES THE MEAN OF N NUMBERS AND THE
15  REM            DEVIATION OF EACH NUMBER FROM THE MEAN
20  REM                      WHERE N<=30
25  LET S=0
30  READ N
35  FOR I=1 TO N
40      READ X(I)
45      LET S=S+X(I)
50  NEXT I
55  PRINT "I","X(I)","X(I)-MEAN"
60  LET M=S/N
65  PRINT "MEAN="M
70  FOR I=1 TO N
75      LET D(I)=X(I)-M
80      PRINT I,X(I),D(I)
90  NEXT I
92  PRINT
95  GO TO 25
96  REM    NOW ENTER THE DATA BEGINNING IN LINE 100 AS FOLLOWS:
97  REM            100 DATA I,X(1),X(2),....,X(I)
100 DATA 5,75,82,71,52,91
105 DATA 10,52,75,76,74,81,82,87,94,51,80
200 END
```

1.8

Prepackaged Programs

Prepackaged programs are programs that have been stored in the memory of a computer. Each program is stored under a specific name. The user of a prepackaged program calls the program out of memory by name, then puts in data in the proper place, and commands the machine to run the program with the given data. In Chapter 6 on elementary statistics we will use some prepackaged statistical programs to solve problems. The user of a prepackaged program is told the name of the program, what it does, where to place the data, and any other pertinent information.

For example, suppose the program just completed in Article 1.7, which computed the arithmetic mean of N numbers and the deviations of each score from the mean or average, was stored under the program name DEMO. You might receive an instruction sheet as follows:

Name: DEMO

Description: This program computes the arithmetic mean of I numbers and the deviation of each number from the arithmetic mean.

Instructions: Enter the data, beginning in line 100 as follows:

$$100 \quad \text{DATA I,X(1),X(2), \ldots ,X(I)}$$

where $I =$ the number of raw scores; $X(1),X(2), \ldots ,X(I) =$ raw scores.

Note: Line 200 is the END statement. If your data statements exceed line 199, the user must type in a new END statement.

EXAMPLE

```
GET-DEMO
100   DATA 2,50,70
RUN

I       X(I)      X(I)-MEAN
MEAN = 60
1       50          - 10
2       70          + 10

I       X(I)      X(I)-MEAN
OUT OF DATA IN LINE 30
```

In some BASIC systems, the command to call a prepackaged program out of memory is as follows:

GET-name   (of the prepackaged program)

Note: This command may change from one system to another. Other systems use a command such as ENTER or LOAD. If an instructor wants to store an original program to be used later on, the command is one such as

SAVE-name   (of program)

Therefore, if we want to execute the program that computes the deviations of a number of scores from their mean, using the prepackaged program DEMO, the procedure will be as follows:

1. Contact the computer and give your identification number. Then, when the computer responds with a statement like READY,

2. Type in

    GET-DEMO
    100   DATA 5,75,82,71,52,91
    101   DATA 10,52,75,76,74,81,82,87,94,51,80
    RUN

3. The output will be as follows:

    DEMO

I	X(I)	X(I)-MEAN
MEAN = 74.2		
1	75	.8
2	82	7.8
3	71	−3.2
4	52	−22.2
5	91	16.3

I	X(I)	X(I)-MEAN
MEAN = 75.2		
1	52	−23.2
2	75	−.2
3	76	.8
4	74	−1.2
5	81	5.8
6	82	6.8
7	87	11.8
8	94	18.8
9	51	−24.2
10	80	4.8

    OUT OF DATA IN LINE 30

Note: If you would like to see how a prepackaged program looks, command the machine to LIST it, as shown in Article 1.6.

The use of prepackaged programs and additional topics in BASIC will be discussed in detail as they are used to solve problems in succeeding chapters.

Problem Set 1.6

1. Give the computer output of the following BASIC program:

```
 2   DIM A(10), B(10)
 4   READ N
 6   FOR I=1 TO N
 8     READ A(I)
10     LET B(I)=A(I)↑2−1
12     PRINT I; A(I); B(I)
14   NEXT I
16   GO TO 4
18   DATA 2,10,−10
20   DATA 5,1,2,4,8,−9
22   END
```

2. (a) State the three errors in the following BASIC program:

```
 5   DIM X(5)
10   FOR I=1 TO 5
15     READ X(I)
20     LET Y(I)=X(I)↑3
25     PRINT, I, X(I), Y(I)
30   NEXT X
32   GO TO 10
35   DATA 1,2,3,4,5
40   DATA 6,7,8,9,10
45   END
```

(b) Now write corrections of these three errors so that this program will run.

3. After your instructor has saved the DEMO program (Article 1.8), call it out of memory and run it with the following data:

```
DATA   4,55,65,72,81
DATA   9,61,52,89,94,71,75,88,97,50
```

4. What statement is missing in the following BASIC program?

```
 10   FOR N=1 TO 7
 20     READ A(N), B(N)
 30     LET C(N)=A(N)−B(N)
 40   NEXT N
 50   FOR N=1 TO 7
 60     PRINT C(N);
 70   NEXT N
 80   DATA 2,9,−7,3,14,22,−81
 90   DATA 19,−8,3,.5,27,−52,8
100   END
```

5. Add the missing statement in Problem 4 and run the program on a computer terminal.

2

Topics in Algebra

2.1

Introduction

This chapter includes some of the topics covered in standard elementary algebra and intermediate algebra courses. The BASIC programming language is used as a practical tool in solving problems related to each of the selected algebraic topics.

2.2

Factors

One of the first and most useful procedures in an elementary algebra course is finding the factors of a *natural number* (the set of natural numbers or *counting numbers* $N = \{1,2,3,\ldots\}$). The natural numbers r and s are factors of a natural number t if $r \cdot s = t$. For example, $2 \cdot 3 = 6$; therefore, 2 and 3 are factors of 6.

We can also say the natural number r is a factor of the natural number t if t/r is a natural number. For example, $6/3 = 2$, which is a natural number; therefore, 3 is a factor of 6.

In Chapter 1 we were given a list of internal functions whose meanings are incorporated in the BASIC compiler (see Article 1.5). When using an internal function, you must supply the proper argument. Let us consider the use of one such internal function.

The Greatest Integer Function

INT(X), where X is any real number, commands the computer to find the greatest integer which is less than or equal to X.

SAMPLE BASIC PROGRAM

```
10 PRINT INT(0);INT(8)
20 PRINT INT(0.9);INT(8.7);INT(-1);INT(-45)
30 PRINT INT(87.88);INT(3/2)
40 END


RUN
                16:33    08/06/75

0      8
0      8    -1    -45
87     1

TIME 0.0 SECS.
```

Figure 2.1

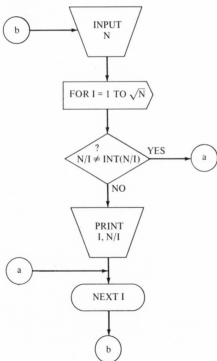

In BASIC we can use a statement such as 20 IF $T/R = INT(T/R)$ THEN 50 to decide whether R is a factor of T. Consider the following illustrations:

1. If $T = 6$ and $R = 3$, then

$$6/3 \overset{?}{=} INT(6/3)$$
$$2 = 2$$

Therefore 3 is a factor of 6.

2. If $T = 6$ and $R = 4$, then

$$6/4 \overset{?}{=} INT(6/4)$$
$$1.5 \neq 1$$

Therefore 4 is not a factor of 6.

Now let us use this procedure above and a theorem from number theory. The latter tells us that if we want to find all the factors of a natural number N, we need only investigate the integers from 1 to $\sqrt{N}$. We then list any factor I found and the factor N/I. (*Note*: If a number I divides N, then so does the number N/I. For example, since 7 divides 21, so does $21/7 = 3$ divide 21). The flowchart (Figure 2.1) and the following BASIC program will print out all the factors of a natural number N.

```
100 PRINT
110 PRINT "ENTER ANY NATURAL NUMBER "
120 INPUT N
130 PRINT " THE FACTORS OF"N; "ARE: "
140 PRINT
150 FOR I= 1 TO SQR(N)
160    IF N/I<>INT(N/I) THEN 180
170    PRINT I;N/I
180 NEXT I
190 GO TO 100
200 END

RUN
              8:13    06/30/75

ENTER ANY NATURAL NUMBER
?36
  THE FACTORS OF 36   ARE:

  1      36
  2      18
  3      12
  4      9
  6      6

ENTER ANY NATURAL NUMBER
?13
  THE FACTORS OF 13   ARE:

  1      13
```

```
ENTER ANY NATURAL NUMBER
? 5034
  THE FACTORS OF 5034     ARE:
  1       5034
  2       2517
  3       1678
  6       839
ENTER ANY NATURAL NUMBER
? 2517
  THE FACTORS OF 2517     ARE:
  1       2517
  3       839
ENTER ANY NATURAL NUMBER
?
STOP.
RAN 0.0 SEC.
```

Figure 2.2

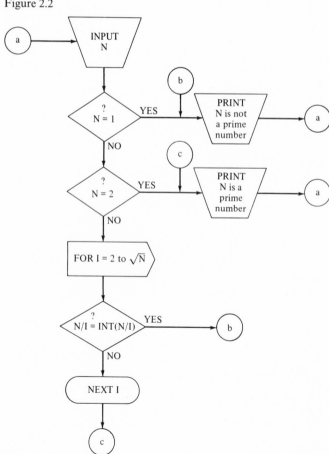

Finding Prime Factors of a Number

In algebraic topics that involve factoring, it becomes necessary to find the prime factors of natural numbers or algebraic expressions. A natural number greater than 1 is a *prime number* if and only if it is divisible only by itself and the number 1. The "if and only if" phrase tells us that both this statement and its converse are true. The numbers 2, 3, 5, and 7 are examples of prime numbers. The natural number 12 is not a prime number because it is divisible by itself, 1, and at least one other natural number. The flowchart (Figure 2.2) and the following BASIC program can direct the computer to decide whether any natural number N is prime.

```
10 REM    THIS PROGRAM DECIDES WHETHER N IS PRIME
20 PRINT "ENTER ANY NATURAL NUMBER "
30 INPUT N
40 IF N=1 THEN 100
50 IF N=2 THEN 130
60 FOR I= 2 TO SQR(N)
70    IF N/I=INT(N/I) THEN 100
80 NEXT I
90 GO TO 130
100 PRINT N;" IS NOT PRIME "
110 PRINT
120 GO TO 20
130 PRINT N;" IS PRIME "
140 PRINT
150 GO TO 20
160 END


RUN

            3:21    06/30/75


ENTER ANY NATURAL NUMBER
?2024
  2024      IS NOT PRIME

ENTER ANY NATURAL NUMBER
?113
  113    IS PRIME

ENTER ANY NATURAL NUMBER
?121133
  121133    IS NOT PRIME

ENTER ANY NATURAL NUMBER
?

STOP.
RAN 0.0 SEC.
```

You may have noticed at the end of each of the programs in this section that the computer keeps asking you to input another number. You can have the computer stop executing your program by depressing the ESC (escape) or BREAK buttons on most Teletype terminals. Another approach is to revise your program so that if you input an $N < 0$, the computer will stop executing the program. We can amend the previous flowchart for deciding whether a number is prime; see Figure 2.3.

Figure 2.3

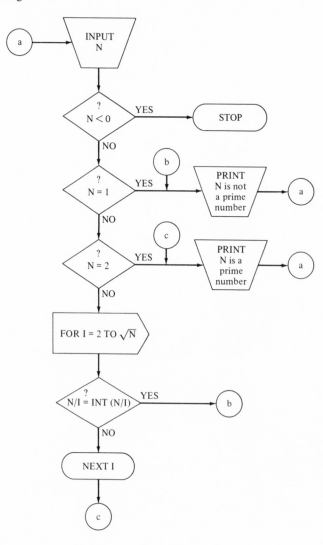

2.3

Subroutines

The GO SUB (Subroutine) and RETURN Statements

In many computer programs a certain sequence of statements must be executed more than once. A programmer can use a subroutine to avoid retyping this sequence of statements:

GENERAL FORMS AND SAMPLE DIAGRAM

Line number GO SUB line number
Line Number RETURN

```
            10   · · ·
            20   · · ·
            30   GO SUB 150
            40   · · ·
            50   · · ·
            60   GO SUB 150
            70   · · ·
            80   · · ·
            90   · · ·
           100   · · ·
           110   GO SUB 150
           120   · · ·
           130   · · ·
           140   STOP
         ┌ 150   · · ·
Subroutine │ 160   · · ·
   150     │ 170   · · ·
         └ 180   RETURN
           190   · · ·
           200   END
```

If this sample diagram were an actual program, statement 30 would command the computer to execute statements 150, 160, 170, and then return to execute statement 40; statement 60 would command the computer to execute statements 150, 160, and 170, and then return to execute statement 70; statement 110 would command the computer to execute statements 150, 160, 170, and then return to execute statement 120.

Sample BASIC PROGRAM

```
10 LET R=50
15 LET D=324
20 GO SUB 100
30 LET R=73
35 LET D=2134
40 GO SUB 100
50 LET R=55
55 LET D=1074
60 GO SUB 100
70 STOP
80 REM    SUBROUTINE 100 COMPUTES AND PRINTS TRAVEL TIME
90 REM         GIVEN DISTANCE AND TIME
100 LET T=D/R
110 PRINT "DISTANCE=";D,"RATE=";R,"TIME=";T
120 RETURN
130 END
```

RUN

```
           15:26    06/24/75

DISTANCE= 324      RATE= 50      TIME= 6.48
DISTANCE= 2134     RATE= 73      TIME= 29.2329
DISTANCE= 1074     RATE= 55      TIME= 19.5273

TIME 0.0 SECS.
```

2.4

A Prepackaged Program for the Prime Factorization of Any Natural Number

One of the sample programs in Article 2.2 decides whether a natural number is prime. In elementary algebra it is extremely useful to be able to list the prime factors of a natural number. For example, $24 = 2 \cdot 2 \cdot 2 \cdot 3$, $36 = 2 \cdot 2 \cdot 3 \cdot 3$, and $34 = 2 \cdot 17$. The following prepackaged program can be used for the prime factorization of any natural number. Each prepackaged program in this textbook includes user's instructions, flowchart, and coding in the BASIC language.

Name: PRIME

Description: This program is used for the prime factorization of any natural number.

Instructions: Enter any natural number N when the computer prints out a question mark. If you want to stop execution of the program, type in an $N < 0$.

Sample Run:

```
RUN

                19:03    07/01/75


ENTER A NATURAL NUMBER TO RUN THE PROGRAM
OR A NEGATIVE NUMBER TO STOP EXECUTION
?113
 113    IS A PRIME NUMBER


ENTER A NATURAL NUMBER TO RUN THE PROGRAM
OR A NEGATIVE NUMBER TO STOP EXECUTION
?720
 THE PRIME FACTORS OF   720   ARE:
 2      2      2      2      3      3      5

ENTER A NATURAL NUMBER TO RUN THE PROGRAM
OR A NEGATIVE NUMBER TO STOP EXECUTION
?3125
 THE PRIME FACTORS OF  3125     ARE:
 5      5      5      5      5

ENTER A NATURAL NUMBER TO RUN THE PROGRAM
OR A NEGATIVE NUMBER TO STOP EXECUTION
?123456
 THE PRIME FACTORS OF   123456  ARE:
 2      2      2      2      2      2      3      643
```

```
ENTER A NATURAL NUMBER TO RUN THE PROGRAM
OR A NEGATIVE NUMBER TO STOP EXECUTION
?999999
  THE PRIME FACTORS OF  999999  ARE:
  3      3      3      7     11     13     37

ENTER A NATURAL NUMBER TO RUN THE PROGRAM
OR A NEGATIVE NUMBER TO STOP EXECUTION
?-9

TIME 0.0 SECS.
```

Let us look at the flowchart (Figure 2.4) for the prepackaged program PRIME. The coding of PRIME follows:

```
100 REM     THIS IS THE PREPACKAGED PROGRAM ENTITLED
110 REM                     PRIME
120 PRINT
130 PRINT
140 PRINT "ENTER A NATURAL NUMBER TO RUN THE PROGRAM"
150 PRINT "OR A NEGATIVE NUMBER TO STOP EXECUTION"
160 INPUT N
170 LET N1=N
180 IF N<0 THEN 500
190 IF N=1 THEN 330
200 IF N<>2 THEN 230
210 PRINT N;" IS A PRIME NUMBER "
220 GO TO 120
230 LET C=0
240 LET I=2
250 GO SUB 400
260 FOR I=3 TO SQR(N1) STEP 2
270    GO SUB 400
290 NEXT I
300 IF N=1 THEN 120
310 IF C=0 THEN 210
320 PRINT N
325 GO TO 120
330 PRINT " 1 DOES NOT HAVE ANY PRIME FACTORS "
340 GO TO 120
350 REM             SUBROUTINE 400 PRINTS
360 REM                     ALL
370 REM             THE PRIME FACTORS
380 REM                     OF N
390 REM     --------------------------------
400 IF N/I<>INT(N/I) THEN 470
410 IF C<>0 THEN 440
420 PRINT " THE PRIME FACTORS OF "N; "ARE: "
430 LET C=1
440 PRINT I;
450 LET N=N/I
460 GO TO 400
470 RETURN
500 END
```

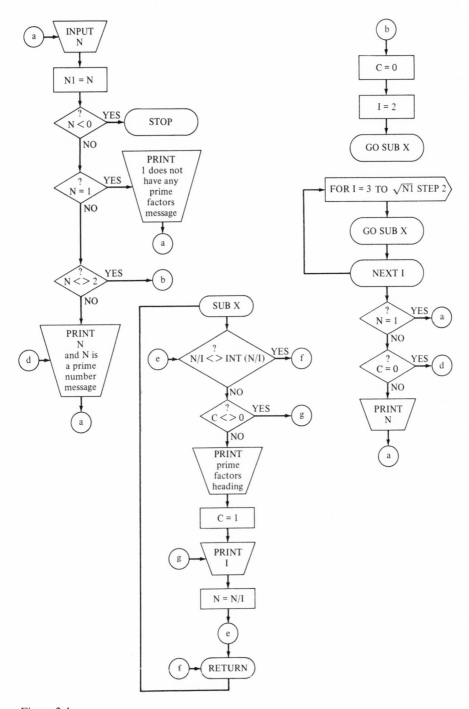

Figure 2.4

Problem Set 2.1

1. Write a BASIC program that will decide whether any natural number is an odd number or an even number.

2. In Article 2.2 the sample output for the program that prints out the factors of a natural number has one minor inconsistency. When N is a perfect square, such as 256, $\sqrt{N}$ (which is a factor of N) is printed out twice. Revise the program so that if N is a perfect square, $\sqrt{N}$ will be printed only once.

3. Revise the BASIC program in Article 2.2 which decides whether a natural number is prime. If someone inadvertently enters a number that is not a natural number, the computer will print out an appropriate message and start the program again.

Figure 2.5

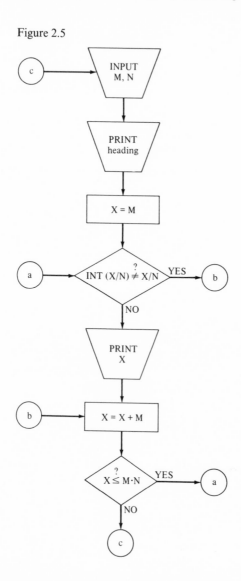

4. Code the flowchart for the revised prime number program in Article 2.2.

5. After your instructor enters the prepackaged program PRIME into your computer, call it out and use it to find the prime factorization for the following numbers: 5734, 64, 11, 9743.

6. The multiples of a natural number n are all numbers of the form nm, where $m = 1,2,3,\ldots$. For example, the multiples of 11 are 11, 22, 33, 44, $\ldots$. Write a BASIC program to print out a list of multiples of the natural number 23. Depress the ESC (escape) or BREAK button, whichever is applicable to your computer, when you decide to direct the computer to stop printing multiples of 23.

7. Write a BASIC program that will read any natural number N and print out a list of multiples of N.

8. In both arithmetic and algebra it is important to find the common multiples of two natural numbers M and N. If X is a multiple of M and X is a multiple of N, then X is a *common multiple* of M and N. For example, 60 is a common multiple of 12 and 4, because $12 \cdot 5 = 60$ and $4 \cdot 15 = 60$. When adding two fractions such as 1/24 and 1/36, we must first find the least common multiple (LCM) of 24 and 36, commonly known as the least common denominator (LCD) of 24 and 36, which is 72. Code the flowchart given in Figure 2.5 to find all the common multiples of two natural numbers M and N which are less than $M \cdot N$. (*Note*: the first multiple printed will be the LCM = LCD.)

9. Run the program in Problem 8 with $M = 27$ and $N = 943$; also, with $M = 1024$ and $N = 92$.

10. Construct a flowchart and write a BASIC program to compute and print out the LCM of any three natural numbers. (Chapter 5 includes a project to generalize this program so that it prints out the LCM for *any number* of natural numbers.)

2.5

Evaluation of Formulas

The evaluation of formulas is an integral part of the study of algebra. The BASIC programming language can be used as a practical tool in the evaluation of formulas.

Degrees Fahrenheit and Degrees Celsius (Formerly Centigrade)

The formula $F = (9/5)C + 32$ allows us to convert degrees Celsius (centigrade) to degrees Fahrenheit. Let us look at the following BASIC program, which utilizes this conversion formula:

```
5 DIM A$(3)
10 REM   THIS PROGRAM CONVERTS DEGREES CELSIUS
20 REM        TO DEGREES FAHRENHEIT
30 PRINT " ENTER THE DEGREES CELSIUS "
40 INPUT C
```

```
50 LET F=(9/5)*C+32
60 PRINT C"DEGREES CELSIUS=";F"DEGREES FAHRENHEIT"
70 PRINT "ENTER YES TO RUN THE PROGRAM AGAIN "
80 PRINT " OR NO TO EXIT FROM THE PROGRAM "
90 INPUT A$
100 IF A$="NO" THEN 140
110 PRINT
120 PRINT
130 GO TO 30
140 END
```

```
RUN

                14:49    09/17/76

 ENTER THE DEGREES CELSIUS
?0
 0     DEGREES CELSIUS= 32    DEGREES FAHRENHEIT
ENTER YES TO RUN THE PROGRAM AGAIN
 OR NO TO EXIT FROM THE PROGRAM
?"YES"


 ENTER THE DEGREES CELSIUS
?28
 28    DEGREES CELSIUS= 82.4    DEGREES FAHRENHEIT
ENTER YES TO RUN THE PROGRAM AGAIN
 OR NO TO EXIT FROM THE PROGRAM
?"YES"


 ENTER THE DEGREES CELSIUS
?-28
-28    DEGREES CELSIUS=-18.4    DEGREES FAHRENHEIT
ENTER YES TO RUN THE PROGRAM AGAIN
 OR NO TO EXIT FROM THE PROGRAM
?"NO"

TIME 0.0 SECS.
```

Solution of the formula $F = (9/5)C + 32$ for C generates a formula for converting degrees Fahrenheit to degrees Celsius:

$$F = (9/5)C + 32$$

$$F - 32 = (9/5)C$$

$$5F - 160 = 9C$$

$$(5F - 160)/9 = C$$

or
$$C = (5F - 160)/9$$

Problem Set 2.2

1. Write a BASIC program that can be used to convert degrees Fahrenheit to degrees Celsius.

2. Use the BASIC program in Problem 1 to convert the following degrees Fahrenheit to degrees Celsius: $F = 32, -21, 89$.

3. Code the flowchart (Figure 2.6), which will convert either from Fahrenheit to Celsius degrees or from Celsius to Fahrenheit degrees, in the BASIC language.

4. Run the program in Problem 3, using your own sample data.

Figure 2.6

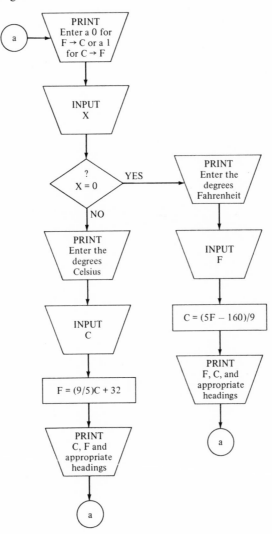

Compound Interest

The formula $A = P(1 + r/k)^{kn}$ is used to compute the total amount of money accumulated for a principal investment. In the formula $A = P(1 + r/k)^{kn}$,

P = initial amount or principal invested

r = interest rate per year

k = number of times interest is compounded each year

n = number of years that P is invested

A = total accumulated amount

For example, if we invest $1,000 at an interest rate of $5\frac{1}{2}\%$ compounded quarterly for four years, then given $P = \$1,000$, $r = 0.055$, $k = 4$, $r = 4$, we would have

$$A = \$1,000(1 + 0.055/4)^{4 \cdot 4}$$

$$= \$1,000(1.01375)^{16}$$

$$= \$1,000(1.24421)$$

$$= \$1224.21$$

Concurrently in many banks, personal savings accounts offer as much as 7.75% interest compounded daily if the principal is left on deposit for at least six years.

The BASIC program on pages 57–58 makes use of the formula $A = P(1 + r/k)^{kn}$ to print out the accumulated amount, given P, r, k, and n.

Geometric Progressions

A *geometric progression* is any sequence of terms of the form $a, ar, ar^2, \ldots, ar^{n-1}$ where

a = first term

r = common ratio of successive terms

$l = ar^{n-1}$ = last term

n = number of terms

The sum of n terms of a geometric progression is denoted by $S = a(r^n - 1)/(r - 1)$. Let us compute the seventeenth term and the sum of the first 17 terms of the geometric progression $10, 5, 5/2, 5/4, \ldots$.

Solution: Given $a = 10$, $r = 1/2$, $n = 17$. Then

$$l = ar^{n-1} = 10(1/2)^{16} \approx 0.000152587$$

```
10 PRINT " ENTER PRINCIPAL TO BE INVESTED "
20 INPUT P
30 PRINT " ENTER INTEREST RATE (IN PERCENT FORM) PER YEAR "
40 INPUT R
50 LET R=R/100
60 PRINT " ENTER THE NUMBER OF TIMES INTEREST IS COMPOUNDED PER YEAR "
70 INPUT K
80 PRINT " ENTER THE NUMBER OF YEARS "
90 INPUT N
100 LET A=P*(1+R/K)↑(K*N)
110 PRINT "TOTAL AMOUNT=$"A
120 PRINT
130 PRINT
140 PRINT
150 GO TO 10
160 END

RUN                    17:44   07/07/75

ENTER PRINCIPAL TO BE INVESTED
?1000
ENTER INTEREST RATE (IN PERCENT FORM) PER YEAR
?5.5
ENTER THE NUMBER OF TIMES INTEREST IS COMPOUNDED PER YEAR
?4
ENTER THE NUMBER OF YEARS
?4
TOTAL AMOUNT=$ 1244.19
```

```
ENTER PRINCIPAL TO BE INVESTED
?2000
ENTER INTEREST RATE (IN PERCENT FORM) PER YEAR
?7.75
ENTER THE NUMBER OF TIMES INTEREST IS COMPOUNDED PER YEAR
?4
ENTER THE NUMBER OF YEARS
?6
TOTAL AMOUNT=$ 3169.85


ENTER PRINCIPAL TO BE INVESTED
?2000
ENTER INTEREST RATE (IN PERCENT FORM) PER YEAR
?7.75
ENTER THE NUMBER OF TIMES INTEREST IS COMPOUNDED PER YEAR
?365
ENTER THE NUMBER OF YEARS
?6
TOTAL AMOUNT=$ 3178.39


ENTER PRINCIPAL TO BE INVESTED
?

STOP.
RAN 0.0 SEC.
```

$$S = a(r^{n-1})/(r-1)$$
$$= 10((1/2)^{17} - 1)/((1/2) - 1)$$
$$\approx 19.9999$$

The following BASIC program computes the last term l and the sum (S) of n terms of a geometric progression, given the first term (a), the common ratio (r), and the number of terms (n).

```
100 DIM B$(3)
110 REM   THIS PROGRAM COMPUTES THE LAST TERM OF A GEOMETRIC PRO-
120 REM            GRESSION AND THE SUM OF THESE TERMS
130 PRINT
140 PRINT
150 PRINT "ENTER: FIRST TERM, COMMON RATIO, AND NUMBER OF TERMS"
160 INPUT A, R, N
170 LET L=A*R†(N-1)
180 LET S=A*(R†N-1)/(R-1)
190 PRINT "THE"N; "TH. TERM="L
200 PRINT "THE SUM OF THE FIRST"N; "TERMS="S
210 PRINT
220 PRINT "ENTER YES TO RUN AGAIN-OR-NO TO STOP"
230 INPUT B$
240 IF B$="YES" THEN 130
250 END

RUN
           20:31    06/30/75

ENTER: FIRST TERM, COMMON RATIO, AND NUMBER OF TERMS
? 10, .5, 17
THE 17    TH. TERM= 1.52533E-04
THE SUM OF THE FIRST 17    TERMS= 19.9998

ENTER YES TO RUN AGAIN-OR-NO TO STOP
? "YES"

ENTER: FIRST TERM, COMMON RATIO, AND NUMBER OF TERMS
?-45.5,-.25, 33
THE 33    TH. TERM=-2.46656E-18
THE SUM OF THE FIRST 33    TERMS=-36.4

ENTER YES TO RUN AGAIN-OR-NO TO STOP
? "NO"

TIME 0.0 SECS.
```

Problem Set 2.3

1. Write a BASIC program that will compute and print out the area of a circle ($A = \pi r^2$), where $\pi \approx 3.14159$, given its radius. (Sample data: $r = 2$, 5.3, 6.14, 1.813.)

2. In the formula $D = RT$, D = distance, R = rate, T = time. Write a BASIC program in which the user is asked to input $X = 1, 2,$ or 3. If $X = 1$ is inputted, the

user must then input values for R and T, and the computer will print out the value for D. If $X = 2$ is inputted, the user must then input values for D and T, and the computer will print out the value for R. Finally, if $X = 3$ is inputted, the user must then input values for D and R, and the computer will print out the value for T. (Sample data: $R = 520$, $T = 3.4$; $D = 3143$, $R = 250$; $D = 1005$, $T = 21$.)

3. A previous section ("Compound Interest") contains a BASIC program to compute the accumulated amount A in the compound interest formula $A = P(1 + r/k)^{kn}$. Write a BASIC program that will compute the principal amount P, given A, r, k, and n. (Sample data: $A = \$2598$, $r = 5\%$, $k = 4$, $n = 4$.)

4. Write a BASIC program that will compute and print out a person's gross weekly pay (G), given his/her hourly rate of pay (R) and the number of hours he/she worked for one week. The person in question is paid $(1.5R)$ for each hour over 35 hours worked in any one week.

5. Write a BASIC program that will compute your total accumulated bank savings at the end of n years (that is, $A = P(1 + r/k)^{kn}$, if you deposit the same amount $(X$ dollars) at the beginning of each year for Y years. (Sample data: $X = \$500$, $Y = 5$, $r = 6\%$, $k = 365$, $n = 10$.)

6. Chapter 1 (Article 1.5) contains a list of predefined BASIC system functions. Three of them are SIN(X), COS(X), and TAN(X), where X is in *radian measure*. Write a BASIC program that will read in Y degrees and print out the sine, cosine, and tangent of Y degrees. (*Note:* X radians $= (\pi/180) \cdot Y$ degrees, where $\pi \approx 3.14159$.) (Sample data: $Y = 50$, 63, and 17 degrees.)

7. An *arithmetic progression* is any sequence of the form $a, a + d, a + 2d, \ldots, a + (n - 1)d$, where $a =$ first term, $d =$ common difference of any two successive terms, $n =$ number of terms, $l = a + (n - 1)d$ is last term, and $S = (n/2) \times [2a + (n - 1)d]$ is the sum of the given n terms. Write a BASIC program in which a user inputs a, n, and d, and the computer prints out l and S.

   Sample progressions:
   (a) 5, 16, 27, 38, 49, 60, 71
   (b) twelve terms of the progression 27, 24, 21, 18, ...

2.6

Conversion from Customary (English) to Metric Units

As a decimal-based system, which somewhat parallels the decimal numeration system, the metric system is now used by over 90% of the nations of the world. Even before the United States Congress passed legislation to adopt the metric system on a gradual, voluntary basis, Americans were already "going metric" in several aspects of their daily lives.

While the shutters of millimeter cameras click across America, auto mechanics work on foreign cars manufactured in countries using metric measurement. Metric units now appear on the labels of many of our own products—cigarettes, films, skis, and drugs.

The most important metric units we will need to know about for everyday living are those for length, mass, capacity (liquid), volume (dry measure), area, and temperature.

Length. The basic metric unit of length is the *meter* (slightly longer than a yard). As a measurement system built in base 10, the metric system provides for easy conversions among its units by use of Latin prefixes to denote subunits and multiples of basic units. Commonly used subunits are denoted by *deci, centi,* and *milli.* The *decimeter* is 1/10 (or 0.1) of a meter in length; the *centimeter* is 1/100 (or 0.01) of a meter (1/10 the length of a decimeter); and the *millimeter* is 1/1000 (or 0.001) of a meter (1/10 the length of a centimeter). Of the multiple meter units—*deka* (10 m), *hecto* (100 m), *kilo* (1000 m)—the most important is the *kilometer,* which is 1000 meters long.

Mass. The *gram,* a unit of mass, is approximately the weight of a paper clip (0.035 ounce). The *kilogram* is equal to 1000 grams. We can also establish subunits (the decigram, centigram, milligram) and multiples (dekagram, hectogram, and kilogram) using relationships analogous to subunits and multiples of the meter, but only the gram and kilogram are widely used.

Capacity. The *liter,* or cubic decimeter (slightly larger than the quart) is used for finding liquid volume (1 liter = 1.057 quart). It has subunits and multiples analogous to those of other metric units.

Volume. The content of dry or solid materials is measured in *cubic meters,* but corresponding terms in the metric system (stere = 1 cubic meter; decistere = 0.10 cubic meter; dekastere = 10 cubic meters, and so on), other than 1 cubic centimeter (0.000001 cubic meter), are not commonly used.

Area. For area, the *square meter, square decimeter,* and *square centimeter* are derived from the meter as the prime units and its subunits. One square decimeter is the same area as 100 square centimeters. The hectare, or square hectometer, is about 2.5 acres.

Temperature. In the metric system we measure temperature in *Celsius degrees* (formerly called centigrade). Water freezes at 0°C and boils at 100°C. (Zero weather in Fahrenheit degrees (0°F) has the approximately equivalent temperature of −18°C.)

CONVERSION

For some quick conversions to metric units we can use the following table of conversion factors, which are approximate but close enough to be useful for all practical purposes. The greater the degree of precision desired, the less "quick" our manual conversions are likely to be. We will later use a prepackaged computer program for more accurate conversions from our customary system of measurement to metric units.

Using Table 2.1, let us do some approximate conversions. To find the length in meters of a flagpole 60 feet in length, we first divide 60 by 3 to get 20 yards. Multiplying 20 by the conversion factor of 0.9, we obtain 18 meters as the

Table 2.1 Approximate conversion factors from customary (English) to metric units

Measure	If you know	You can get	If you multiply by
Length	inches (in.)	millimeters (mm)	25
	feet (ft)	centimeters (cm)	30
	yards (yd)	meters (m)	0.9
	miles (mi)	kilometers (km)	1.6
Area	square inches (in.²)	square centimeters (cm²)	6.5
	square feet (ft²)	square meters (m²)	0.09
	square yards (yd²)	square meters (m²)	0.8
	square miles (mi²)	square kilometers (km²)	2.6
	acres	square hectometers or hectares (ha)	0.4
Mass (dry weight)	ounces (oz)	grams (g)	28
	pounds (lb)	kilograms (kg)	0.45
Capacity (liquid)	fluid ounces (fl oz)	milliliters (ml)	30
	quarts (qt)	liters (l)	0.95
	gallons (gal)	liters (l)	3.8
Volume (solid content)	cubic feet (ft³)	cubic meters (m³)	0.03
	cubic yards (yd³)	cubic meters (m³)	0.76
Temperature	degrees Fahrenheit (°F)	degrees Celsius (°C)	5/9 (after subtracting 32)

flagpole's metric length. If I traveled 225 miles in my new car, how far did I go in kilometers (km)? Multiplying 225 by 1.6, we obtain 360.0 km as the distance I traveled.

What is the length in millimeters (mm) of a pencil 4.5 inches long? We multiply 4.5 by 25 to find the pencil's length as 112.5 mm. A bookshelf is 6 feet 3 inches long. What is its length in centimeters (cm)? We first convert 6 feet 3 inches to 6.25 feet, and then multiply 6.25 by 30 to get 187.50 cm as our result.

How much does an apple weighing 3 ounces weigh in grams? Multiplying 3 by 28, we get 84 grams as the weight of the apple. John's scale indicates that he weighs 175 pounds. How many kilograms does he weigh? Multiplying 175 by 0.45, we find that John's weight is 78.75 kg.

How many milliliters are contained in 2 fluid ounces of Charmaine perfume? Multiplying 2 by 30 we obtain 60 ml as the volume of the perfume. To convert 16 quarts of milk to liters, we multiply 16 by 0.95 to get 15.20. We can also determine that 12 gallons of gasoline are equivalent to 45.6 liters of gasoline.

We can convert the area of a photograph measuring 3 inches by 4 inches, or 12 square inches, to square centimeters (or cm^2) if we multiply 12 by 6.5 to obtain 78 cm^2. How would you calculate the area of the cover of this textbook in square centimeters? The top surface of Alice's new desk measures 4 feet in length and $2\frac{1}{2}$ feet in width. What is the area of this surface in square meters? We first find the area to be 4 $\times$ $2\frac{1}{2}$, or 10 square feet, then multiply 10 by 0.09 to get 0.90 square meter. We can also determine that 5 acres of land are equivalent in measurement to 2.0 hectares (ha) by multiplying 5 $\times$ 0.4.

The normal body temperature is 98.6 degrees on the Fahrenheit (F) scale. What is this measurement in degrees Celsius (C)? Subtracting 32 from 98.6, we obtain 66.6; then multiplying 66.6 by the conversion factor 5/9, we obtain 37.0°C as the equivalent in degrees Celsius. In 1714 Gabriel Fahrenheit determined on his thermometer that water boils at 212 degrees. What is this temperature equivalent in degrees Celsius (C)? Subtracting 32 from 212, we obtain 180; then multiplying 180 by 5/9, we get 100°C. Fahrenheit also found that water freezes at 32 degrees. On the Celsius scale, what is the freezing point of water?

2.7

A Prepackaged Program for Converting from Customary (English) to Metric Units

In Article 2.6 approximate formulas were used to convert English measures to metric units. The following more exact equivalents will be used in the prepackaged program entitled METRIC:

    1 yard = 0.914 meter
    1 mile = 1.610 kilometers
    1 inch = 25.4 millimeters

1 foot = 30.5 centimeters
1 ounce = 28.35 grams
1 pound = 0.454 kilogram
1 fluid ounce = 29.71 milliliters
1 quart = 0.951 liter
1 sq. inch = 6.452 sq. centimeters
1 sq. foot = 0.0929 sq. meter
1 acre = 0.4046 hectare

Name: METRIC

Description: This program converts customary (English) measures to their metric equivalents.

Sample Computer Output:

```
RUN


                9:34    07/03/75

TYPE IN A            TO CONVERT FROM    TO

1                    YARDS              METERS
2                    MILES              KILOMETERS
3                    INCHES             MILLIMETERS
4                    FEET               CENTIMETERS
5                    OUNCES             GRAMS
6                    POUNDS             KILOGRAMS
7                    FLUID OUNCES       MILLILITERS
8                    QUARTS             LITERS
9                    SQUARE INCHES      SQUARE CENTIMETERS
10                   SQUARE FEET        SQUARE METERS
11                   ACRES              HECTARES
       OR A 0 TO STOP



?1
 ENTER THE ENGLISH MEASURE
?20
 20   YARDS= 18.28   METERS



?2
 ENTER THE ENGLISH MEASURE
?225
 225 MILES= 362.25 KILOMETERS
```

```
?4
 ENTER THE ENGLISH MEASURE
?6.25
 6.25    FEET= 190.625    CENTIMETERS


?5
 ENTER THE ENGLISH MEASURE
?3
 3    OUNCES= 85.05    GRAMS


?6
 ENTER THE ENGLISH MEASURE
?175
 175 POUNDS= 79.45    KILOGRAMS


?7
 ENTER THE ENGLISH MEASURE
?2
 2    FLUID OUNCES= 59.42    MILLILITERS


?8
 ENTER THE ENGLISH MEASURE
?16
 16    QUARTS= 15 216  LITERS


?9
 ENTER THE ENGLISH MEASURE
?12
 12    SQ.INCHES= 77.424  SQ.CENTIMETERS


?10
 ENTER THE ENGLISH MEASURE
?10
 10    SQ.FEET= .929    SQ.METERS


?11
 ENTER THE ENGLISH MEASURE
?5
 5    ACRES= 2.023    HECTARES


?0

TIME 0.0 SECS.
```

Note: When running the prepackaged program METRIC, a user should tear off the initial table printed by the computer before entering specific customary measures.

Let us look at the flowchart for METRIC (see Figure 2.7). The coding of METRIC is as follows:

```
10 REM    THIS IS THE PREPACKAGED PROGRAM ENTITLED:
20 REM              METRIC
30 PRINT "TYPE IN A","TO CONVERT FROM","TO "
40 PRINT
50 PRINT "1","YARDS","METERS"
60 PRINT "2","MILES","KILOMETERS"
70 PRINT "3","INCHES","MILLIMETERS"
80 PRINT "4","FEET","CENTIMETERS"
90 PRINT "5","OUNCES","GRAMS"
100 PRINT "6","POUNDS","KILOGRAMS"
110 PRINT "7","FLUID OUNCES","MILLILITERS"
120 PRINT "8","QUARTS","LITERS"
130 PRINT"9","SQUARE INCHES","SQUARE CENTIMETERS"
135 PRINT "10","SQUARE FEET","SQUARE METERS"
140 PRINT "11","ACRES","HECTARES"
145 PRINT "   OR A 0 TO STOP   "
150 PRINT
155 PRINT
160 PRINT
165 INPUT K
170 IF K=0 THEN 420
180 PRINT " ENTER THE ENGLISH MEASURE "
185 INPUT X
190 IF K= 1 THEN 410
200 IF K=2 THEN 400
210 IF K=3 THEN 390
220 IF K=4 THEN 380
230 IF K=5 THEN 370
240 IF K=6 THEN 360
245 IF K=7 THEN 350
250 IF K=8 THEN 340
260 IF K=9 THEN 330
280 IF K=10 THEN 320
290 IF K<>11 THEN 420
300 PRINT X"ACRES=";X*0.4046"HECTARES"
310 GO TO 150
320 PRINT X"SQ.FEET=";X*0.0929"SQ.METERS"
325 GO TO 150
330 PRINT X"SQ.INCHES=";X*6.452"SQ.CENTIMETERS"
335 GO TO 150
340 PRINT X"QUARTS=";X*0.951"LITERS"
345 GO TO 150
350 PRINT X"FLUID OUNCES=";X*29.71"MILLILITERS"
355 GO TO 150
360 PRINT X"POUNDS=";X*0.454"KILOGRAMS"
365 GO TO 150
370 PRINT X"OUNCES=";X*28.35"GRAMS"
```

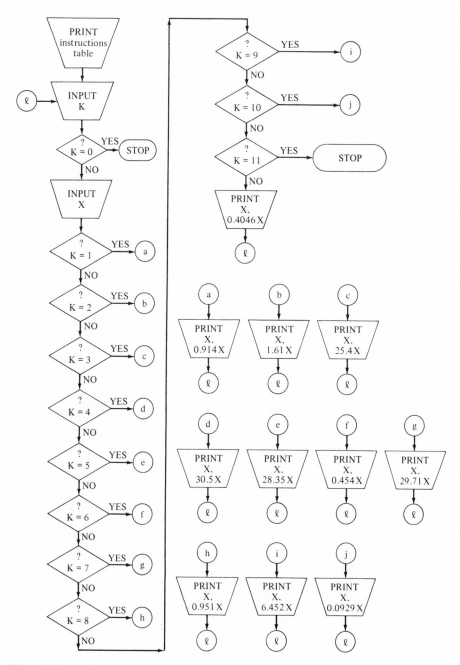

Figure 2.7

```
375 GO TO 150
380 PRINT X "FEET="; X*30.5 "CENTIMETERS"
385 GO TO 150
390 PRINT X "INCHES="; X*25.4 "MILLILITERS"
395 GO TO 150
400 PRINT X "MILES="; X*1.61 "KILOMETERS"
405 GO TO 150
410 PRINT X "YARDS="; X*0.914 "METERS"
415 GO TO 150
420 END
```

2.8

Relations and Functions

The Real Number System

The language of sets and set theory will be developed in Chapter 5 of this textbook. For now it is sufficient to say that a *set* is a collection of objects, and capital letters are used to name a set. One way to describe a set is to list its objects, or *elements*, separated by commas, in a pair of braces. For example:

$$A = \{1,7,11\}$$

$$B = \{2,4,6,8, \ldots\}$$

$$C = \{\text{New York, New Jersey, California}\}$$

$$D = \{(2,4), (3,9), (4,16), (5,25)\}$$

$$E = \{P_1, P_2, P_3, \ldots, P_n\}$$

The set of all positive and negative numbers and zero is called the set of *real* numbers, which may be denoted by the symbol $\mathscr{R}$. Thus, -3, 2, 5/19, 0, $+7$, 10, and $-0.3333 \ldots$ are all real numbers.

The *natural* or *counting numbers* may be denoted by the set $N = \{1,2,3, \ldots\}$. If t is a natural number, what values of t will make the following statements true?

$$t + 5 = 8$$

$$t - 5 = 8$$

$$t + 5 \geq 8$$

$$t + 5 = 5$$

The *cardinal*, or whole, numbers may be denoted by the set $C = \{0,1,2,3, \ldots\}$. If u is a cardinal number, what values of u will make the following statements true?

$$u + 5 = 5$$

$$u - 5 \leq 8$$

$$u + 5 = 2$$

The set of all positive and negative integers and zero (which is nonpositive and nonnegative) may be denoted by the set $Z = \{\ldots, -3, -2, -1, 0, 1, 2, 3, \ldots\}$. If z is an integer, what values of z will make the following statements true?

$$z + 5 = 2$$

$$z - 5 \leq 2$$

$$5z = 2$$

A *rational* number q is any real number that can be written in the form r/s, where r and s are integers and $s \neq 0$. Every rational number can be expressed as a *terminating decimal* or a *repeating* (in some particular order with a repeating block of digits) *decimal*. For example,

$$-7 = -7/1 = -7.0$$

$$3/4 = 0.75$$

$$1/3 = 0.3333\ldots$$

$$-27/99 = -0.272727\ldots$$

$$3/22 = 0.13636\ldots$$

If q is a rational number, what values of q will make the following statements true?

$$5q = 2$$

$$8q + 1 = 3$$

$$8q \leq -2$$

$$q^2 = 2$$

An *irrational* number is any real number that *cannot* be expressed in the form r/s, where r and s are integers and $s \neq 0$. An irrational number is any nonterminating or nonrepeating decimal. For example,

$$\sqrt{3} \approx 1.7321, \qquad \pi \approx 3.1416$$

The values of irrational numbers cannot be computed exactly and are approximated by some rational number. Therefore, if $q^2 = 2$, then $q = \pm\sqrt{2} \approx \pm 1.4142$ and $\sqrt{3} \approx \pm 1.732$. (See Table 1 in Appendix H.)

The real number system consists of all rational numbers and all irrational numbers.

Relations versus Functions

The *Cartesian product* of two sets A and B, denoted by $A \times B$, is the set of all possible ordered pairs, such that the first element in each ordered pair is contained in set A and the second element in each ordered pair is contained in set B. For example, if $A = \{1,2,3\}$ and $B = \{1,2\}$, then

$$A \times B = \{(1,1), (1,2), (2,1), (2,2), (3,1), (3,2)\}$$

The graph of $A \times B$ is given in Figure 2.8.
    Also,

$$B \times A = \{(1,1), (1,2), (1,3), (2,1), (2,2), (2,3)\}$$

and its graph is given in Figure 2.9. It is clear from their respective graphs that $A \times B \neq B \times A$.

If $Z = \{\ldots, -3, -2, -1, 0, 1, 2, 3, \ldots\}$, then $Z \times Z$ represents every point whose rectangular coordinates are integers on the Cartesian or coordinate plane where a vertical and a horizontal axis intersect. Look at the graph of $Z \times Z$ in Figure 2.10.

If $\mathscr{R} = \{\text{real numbers}\}$, then $\mathscr{R} \times \mathscr{R}$ represents all possible points on the real or Cartesian plane used for graphing real relations and functions in elementary algebra. When ordered pairs of real numbers are assigned to points of a plane, we say we have a *Cartesian coordinate system*. The first number of an ordered pair is called the *abscissa* and the second number is called the *ordinate*.

Figure 2.8

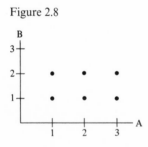

Figure 2.9

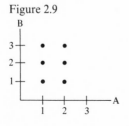

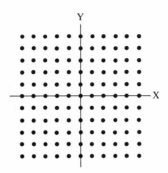

Figure 2.10

A *relation* from a set A into a set B is any set R such that each element in R consisting of an ordered pair is an element in $A \times B$.

A *function* from set A into a set B is a special relation from A to B in which *no two first elements* of an ordered pair are the same. For example, if $A = \{1,2,3\}$ and $B = \{1,2\}$, then $A \times B = \{(1,1), (1,2), (2,1), (2,2), (3,1), (3,2)\}$.

Each of the following sets represents relations from A into B:

$$R_1 = \{(1,1), (1,2), (2,1)\}$$

$$R_2 = \{(1,1), (2,2), (3,2)\}$$

$$R_3 = \{(3,1)\}$$

$$R_4 = A \times B$$

$$R_5 = \{(1, 1), (2,1), (3,1)\}$$

Notice that only R_2, R_3, and R_5 represent functions from A into B. Explain why R_1 and R_4 are *not* functions from A into B.

If $X = Y = \mathscr{R} = \{\text{real numbers}\}$, then $\mathscr{R} \times \mathscr{R}$ represents the coordinate or Cartesian plane. Each of the graphs in Figure 2.11 represents a relation in $\mathscr{R} \times \mathscr{R}$. Which of the relations r_1, r_2, r_3 illustrated in Figure 2.11 does not represent a function in $\mathscr{R} \times \mathscr{R}$?

Figure 2.11

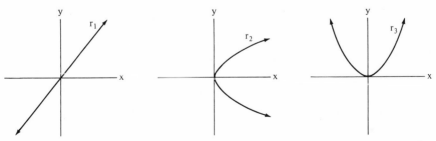

Domain and Range of Relations and Functions

The *domain* of a relation (r) or a function (f) is the set of numbers consisting of the *first elements* in the ordered pairs comprising r and f. The *range* of a relation (r) or function (f) is the set consisting of the *second elements* in the ordered pairs comprising r and f. In the previous example (see preceding section) of relations from A to B, where $A = \{1,2,3\}$ and $B = \{1,2\}$,

$$R_1 = \{(1,1), (1,2), (2,1)\},$$
$$\text{domain} = \{1,2\}, \text{range} = \{1,2\}$$

$$R_2 = \{(1,1), (2,2), (3,2)\} = F_1 \text{ (a function)},$$
$$\text{domain} = \{1,2,3\}, \text{range} = \{1,2\}$$

$$R_3 = \{(3,1)\} = F_2 \text{ (a function)},$$
$$\text{domain} = \{3\}, \text{range} = \{1\}$$

$$R_4 = A \times B,$$
$$\text{domain} = A, \text{range} = B$$

$$R_5 = \{(1,1), (2,1), (3,1)\} = F_3 \text{ (a function)},$$
$$\text{domain} = \{1,2,3\}, \text{range} = \{1\}$$

In the example where $X = Y = \mathcal{R} = \{\text{real numbers}\}$, the relations or functions (see Figure 2.12) were illustrated graphically.

Figure 2.12

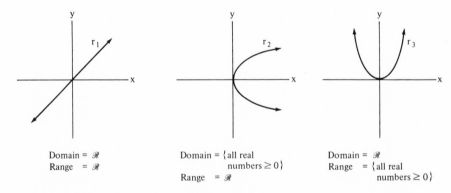

Domain = $\mathcal{R}$ Domain = {all real   Domain = $\mathcal{R}$
Range = $\mathcal{R}$ numbers ≥ 0}   Range = {all real
                            Range = $\mathcal{R}$ numbers ≥ 0}

Problem Set 2.4

1. If $A = \{2,7,8\}$, $B = \{3,7\}$, find:
   (a) $A \times B$ (c) $A \times A$
   (b) $B \times A$ (d) $B \times B$

2. Which of the following sets represent relations from B into A, where $A = \{2,7,8\}$ and $B = \{3,7\}$?

$\quad R_1 = \{(3,2)\}$

$\quad R_2 = \{(3,2), (3,3)\}$

$\quad R_3 = \{(3,2), (3,8), (7,7)\}$

$\quad R_4 = \{(3,2), (7,7), (7,8)\}$

$\quad R_5 = \{(3,2), (7,8)\}$

$\quad R_6 = \{(3,2), (8,8)\}$

3. Which of the sets $R_1, R_2, R_3, R_4, R_5, R_6$ in Problem 2 are functions from B into A?

4. If $A = \{1,2,3,4,7\}$, then give
(a) three examples of relations from A into A.
(b) three examples of functions from A into A.
(c) an example of a relation from A into A that is not a function from A into A.

5. Tell which graphs in Figure 2.13 represent functions in the coordinate or Cartesian plane.

6. State the domain and range for each of the relations in Problem 2 of this problem set.

Figure 2.13

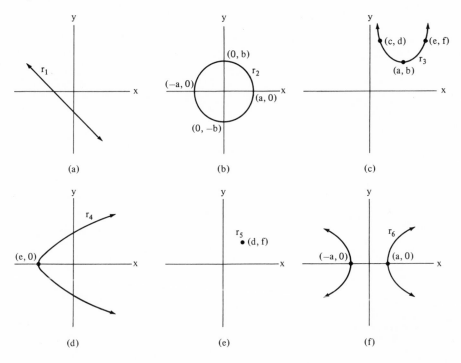

(a) (b) (c)

(d) (e) (f)

7. State the domain and range for each of the relations represented graphically in Problem 5 of this problem set.

8. Which of the following statements is true?
   (a) Every relation is a function.
   (b) Every function is a relation.

2.9

Real Functions, Graphs, and Equations

Function Notation

One approach illustrating rules for functions in the coordinate plane is to write an equation solved for y in terms of x. For example, $y = x^2 - 2$. Such an equation tells us how to find the second (y) element of an ordered pair on the graph of the function, given the first (x) element of the ordered pair.

1. If $y = x^2 - 2$ and $x = 2$, then $y = 2^2 - 2 = 2$, which gives us the ordered pair (2,2).

2. If $y = x^2 - 2$ and $x = -2$, then $y = (-2)^2 - 2 = 2$, which gives us the ordered pair $(-2,2)$.

Another way to illustrate rules for functions in the coordinate plane is to use the following function notation:

$$y = x^2 - 2 \qquad \text{can be represented by } f(x) = x^2 - 2, \text{ which defines the rule for this function } f.$$

$$s = t^2 - 7t + 1 \qquad \text{can be represented by } g(t) = t^2 - 7t + 1, \text{ which defines the rule for a function } g.$$

If $g(t) = t^2 - 7t + 1$,

$$g(-3) = (-3)^2 - 7(-3) + 1 = 31$$

$$g(0) = 0^2 - 7(0) + 1 = 1$$

$$g(3) = 3^2 - 7(3) + 1 = -11$$

Therefore, $(-3,31), (0,1)$, and $(3,-11)$ all lie on the graph of the function g where $g(t) = t^2 - 7t + 1$.

Linear Functions

The general form of a linear (straight line) function is $Ax + By = C$, where A, B, and C are integers and $B \neq 0$. This general or integral form can be solved for y, resulting in the *slope-intercept* or linear form of the equation, or $y =$

$(-A/B)x + C/B$, which may be expressed as

$$f(x) = mx + b,$$

where $m = (-A/B) = $ slope $= $ (change in y/change in x) between any two points on the graph of f, and $b = C/B = $ the y-intercept on the graph of $f(x)$.

The y-intercept is the point (o,b) where the straight line intersects or crosses the Y-axis. If the line crosses the Y-axis at $(0,5)$ for example, then the value of the y-intercept or $b = 5$.

If $x_1 \neq x_2$ (so that their difference is not equal to 0), we can determine the slope m of the straight line joining the points whose coordinates are (x_1, y_1) and (x_2, y_2) by computing

$$m = \frac{y_2 - y_1}{x_2 - x_1}$$

For example, if a straight line passes through the points $(4,5)$ and $(-3, -7)$, then

$$m = \frac{-7 - 5}{-3 - 4} \quad \text{or} \quad m = \frac{-12}{-7} = \frac{12}{7}$$

Any two points on the graphs of a linear function determine its *straight-line graph*. For example, if we are given $3x + 2y = 7$, then

$$y = f(x) = (-3/2)x + 7/2$$

$$f(0) = 7/2 \quad \text{so we have the ordered pair } (0, 7/2)$$

$$f(2) = 1/2 \quad \text{so we have the ordered pair } (2, 1/2)$$

By plotting these two points on a set of X- and Y-axes, we can construct or draw the straight-line graph of $y = (-3/2)x + 7/2$, as shown in Figure 2.14.

Figure 2.14

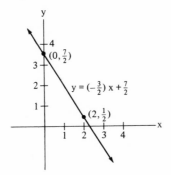

Do you see that the value of the y-intercept or b for this equation is $7/2$? Again, if we are given $2y = 7$ or $y = g(x) = 7/2$, we can find

$$g(0) = 7/2 \quad \text{and} \quad g(1) = 7/2, \text{ etc.}$$

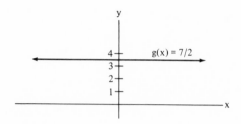

Figure 2.15

Then g (any real x) $= 7/2$, and its graph is plotted in Figure 2.15.

Does $f(x) = c$, where c is a constant, represent a relation or a function? Why?

The following computer program prints out a table of values for the linear function $Ax + By = C$ or $f(x) = (-A/B)x + (C/B)$, given A, B, and C are integers and $B \neq 0$.

```
10 REM   THIS PROGRAM PRINTS OUT A TABLE OF VALUES FOR:
20 REM           AX+BY=C WHERE BOTH A AND B<>0
30 PRINT
40 PRINT
50 PRINT "ENTER A,B,C FOR AX+BY=C"
60 INPUT A,B,C
70 IF A<>0 THEN110
80 IF B<>0 THEN110
90 PRINT "BOTH A AND B CANNOT EQUAL 0"
100 GO TO 30
110 IF B<0 THEN 140
120 PRINT A;"X+"B;"Y="C
130 GO TO 150
140 PRINT A;"X"B;"Y="C
150 PRINT
160 PRINT "X","Y"
170 IF B=0 THEN 230
180 IF A=0 THEN 280
190 FOR X= 0 TO C/A STEP C/(2*A)
200     PRINT X,(-A/B)*X+C/B
210 NEXT X
220 GO TO 30
230 PRINT "NOT A FUNCTION"
240 FOR Y=-1 TO 1
250     PRINT C/A,Y
260 NEXT Y
270 GO TO 30
280 FOR X=-1 TO 1
290     PRINT X,C/B
300 NEXT X
310 GO TO 30
320 END
```

```
RUN
                9:41    07/08/75


ENTER A,B,C FOR AX+BY=C
?2,3,12
 2    X+ 3    Y= 12

X                 Y
 0                4
 3                2.
 6                9.53674E-07


ENTER A,B,C FOR AX+BY=C
?2,-3,12
 2    X-3    Y= 12

X                 Y
 0                -4
 3                -2.
 6                -9.53674E-07


ENTER A,B,C FOR AX+BY=C
?0,3,12
 0    X+ 3    Y= 12

X                 Y
-1                4
 0                4
 1                4


ENTER A,B,C FOR AX+BY=C
?2 ,0,12
 2    X+ 0    Y= 12

X                 Y
NOT A FUNCTION
 6                -1
 6                0
 6                1


ENTER A,B,C FOR AX+BY=C
?0,0,12
BOTH A AND B CANNOT EQUAL 0


ENTER A,B,C FOR AX+BY=C
?

STOP.
RAN 0.0 SEC.
```

If we let $B = 0$ in the straight-line equation $Ax + By = C$, the resulting equation $Ax = C$ (if $A \neq 0$) or $Ax + C = 0$ is the *general form* of a linear equation that has exactly one real solution. For example,

$$5(4x - 3) + 2x = 7x - 8$$

$$20x - 15 + 2x = 7x - 8$$

$$22x - 15 = 7x - 8$$

$$15x - 15 = -8$$

$$15x = 7 \qquad \text{(general form)}$$

$$x = 7/15$$

Does the linear equation $Ax + C = 0$ represent a relation or function? Why?

Quadratic Functions

The general form of a quadratic (parabolic) function is $y = f(x) = ax^2 + bx + c$, where a, b, and c are real numbers and $a \neq 0$. For example, if $f(x) = x^2 + 3$,

1. $f(-2) = (-2)^2 + 3 = 7$; then we have the ordered pair $(-2,7)$.

2. $f(0) = 0^2 + 3 = 3$; then we have the ordered pair $(0,3)$.

3. $f(2) = 2^2 + 3 = 7$; then we have the ordered pair $(2,7)$.

With these three ordered pairs we can plot the graph of $f(x) = x^2 + 3$, as in Figure 2.16. This type of graph is called a *parabola*. We can see the form of the parabola in the spray of a water fountain, in the cable of a suspension bridge, and in the trajectory or curved path of a missile.

If $a > 0$ in $f(x) = ax^2 + bx + c$, then the graph of f opens *upward* or is concave upward; if $a < 0$, then the graph of f opens *downward* or is concave downward. Every parabola has a *vertex* or point at which the parabola reaches its maximum (highest) or minimum (lowest) point. We can simplify the graphing

Figure 2.16

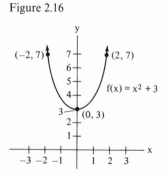

of a parabola by finding the coordinates of its vertex first. Consider:

$$f(x) = ax^2 + bx + c$$

$$= a\left(x^2 + \frac{b}{a}x\right) + c$$

By a process called *completing the square* we obtain

$$= a\left(x^2 + \frac{b^2}{a}x + \frac{b^2}{4a^2}\right) + c - \frac{b^2}{4a}$$

$$= a\left(x + \frac{b}{2a}\right)^2 + \frac{4ac - b^2}{4a}$$

The straight line $x = -b/2a$ serves as an *axis of symmetry* for the parabola; that is,

$$f\left(T - \frac{b}{2a}\right) = f\left(-T - \frac{b}{2a}\right)$$

for any real number T. The point at which the axis of symmetry intersects the graph of the parabola is called the *vertex* of the parabola. The value $x = -b/2a$ generates the ordered pair $(-b/2a, f(-b/2a))$, which *locates* the vertex of the parabola. If $f(x) = -x^2 + 5x + 6$, $-b/2a = -5/-2 = 5/2$, then

$$f(0) = 6$$

$$f(5/2) = 49/4$$

$$f(5) = 6$$

We can use these three ordered pairs to plot the graph of $f(x)$ in Figure 2.17. Notice that the graph of $f(x)$ crosses the X-axis twice.

Figure 2.17

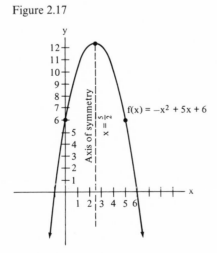

If $g(x) = x^2 + 6x + 9$, then $-b/2a = -6/2 = -3$, and

$$g(-6) = 9$$
$$g(-3) = 0$$
$$g(0) = 9$$

Using these three ordered pairs we plot the graph of $g(x)$ in Figure 2.18. You can see that the graph of $g(x)$ touches or is tangent to the X-axis once.

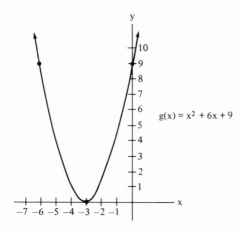

Figure 2.18

If $h(x) = x^2 + x + 1$, then

$$-b/2a = -1/2$$

and

$$h(-1) = 1$$
$$h(-1/2) = 3/4$$
$$h(0) = 1$$

We now plot the graph of $h(x)$ in Figure 2.19. Observe that the graph of $h(x)$ does not intersect or cross the X-axis.

Figure 2.19

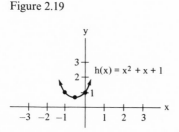

If we let $y = f(x) = 0$ in $y = f(x) = ax^2 + bx + c$, the resulting equation $ax^2 + bx + c = 0$ is the *general form* of a quadratic equation that has at most two real solutions, or *roots*. You saw that the graph of $f(x) = -x^2 + 5x + 6$ intersected the X-axis twice; these two intersections indicate that $-x^2 + 5x + 6 = 0$ has two *real* roots. Since the graph of $g(x) = x^2 + 6x + 9$ is tangent to the X-axis, the equation $x^2 + 6x + 9 = 0$ has *one* real root. The graph of $h(x) = x^2 + x + 1$ does not intersect the X-axis; therefore, $x^2 + x + 1 = 0$ has *no* real roots.

In elementary algebra we are shown how to solve quadratic equations (such as $x^2 + 5x + 6 = 0$) by *factoring*. If $x^2 + 5x + 6 = 0$, then $(x + 2)(x + 3) = 0$. THEN

$$x + 2 = 0 \quad \text{or} \quad x + 3 = 0$$

and

$$x = -2 \quad \text{or} \quad x = -3$$

Therefore, $x = -2$ and $x = -3$ are the two real solutions or roots of the equation $x^2 + 5x + 6 = 0$. By first substituting the value $x = -2$ and then the value $x = -3$, we can verify or *check* that -2 and -3 are real roots of the equation. Thus, $(-2)^2 + 5(-2) + 6 = 0$ gives us $4 - 10 + 6 = 0$; and $(-3)^2 + 5(-3) + 6 = 0$ gives us $9 - 15 + 6 = 0$.

In order to solve other quadratic equations such as $x^2 + 5x + 3 = 0$, we can use the *quadratic formula*, which is derived from the equation $ax^2 + bx + c = 0$. If $ax^2 + bx + c = 0$, then

$$x^2 + (b/a)x + (c/a) = 0$$

$$(x^2 + (b/a)x + b^2/4a^2) + ((c/a) - b^2/4a^2) = 0$$

$$((x + b)/2a)^2 + ((4ac - b^2)/4a^2) = 0$$

$$((x + b)/2a)^2 = (b^2 - 4ac)/4a^2$$

$$(x + b)/2a = \pm\sqrt{(b^2 - 4ac)}/2a$$

$$x = (-b \pm \sqrt{b^2 - 4ac})/2a$$

In the example, $x^2 + 5x + 3 = 0$; and $a = 1, b = 5, c = 3$.

Then

$$x = (-5 \pm \sqrt{5^2 - 4 \cdot 1 \cdot 3})/(2 \cdot 1)$$

$$= (-5 \pm \sqrt{13})/2$$

and

$$x_1 = (-5 + \sqrt{13})/2 \qquad x_2 = (-5 - \sqrt{13})/2$$

or

$$x_1 \approx -0.69722 \qquad x_2 \approx -4.30277$$

The flowchart in Figure 2.20 can be used to write a computer program to solve or find the real roots of any quadratic equation. *Remember*: for $ax^2 + bx + c = 0$, $x = (-b \pm \sqrt{b^2 - 4ac})/2a$.

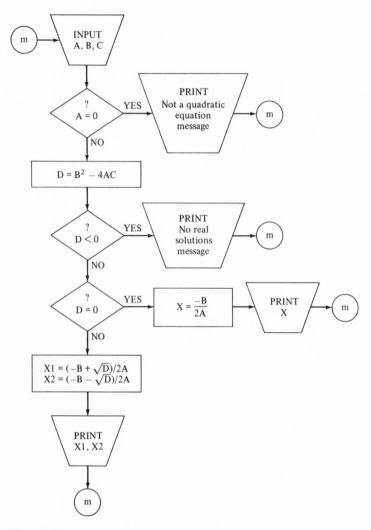

Figure 2.20

2.10

User Defined Functions

The DEF (Definition) Statement

GENERAL FORM

Line number DEF FNm(n) = rule for a function of *n*, where *m* and *n* are any letters of the alphabet and *m* designates the name of the function. The DEF statement tells the computer how to evaluate a function, given a particular argument *n*. Computation takes place only when a statement containing DEF FNm(n) is assigned a particular value for *n* and is subsequently executed.

For example, suppose we want to use the DEF statement to print out a table of the first ten counting numbers and their squares.

Solution:

```
10 DEF FNA(X)=X↑2
20 FOR I=1 TO 10
30    PRINT I,FNA(I)
40 NEXT I
50 END
RUN
```

```
          15:47    06/24/75

    1                1
    2                4
    3                9
    4               16
    5               25
    6               36
    7               49
    8               64
    9               81
   10              100

  TIME 0.0 SECS.
```

It is not necessary to use the DEF statement in the previous program, but in more complex problems it will be convenient to use such a definition statement.

Problem Set 2.5

1. Plot the graphs of the functions *f* and *g*, where $f(x) = 5x - 3$ and $g(t) = 2t^2 - 8t + 5$.

2. Given the following rules for the functions *h* and *p*:
$$h(r) = -5r - (7/5), \qquad p(s) = 2s^2 - s + 9$$
find $h(3)$, $h(-1/2)$, $h(t)$; and $p(5)$, $p(-3/5)$, $p(a + 2)$.

3. Code the flowchart in Article 2.9 (Figure 2.20) for solving any quadratic equation in the BASIC language.

4. Use your program in Problem 3 to solve the following equations:
   (a) $-5x^2 - 0.3x + 7 = 0$
   (b) $25t^2 - 3t + 2 = 0$
   (c) $25t^2 - 3t - 2 = 0$

5. Write a BASIC program to print out a table of values for $(x, f(x))$, where $f(x) = 5x^2 - 17x + 2$ and $x = -1, -0.9, -0.8, \ldots, 0, 0.1, 0.2, \ldots, 1$.

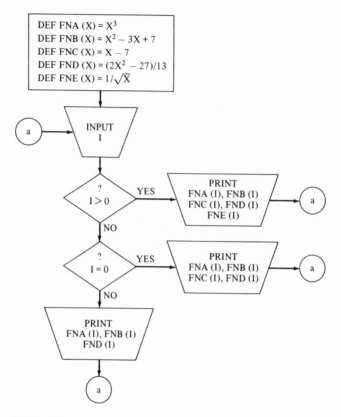

Figure 2.21

6. Write DEF statements for the following functions of x:
  (a) $f_1 = x^3$
  (b) $f_2 = x^2 - 3x + 7$
  (c) $f_3 = x - 7$
  (d) $f_4 = (2x^2 - 27)/13$
  (e) $f_5 = 1/x$

7. Code the flowchart in Figure 2.21 in the BASIC programming language.

8. Run the program you coded for Problem 7 by inputting $I = 19, -27, 34, 0$.

9. Code the flowchart in Figure 2.22 in the BASIC language so that it will print out enough information for you to plot the graph of $y = f(x) = ax^2 + bx + c$, where $a \neq 0$.

10. (a) Run the program in Problem 9 with the functions f and g defined by $f(x) = -5x^2 - 3x + 2$ and $g(t) = t^2 + 5t - 7$.
  (b) Use the printed information to plot graphs of f and g.

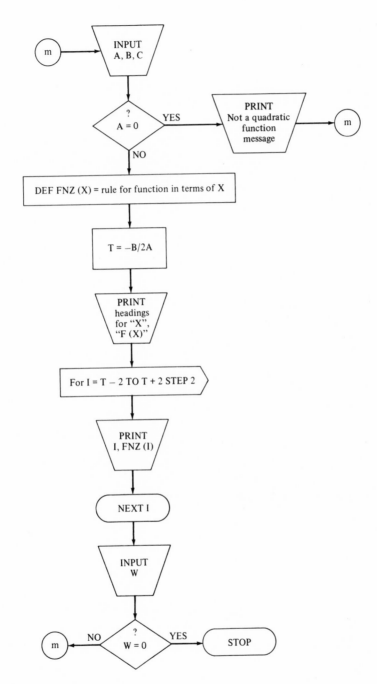

Figure 2.22

"Polynomial Functions"

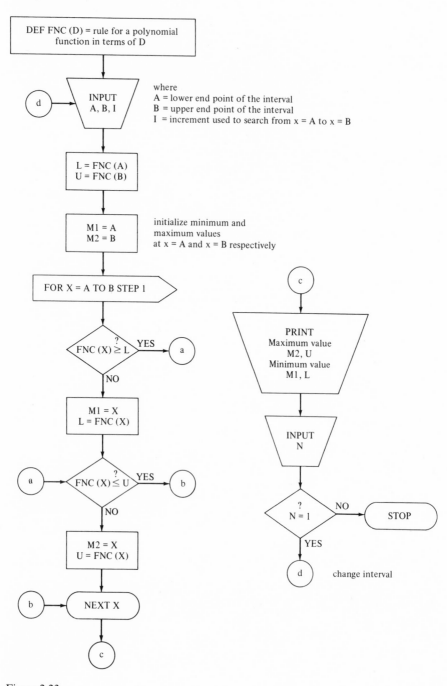

Figure 2.23

```
5 REM     THIS PROGRAM WILL SEARCH FOR APPROXIMATE MAXIMUM
10 REM        AND MINIMUM VALUES OF A FUNCTION DEFINED
15 REM           ON THE INTERVAL [A,B]
20 REM        YOU MUST ENTER THE FUNCTION IN LINE 60
25 REM           AS FOLLOWS: 60 DEF FNC(D)=...
30 PRINT
40 PRINT
50 PRINT
70 PRINT "ENTER LOWER ENDPOINT,UPPER ENDPOINT,AND INCREMENT ON[A,B]"
80 INPUT A,B,I
90 LET L=FNC(A)
100 LET U=FNC(B)
110 LET M1=A
120 LET M2=B
130 FOR X=A TO B STEP I
140     IF FNC(X)>=L THEN 170
150     LET M1=X
160     LET L=FNC(X)
170     IF FNC(X)<=U THEN 200
180     LET M2=X
190     LET U=FNC(X)
200 NEXT X
210 PRINT "THE MAXIMUM POINT ON [A,B] HAS THE COORDINATES:"
220 PRINT "X=";M2;"Y=";U
240 PRINT "THE MINIMUM POINT ON [A,B] HAS THE COORDINATES:"
250 PRINT "X=";M1;"Y=";L
260 PRINT "ENTER 1 TO CHANGE INTERVAL OR 0 TO CHANGE FUNCTION"
270 INPUT N
280 IF N=1 THEN 30
290 END
```

Polynomial Functions

The general form for the rule of a polynomial function of degree n is $y = f(x) = a_n x^n + a_{n-1} x^{n-1} + \cdots + a_1 x + a_0$, where n is a natural number and $a_n \neq 0$. For example:

$f(x) = 3x - 7$ is a polynomial function of degree 1.

$g(t) = 5t^2 - 3t + 2$ is a polynomial function of degree 2.

$h(r) = 9r^3 - 3r + 1$ is a polynomial function of degree 3.

$p(s) = 0.95s^8 - 7s^3 + 4$ is a polynomial function of degree 8.

In graphing a second-degree polynomial function ($f(x) = ax^2 + bx + c$, where $a \neq 0$), we were able to find the extreme or critical value of the function by means of the formula $x = -b/2a$. Finding extreme values of polynomial functions of degree $n > 3$ requires methods from the calculus. The computer can be used to *approximate* maximum or minimum values for a function defined on a given interval. Note that the maximum (or minimum) *value* of the function is the *second* coordinate of the maximum (or minimum) point.

The BASIC program on pages 86–87 searches for maximum and minimum points of a polynomial function in the interval $[a,b]$; that is, from $x = a$ to $x = b$, inclusive.

```
60  DEF FNC( D)= Dt 3+ Dt 2- 6* D
RUN
                18:54    07/14/75
ENTER LOWER ENDPOINT, UPPER ENDPOINT, AND INCREMENT ON[A, B]
?- 3, 2, .01
THE MAXIMUM POINT ON [A, B] HAS THE COORDINATES:
X=-1.78997    Y= 8.20876
THE MINIMUM POINT ON [A, B] HAS THE COORDINATES:
X= 1.12004    Y=-4.06067
ENTER 1 TO CHANGE INTERVAL OR 0 TO CHANGE FUNCTION
?0
TIME 0.1 SECS.
60  DEF FNC( D)= Dt 3+ 6* Dt 2- 13*D- 42
RUN
                18:57    07/14/75
ENTER LOWER ENDPOINT, UPPER ENDPOINT, AND INCREMENT ON[A, B]
?- 7, -2, .01
THE MAXIMUM POINT ON [A, B] HAS THE COORDINATES:
X=-4.88995    Y= 48.1124
THE MINIMUM POINT ON [A, B] HAS THE COORDINATES:
X=-7    Y= 0
ENTER 1 TO CHANGE INTERVAL OR 0 TO CHANGE FUNCTION
?1
```

```
ENTER LOWER ENDPOINT, UPPER ENDPOINT, AND INCREMENT ON[A,B]
?-2,3,.01
THE MAXIMUM POINT ON [A,B] HAS THE COORDINATES:
X= 3     Y= 0
THE MINIMUM POINT ON [A,B] HAS THE COORDINATES:
X= .890027     Y=-48.1124
ENTER 1 TO CHANGE INTERVAL OR 0 TO CHANGE FUNCTION
?0
TIME 0.1 SECS.
```

This printout information can be used to plot the following graphs.

(a) $y = f(x) = x^3 + x^2 - 6x = x(x^2 + x - 6) = x(x + 3)(x - 2)$

The approximate maximum point is at $(-1.79, 8.21)$; the approximate minimum point is at $(1.12, -4.06)$; and the three zeros of the function exist at $(-3,0), (0,0)$, and $(2,0)$. See Figure 2.24.

(b) $y = f(x) = x^3 + 6x^2 - 13x - 42$

The approximate maximum point is at $(-4.88, 48.11)$; the approximate minimum point is at $(0.89, -48.11)$; and three zeros of the function exist at $(-7,0)$, $(-2,0)$, and $(3,0)$, two of which we obtained in our computer search for maximum and minimum points. See Figure 2.25.

Figure 2.24

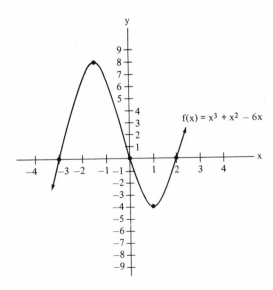

$f(x) = x^3 + x^2 - 6x$

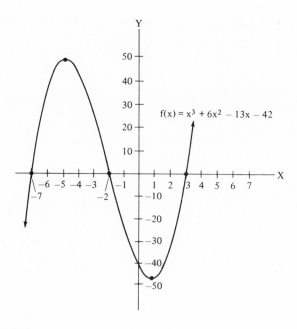

Figure 2.25

Roots of Polynomials

If we let $y = f(x) = 0$ in

$$y = f(x) = a_nx^n + a_{n-1}x^{n-1} + \cdots + a_1x + a_0$$

the resulting equation is

$$a_nx^n + a_{n-1}x^{n-1} + \cdots + a_1x + a_0 = 0$$

where n is a natural number and $a_n \neq 0$ is a polynomial equation of degree n, which has at most n real solutions or roots. If the expression in a polynomial equation can be factored, its solution is elementary. For example:

$$x^3 + x^2 - 6x = 0$$
$$x(x^2 + x - 6) = 0$$
$$\underline{x(x + 3)(x - 2) = 0}$$

$x = 0$	$x + 3 = 0$	$x - 2 = 0$
	$x = -3$	$x = 2$

Thus, 0, -3, and 2 are the three real roots of this cubic or third-degree equation.

If the polynomial expression cannot be factored, the solution of the polynomial equation involves methods from advanced algebra or the calculus. One method used for approximating roots of a polynomial equation is the method known as *binary chopping*. This method allows you to search for one root of a polynomial equation in the interval $[a,b]$, provided $f(a)$ and $f(b)$ have *opposite signs*. Notice that each of the following graphs of $f(x)$ and $g(x)$ in Figure 2.26 intersects the X-axis.

If a polynomial function is defined on an interval $[a,b]$, where $f(a) > 0$ and $f(b) < 0$, then there must be a value for x in the interval $[a,b]$ where the graph of f crosses the X-axis, as shown in the graph of $f(x)$ in Figure 2.26. This value of x is a *zero* of the polynomial function and a *root* of the polynomial equation. Similarly, if $g(a) < 0$ and $g(b) > 0$ for a polynomial function, there must be a value for x in $[a,b]$ where the graph of g crosses the X-axis, as shown in the graph of $g(x)$ in Figure 2.26. This value of x is a zero of the polynomial function and a root of the polynomial equation.

In the method of binary chopping we simply inspect the sign of the function at the *midpoint* of $[a,b]$—that is, where $x = (a + b)/2$—when $f(a)$ and $f(b)$ have opposite signs. If $f(a) > 0$, $f(b) < 0$, and $x = (a + b)/2$ for a polynomial function, then:

1. If $f(x) \approx 0$, there is an approximate root at x.

2. If $f(x) < 0$, there is a root in the interval $[a,x]$.

3. If $f(x) > 0$, there is a root in the interval $[x,b]$.

If $f(a) < 0$, $f(b) > 0$, and $x = (a + b)/2$ for a polynomial function, then:

1. If $f(x) \approx 0$, there is an approximate root at x.

Figure 2.26

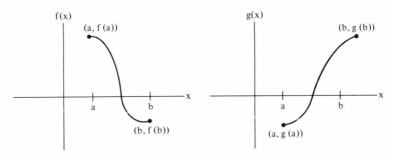

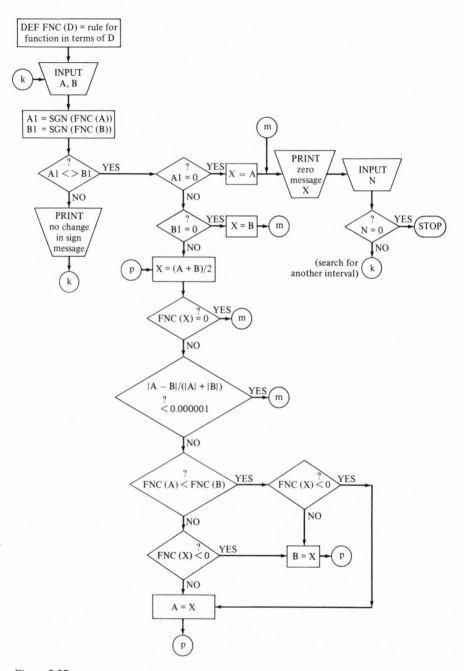

Figure 2.27

2. If $f(x) < 0$, there is a root in the interval $[x,b]$.

3. If $f(x) > 0$, there is a root in the interval $[a,x]$.

Let us construct a flowchart (Figure 2.27) that uses the method of binary chopping to search for a root of a polynomial equation; then code this flowchart in BASIC, as in the following printout, and run it with some sample polynomial equations.

```
5 REM     THIS PROGRAM SEARCHES FOR ONE ROOT OF A
10 REM              POLYNOMIAL EQUATION IN
15 REM               THE INTERVAL [A,B]
20 REM      YOU MUST ENTER THE RULE OF THE FUNCTION IN LINE 30
25 REM             AS FOLLOWS:  30 DEF FNC(D)=...
40 PRINT
50 PRINT
60 PRINT "ENTER THE ENDPOINTS OF THE INTERVAL"
70 INPUT A,B
80 LET A1=SGN(FNC(A))
90 LET B1=SGN(FNC(B))
100 IF A1<>B1 THEN 130
110 PRINT "NO CHANGE IN SIGN--CHOOSE ANOTHER INTERVAL[A,B]"
120 GO TO 40
130 IF A1=0 THEN 150
140 IF B1=0 THEN 220
145 GO TO 250
150 LET X=A
160 PRINT "ONE ROOT AT X="X
170 PRINT
180 PRINT "ENTER A 0 TO STOP OR A 1 TO SEARCH ANOTHER INTERVAL"
190 INPUT N
200 IF N=0 THEN 350
210 GO TO 40
220 LET X=B
230 GO TO 160
240 REM            -----BINARY ROOT CHOPPING-----
250 LET X=(A+B)/2
260 IF FNC(X)=0 THEN 160
270 IF ABS(A-B)/(ABS(A)+ABS(B))<.000001 THEN 160
280 IF FNC(A)<FNC(B) THEN 320
290 IF FNC(X)<0 THEN 330
300 LET A=X
310 GO TO 250
320 IF FNC(X)<0 THEN 300
330 LET B=X
340 GO TO 250
350 END
```

```
30 DEF FNC(D)=D↑3+D↑2-6*D
RUN

ROOT          17:40    07/15/75


ENTER THE ENDPOINTS OF THE INTERVAL
?-5,-1
ONE ROOT AT X=-3

ENTER A 0 TO STOP OR A 1 TO SEARCH ANOTHER INTERVAL
?1


ENTER THE ENDPOINTS OF THE INTERVAL
?-1,1
ONE ROOT AT X= 0

ENTER A 0 TO STOP OR A 1 TO SEARCH ANOTHER INTERVAL
?1


ENTER THE ENDPOINTS OF THE INTERVAL
?1,5
ONE ROOT AT X= 2

ENTER A 0 TO STOP OR A 1 TO SEARCH ANOTHER INTERVAL
?0

TIME 0.0 SECS.
```

```
30 DEF FNC(D)=D↑3+6*D↑2-13*D-42
RUN

ROOT          17:43    07/15/75


ENTER THE ENDPOINTS OF THE INTERVAL
?-10,-5
ONE ROOT AT X=-7

ENTER A 0 TO STOP OR A 1 TO SEARCH ANOTHER INTERVAL
?1


ENTER THE ENDPOINTS OF THE INTERVAL
?-5,0
ONE ROOT AT X=-2

ENTER A 0 TO STOP OR A 1 TO SEARCH ANOTHER INTERVAL
?1
```

```
ENTER THE ENDPOINTS OF THE INTERVAL
?0,2
NO CHANGE IN SIGN--CHOOSE ANOTHER INTERVAL[A,B]

ENTER THE ENDPOINTS OF THE INTERVAL
?0,5
ONE ROOT AT X= 3

ENTER A 0 TO STOP OR A 1 TO SEARCH ANOTHER INTERVAL
?0

TIME 0.0 SECS.
```

Problem Set 2.6

1. Give the degree of the following polynomial functions:
  (a) $f(x) = x^3 - 3x^2 + 2x$
  (b) $g(t) = t^2 - t^4 + 5t^3 - 22$
  (c) $h(r) = r^5 - r^9$
  (d) $j(s) = s - 3$

2. Use the maximum and minimum point-searching program given under the section "Polynomial Functions" to search for such points of the following polynomial functions in the given intervals:
  (a) $f(x) = x^3 - 3x^2 + 3$ in the intervals $[0,1]$, $[1,2]$.
  (b) $g(t) = t^2 - t^4 + 5t^3 - 22$ in the intervals $[-1,-0.05]$, $[0,1]$, $[1,5]$.
  (c) $h(x) = x^3 + x^2 - 6x$ in the intervals $[-3,0]$, $[0,2]$.

3. Use the root-searching program given under "Roots of Polynomials" to search for roots of the following polynomial equations:
  (a) $x^3 - 3x^2 + 2x = 0$
  (b) $t^4 - 5t^3 - t^2 + 22 = 0$
  (c) $x^3 + x^2 - 6x = 0$
  (d) $x^3 + x^2 - 6x + 9 = 0$
  (e) $r^9 - r^5 = 0$

4. Write a BASIC program to compute and print out a table of values for $(x, f(x))$, where $f(x) = x^3 + x^2 - 6x$ and $x = -3, -2.9, -2.8, \ldots, 0, 0.1, 0.2, \ldots, 2$.

5. Run the following BASIC program:

```
10   PRINT "X","F(X)","G(X)"
20   DEF FNF(A)=X↑2+1
30   DEF FNG(B)=X↑3-1
40   FOR X=1 TO 2 STEP 0.1
50      PRINT X,FNF(X),FNG(X)
60   NEXT X
70   END
```

6. The notation $n!$ is read as "n factorial" and is defined as follows:

$$n! = n(n - 1)(n - 2)\ldots(1)$$

where $n = 1,2,3,\ldots$; that is,

$$1! = 1$$
$$2! = 2 \cdot 1 = 2$$
$$3! = 3 \cdot 2 \cdot 1 = 6$$
$$4! = 4 \cdot 3 \cdot 2 \cdot 1 = 24$$
$$5! = 5 \cdot 4 \cdot 3 \cdot 2 \cdot 1 = 120$$

Note: $n! = n(n - 1)!$ or

$$6! = 6 \cdot 5! = 6 \cdot 120 = 720$$
$$7! = 7 \cdot 6! = 7 \cdot 720 = 5040$$

Write a BASIC program to print out the following table:

N	N FACTORIAL
1	1
2	2
3	6
⋮	⋮
20	?

2.11

A Prepackaged Program for Plotting Functions Defined on the Interval [A,B]

The TAB function in the BASIC language can be used to simulate the graph of a function defined on the interval $[A,B]$. We must realize that the computer tabs or moves horizontally $0, 1, 2, 3, \ldots, 70$ places (that is, it moves an *integral* number of spaces); therefore we can only simulate when plotting the $y = f(x)$ value in the ordered pair (x,y) of a function. For example, the following BASIC program prints out a table of values for the function f defined by $y = f(x) = x^2 - 1$ and merely simulates the shape of its graph with the X-axis running vertically along the paper.

```
10 PRINT "X","Y"
20 FOR X=-4 TO 4
30     LET Y=X↑2-1
40       PRINT X,Y;TAB(Y+30);"."
50 NEXT X
60 END
```

```
RUN
X                    Y
 -4                  15                                        •
 -3                   8                              •
 -2                   3                        •
 -1                   0                   •
  0                  -1               •
  1                   0                   •
  2                   3                        •
  3                   8                              •
  4                  15                                        •

*READY
```

Let us look at the instruction sheet for a more sophisticated prepackaged program called GRAPH, which simulates the graph of a function defined on the interval $[A,B]$:

Name: GRAPH

Description: This program simulates the graph of a function on the interval $[A,B]$, provided the function $f = \{(x, f(x))\}$ is defined for each point in $[A,B]$.

Instructions: Before running the program you must define the function in line 40 as follows:

40 DEF FNC(Z) = rule for function in terms of Z. After typing in the RUN command you must enter:

1. lower limit, upper limit, and increment for x.

2. lower limit, upper limit, and increment for $y = f(x)$.

Sample Computer Run:

```
40 DEF FNC(D)=D†2-1
RUN

ENTER LOWER LIMIT,UPPER LIMIT,INCREMENT ON X-AXIS

? -3,3,.1
ENTER LOWER LIMIT,UPPER LIMIT,INCREMENT ON Y-AXIS

? -2,2,.1
```

X-AXIS

```
*READY
40 DEF FNC(D)=D↑3+D↑2-6*D
RUN

ENTER LOWER LIMIT,UPPER LIMIT,INCREMENT ON X-AXIS

? -4,4,.1
ENTER LOWER LIMIT,UPPER LIMIT,INCREMENT ON Y-AXIS

? -2,2,.1
```

X-AXIS

```
*READY
```

The flowchart for GRAPH is given in Figure 2.28. Now look at the coding of GRAPH, as shown in the following printout.

```
0010 REM          THIS PROGRAM SIMULATES THE GRAPH OF A FUNCTION DEFINED
0020 REM                    ON AN INTERVAL [A,B]
0025 REM          ENTER THE RULE FOR THE FUNCTION IN LINE 40 AS FOLLOWS:
0030 REM                    40 DEF FNC(D)=...
0050 PRINT
0060 PRINT "ENTER LOWER LIMIT,UPPER LIMIT,INCREMENT ON X-AXIS"
0070 INPUT A,B,I1
0080 PRINT "ENTER LOWER LIMIT,UPPER LIMIT,INCREMENT ON Y-AXIS"
0090 INPUT C,D,I2
0110 LET Y1=0
0120 IF (D-C)/I2<=70 THEN 0140
0130 PRINT "THE RANGE OF THE Y-AXIS IS TOO LARGE"
0135 GOTO 0050
0140 IF SGN(A)=SGN(B)THEN     0170
0150 IF SGN(C)=SGN(D)THEN     0190
0160 GOTO 0200
0170 LET X1=A
0180 IF SGN(C)<>SGN(D) THEN 0200
0190 LET Y1=C
0200 LET Y1=(Y1-C)/I2
0210 LET D=(D-C)/I2
0220 FOR X=A TO B STEP I1
0230    LET Y=(FNC(X)-C)/I2
0240    LET Y=INT(Y+.5)
0250    IF Y>D THEN     0340
0260    IF Y<C THEN     0340
0270    IF Y1>=Y THEN     0300
0280    PRINT  TAB (Y1);"-"; TAB (Y);"."
0290    GOTO 0340
0300    IF Y1>Y GOTO 0330
0310    PRINT  TAB (Y);"."
0320    GOTO 0340
0330    PRINT  TAB (Y);"."; TAB (Y1);"-"

0340 NEXT X
0350 PRINT  TAB (Y1);"X-AXIS"
0360 END
```

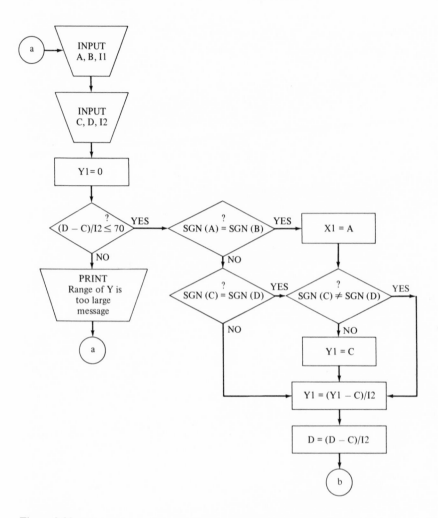

Figure 2.28

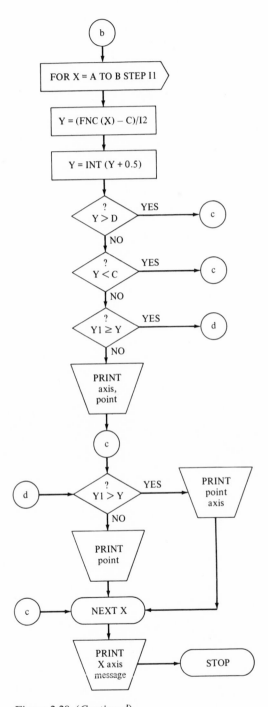

Figure 2.28 (*Continued*)

Problem Set 2.7

1. Use the prepackaged program GRAPH to simulate the graphs of the following functions on the given intervals:

(a) $f(x) = x^3 - 3x^2 + 2$ $[-3,3]$

(b) $g(t) = t^2 - t^4 + 5t^3 - 22$ $[-1,3]$

(c) $h(x) = x^3 + x^2 - 6x$ $[-3,2]$

(d) $f(t) = \sqrt{t^2 - 9}$ $[-3,3]$

(e) $g(r) = r^5 - 4^9$ $[-1,1]$

3

Systems of Linear Equations
And Inequalities

3.1

Introduction

In Chapter 2 we gave the general form of the equation of a straight line as $Ax + By = C$ such that not both A and B equal 0. $Ax + By = C$ is referred to as a *linear equation in two variables*. Although $2x + 3y - 4z = 7$ and $8a + 2b - 3c + 4d = -19$ are referred to as linear equations in three and four variables, respectively, their graphs are not straight lines. The graph of $3x + 2y - 4z = 7$ is a real plane; the graph of $8a + 2b - 3c + 4d = -19$ cannot be drawn and is referred to as a *hyperplane*.

Many applications of mathematics in business, economics, and other social sciences involve the solution of systems of linear equations or systems of linear inequalities. This chapter deals with the definition and solution of different types of systems of linear equations and systems of linear inequalities.

3.2

Systems of Linear Equations:
Two Variables in Two Equations (2 × 2)

The general form of two linear equations in two variables is

$$a_1 x + b_1 y = c_1$$

$$a_2 x + b_2 y = c_2$$

where x and y are the variables; a_1, b_1, a_2, b_2 are the coefficients of the variables (both a_1 and b_1 or both a_2 and b_2 cannot equal 0); and c_1 and c_2 are the numerical coefficients or constant terms. Notice that in any linear equation, $Ax + By = C$, each term is either a constant or monomial (single term) of degree 1. Thus, $2x + 3y = 10$ is a linear equation, but $y = x^2$ and $xy = 8$ are *not* linear equations, and their graphs are not straight lines.

For example, consider the following three systems of two linear equations in two variables:

(a) $\quad x + 2y = 6$
$\qquad 2x - y = 7$

(b) $\quad 2x - y = 5$
$\qquad 4x - 2y = 8$

(c) $\quad 2x - y = 5$
$\qquad 4x - 2y = 10$

When solving a system of linear equations, we are looking for the number of common solutions. That is, in the system $x + 2y = 6$ and $2x - y = 7$, $x + 2y = 6$ has an infinite number of solutions (any ordered pair lying on the straight-line graph of $x + 2y = 6$), as does $2x - y = 7$. We want to solve only for the *common solution*, or for an *ordered pair* (x, y) that makes both $x + 2y = 6$ and $2x - 7 = 7$ true statements. Because two such equations represent two conditions imposed at the same time on the same variables x and y, this system of two equations is called *simultaneous equations*.

Graphical Solutions

One method used for solving a system of two linear equations in two unknowns is the *graphical method*, by which we plot or graph each linear equation on the same set of axes and look for a possible point of intersection of the two graphs which represents a *common solution*. Let us use the graphical method to illustrate the three possible types of solutions of systems of linear or first-degree equations (see Figure 3.1). Again let us consider the previously given systems of two linear equations in two unknowns:

(a) $\quad x + 2y = 6$
$\qquad 2x - y = 7$

Note: The graphs of $x + 2y = 6$ and $2x - y = 7$ intersect at the point $(4,1)$. Therefore, the ordered pair $(4,1)$ is the *common solution* or *root* of this given system of equations. Substituting the values of x and y in each equation, we obtain $4 + 2(1) = 6$ and $2(4) - 1 = 7$, and thus *check* or *verify* that $(4,1)$ is a solution of *both* original equations. Such a system of linear equations in which there is *only one common solution* is said to be a *consistent system* of independent linear equations.

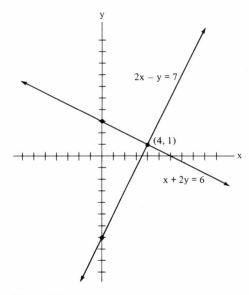

Figure 3.1

(b) $2x - y = 5$

   $4x - 2y = 8$

Note: In Figure 3.2, the graphs of $2x - y = 5$ and $4x - 2y = 8$ are parallel (do not intersect). Therefore, there are no *common solutions* to this given system of equations. Such a system of linear equations is said to be an *inconsistent system*. Do you see that the slopes of these two lines are equal? Parallel lines have *equal slopes*.

Figure 3.2

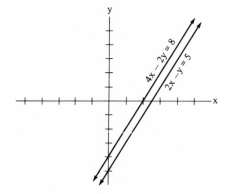

(c) $2x - y = 5$
   $4x - 2y = 10$

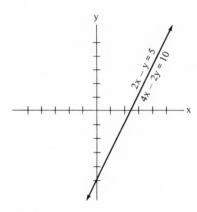

Figure 3.3

Note: The graphs of $2x - y = 5$ and $4x - 2y = 10$ in Figure 3.3 are *equivalent* (represent the same straight line). Therefore, we can find an *infinite number of solutions* to this given system of equations. Such a system of linear equations is said to be a *dependent system* of equivalent linear equations; that is, one equation is dependent on the other, or its coefficients are multiples of the other equation's coefficients. If we multiply each term in the equation $2x - y = 5$ by 2, we obtain the equation $4x - 2y = 10$.

The graphic method is not used frequently because if there does exist a unique solution (x, y), where either x or y or both x and y do not represent whole or integral values, we would have to estimate or approximate these values at the point of intersection of the two straight lines on their graph. How could you read accurately the point of intersection of two straight lines on a graph at $(5/9, 31/17)$? If you *estimate* the values of x and y at the point of intersection (x, y) on a graph, will your approximate values check or verify *both* original equations?

Elimination Method of Solving Two Simultaneous Equations

The *elimination method* for solving a (2×2) system of linear equations involves the elimination of one of the variables x or y by *adding* two equations or *subtracting* one equation from the other equation. For example:

(a) $x + 2y = 6$
    $2x - y = 7$

Multiply $x + 2y = 6$ by 2 in order to obtain

$$2x + 4y = 12$$
$$\underline{2x - y = 7}$$

Subtract $2x - y = 7$ from $2x + 4y = 12$ in order to obtain

$$5y = 5 \qquad \text{or} \qquad y = 1$$

If $y = 1$, then $x + 2(1) = 6$ or $x = 4$, which gives us *one common solution* of (4,1) (*consistent*).

(b) $2x - y = 5$
$\ 4x - 2y = 8$

Multiply $2x - y = 5$ by 2 to obtain

$$4x - 2y = 10$$
$$\underline{4x - 2y = 8}$$

Subtract $4x - 2y = 8$ from $4x - 2y = 10$ to obtain

$$0 = 2$$

which is a false statement and indicates that there are *no common solutions* (*inconsistent*).

(c) $2x - y = 5$
$\ 4x - 2y = 10$

Multiply $2x - y = 5$ by 2 to obtain

$$4x - 2y = 10$$
$$\underline{4x - 2y = 10}$$

Subtract and obtain

$$0 = 0$$

which indicates that there are an *infinite number of common solutions* (*dependent*).

(d) $3t - 7r = 9$
$\ -2t + 9r = 1$

Multiply $3t - 7r = 9$ by 2 and $-2t + 9r = 1$ by 3 to obtain

$$6t - 14r = 18$$
$$\underline{-6t + 27r = 3}$$

Add the two equations to obtain

$$13r = 21 \qquad \text{or} \qquad r = 21/13$$

Now substitute $r = 21/13$ in the first equation. Then

$$3t - 7(21/13) = 9$$
$$3t = 9 + 7(21/13)$$
$$39t = 117 + 147$$
$$39t = 264$$
$$t = 264/39$$
$$t = 88/13$$

Therefore, the common solution is at the point $(88/13, 21/13)$.

Check:

$$3(88/13) - 7(21/13) \overset{?}{=} 9 \qquad and \qquad -2(88/13) + 9(31/13) \overset{?}{=} 1$$
$$264/13 - 147/13 \overset{?}{=} 9 \qquad\qquad\qquad (-176/13) + (189/13) \overset{?}{=} 1$$
$$117/13 = 9 \qquad\qquad\qquad\qquad\qquad 13/13 = 1$$
$$9 = 9 \qquad\qquad\qquad\qquad\qquad\qquad 1 = 1$$

Solutions of (2 × 2) Systems of Linear Equations by Determinants

In order to program a computer to solve a (2×2) system of linear equations, we need to introduce a numerical method for solving such a system. Consider the solution of the general form of a (2×2) system of linear equations:

$$a_1 x + b_1 y = c_1$$
$$a_2 x + b_2 y = c_2$$

Multiply the first equation by a_2; then multiply the second equation by a_1. We thus obtain

$$a_1 a_2 x + a_2 b_1 y = a_2 c_1$$
$$a_1 a_2 x + a_1 b_2 y = a_1 c_2$$

Subtracting the second equation from the first, we obtain

$$a_2 b_1 y - a_1 b_2 y = a_2 c_1 - a_1 c_2$$
$$(a_2 b_1 - a_1 b_2)y = a_2 c_1 - a_1 c_2$$
$$y = (a_2 c_1 - a_1 c_2)/(a_2 b_1 - a_1 b_2)$$

or

$$y = (a_1 c_2 - a_2 c_1)/(a_1 b_2 - a_2 b_1)$$
$$\text{if } a_1 b_2 - a_2 b_1 \neq 0$$

Similarly, we can eliminate y and obtain $x = (b_2c_1 - b_1c_2)/(a_1b_2 - a_2b_1)$.

The solution of the general (2×2) system of simultaneous linear equations shows us that we can solve for x and y by performing arithmetic operations on the given coefficients of x and y, and on the numerical coefficients.

Second-Order Determinants

If we are given a (2×2) *square array* of individual entries or *elements* (that is, 2 rows and 2 columns of elements) such as

$$\begin{vmatrix} a & b \\ c & d \end{vmatrix}$$

we can determine or compute the numerical value or *determinant* (D) for this square array as follows:

$$\begin{vmatrix} a & b \\ c & d \end{vmatrix} = ad - bc$$

For example,

$$\begin{vmatrix} 2 & 5 \\ -1 & 3 \end{vmatrix} = 6 - (-5) = 11$$

and

$$\begin{vmatrix} 4 & -0.5 \\ 9 & 0 \end{vmatrix} = 0 - (-4.5) = 4.5$$

The determinant solution for any (2×2) system of linear equations

$$a_1x + b_1y = c_1$$
$$a_2x + b_2y = c_2$$

is (x,y), where

$$x = \frac{\begin{vmatrix} c_1 & b_1 \\ c_2 & b_2 \end{vmatrix}}{D}$$

and

$$y = \frac{\begin{vmatrix} a_1 & c_1 \\ a_2 & c_2 \end{vmatrix}}{D} \quad \text{and} \quad D = \begin{vmatrix} a_1 & b_1 \\ a_2 & b_2 \end{vmatrix} \neq 0$$

if a unique common solution exists. If $D = 0$, then there is either an infinite number of common solutions or no common solutions. Consider the following system of two linear equations in which we previously found the common solution to be $(88/13, 21/13)$, where $t = (88/13)$ and $r = (21/13)$. For these simultaneous equations,

$$3t - 7r = 9$$
$$-2t + 9r = 1$$

the determinant solution is as follows:

$$t = \frac{\begin{vmatrix} 9 & -7 \\ 1 & 9 \end{vmatrix}}{D} \quad \text{and} \quad r = \frac{\begin{vmatrix} 3 & 9 \\ -2 & 1 \end{vmatrix}}{D}$$

where

$$D = \begin{vmatrix} 3 & -7 \\ -2 & 9 \end{vmatrix} = 27 - (14) = 13 \neq 0$$

Therefore, there *is* a unique or common solution. Then

$$t = \frac{\begin{vmatrix} 9 & -7 \\ 1 & 9 \end{vmatrix}}{13} = (81 - (-7))/13 = 88/13$$

and

$$r = \frac{\begin{vmatrix} 3 & 9 \\ -2 & 1 \end{vmatrix}}{13} = (3 - (-18))/13 = 21/13$$

and the common solution is $(88/13, 21/13)$.

In the systems $(2x - y = 5$ and $4x - 2y = 8)$ and $(2x - y = 5$ and $4x - 2y = 10)$,

$$D = \begin{vmatrix} 2 & -1 \\ 4 & -2 \end{vmatrix} = -4 - (-4) = 0$$

This zero value of D indicates that there does *not* exist a unique or common solution to either system. Note that in the system $(2x - y = 5$ and $4x - 2y = 10)$ the respective x, y and numerical coefficients are in proportion (that is, $2/4 = -1/-2 = 5/10$), which indicates that the system is *dependent*. If $D = 0$ and the respective x, y and numerical coefficients are not in proportion, the system is *inconsistent*.

Computer Application

Consider the following programming project:

Given: $a_1, b_1, c_1, a_2, b_2, c_2$, where a_2, b_2, and $c_2 \neq 0$ for

$$a_1 x + b_1 y = c_1$$
$$a_2 x + b_2 y = c_2$$

Wanted: A flowchart to solve any system of two linear equations with two variables.

Desired Output:

$$A1 = \cdots B1 = \cdots C1 = \cdots$$
$$A2 = \cdots B2 = \cdots C2 = \cdots$$
$$X = \cdots Y = \cdots$$

or

INCONSISTENT—NO COMMON SOLUTIONS

or

DEPENDENT—INFINITE NUMBER OF COMMON SOLUTIONS

Figure 3.4

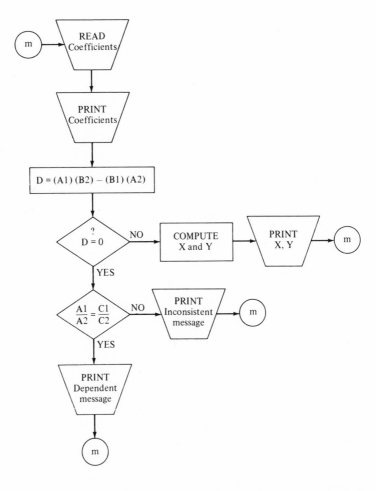

Solution (See Figure 3.4):

$$(A1)X + (B1)Y = C1$$
$$(A2)X + (B2)Y = C2$$

$$X = \frac{\begin{vmatrix} C1 & B1 \\ C2 & B2 \end{vmatrix}}{D}$$

$$Y = \frac{\begin{vmatrix} A1 & C1 \\ A2 & C2 \end{vmatrix}}{D}$$

where

$$D = \begin{vmatrix} A1 & B1 \\ A2 & B2 \end{vmatrix} \neq 0$$

Problem Set 3.1

1. Use the graphic method to solve the following systems of linear equations:
   (a) $2x - y = 3$ (b) $3t - 7r = 9$ (c) $2a - 7b = 5$
   $4x + 2y = 2$ $9t - 21r = 1$ $-3a + b = 2$

2. State the type of system of linear equations (consistent, inconsistent, or dependent) for each system in Problem 1.

3. Use the elimination method to solve each of the following systems of simultaneous linear equations:
   (a) $5w - 3z = 1$ (b) $-5a + 17b = 1$ (c) $-x + 5y = 1$
   $2w - z = 9$ $3a + 2b = 3$ $2x - 7y = -7$

   (d) $5x - 3y = 7$ (e) $2a + 3b = 11$ (f) $2x - 5y = 9$
   $-15x + 9y = 1$ $-6a + 9b = 33$ $3x = 11$

4. Evaluate each of the following second-order determinants:
   (a) $\begin{vmatrix} 2 & 0 \\ -5 & 17 \end{vmatrix}$ (b) $\begin{vmatrix} -3 & -4 \\ 5 & -17 \end{vmatrix}$ (c) $\begin{vmatrix} 9 & 0.3 \\ 7.1 & 21 \end{vmatrix}$

   (d) $\begin{vmatrix} w & x \\ y & z \end{vmatrix}$ (e) $\begin{vmatrix} 1 & 1 \\ 1 & 1 \end{vmatrix}$ (f) $\begin{vmatrix} 19 & 3 \\ 2 & -1 \end{vmatrix}$

5. Code flowchart in Figure 3.4 for solving any system of two linear equations in two unknowns in the BASIC programming language.

6. Run the program you constructed in Problem 5, using each of the systems of equations in Problem 3 as sample data.

3.3

**Systems of Linear Equations:
Three Variables and Three Equations (3 × 3)**

The general form of three linear equations in three variables is

$$a_1 x + b_1 y + c_1 z = d_1$$
$$a_2 x + b_2 y + c_2 z = d_2$$
$$a_3 x + b_3 y + c_3 z = d_3$$

where x, y, and z are the variables.

Elimination Method of Solving Three Simultaneous Equations

The *elimination method* for solving a (3 × 3) system of linear equations involves the elimination of two of the unknowns by adding or subtracting equations. For example, consider the following system of equations:

(1) $\qquad x + y - z = 9$
(2) $\qquad 2x + y + 2z = 15$
(3) $\qquad 3x - 2y + z = 4$

Multiplying Equation (1) by 2 and adding it to Equation (2), we obtain

$$2x + 2y - 2z = 18$$
$$2x + y + 2z = 15$$
$$\overline{4x + 3y \qquad = 33}$$

Now add Equations (1) and (3) to obtain

$$x + y - z = 9$$
$$3x - 2y + z = 4$$
$$\overline{4x - y \qquad = 13}$$

Now solve the resulting (2 × 2) system:

$$4x + 3y = 33$$
$$4x - y = 13$$
$$\overline{\qquad 4y = 20}$$

or $y = 5$.

If $4x - y = 13$, then

$$4x - 5 = 13$$
$$4x = 18$$

or $x = 4.5$.

Since $x + y - z = 9$, then $4.5 + 5 - z = 9$, where $-z = -0.5$ or $z = 0.5$. Therefore, the common solution is at the point in space $(4.5, 5, 0.5)$, where $x = 4.5$, $y = 5$, and $z = 0.5$.

Check: We have $x + y - z = 9$, and $2x + y + 2z = 15$, and $3x - 2y + z = 4$; or, $4.5 + 5 - 0.5 = 9$, and $2(4.5) + 5 + 2(0.5) = 15$, and $3(4.5) - 2(5) + 0.5 = 4$. Then

$$9 = 9; \qquad 15 = 15; \qquad 4 = 4$$

Third-Order Determinants

If we are given a (3×3) square array of individual entries or elements (that is, three rows and three columns of elements), such as

$$\begin{vmatrix} a_1 & b_1 & c_1 \\ a_2 & b_2 & c_2 \\ a_3 & b_3 & c_3 \end{vmatrix}$$

we can determine or compute the *determinant* for this square array of elements as follows:

$$\begin{vmatrix} a_1 & b_1 & c_1 \\ a_2 & b_2 & c_2 \\ a_3 & b_3 & c_3 \end{vmatrix} = a_1 \begin{vmatrix} b_2 & c_2 \\ b_3 & c_3 \end{vmatrix} - b_1 \begin{vmatrix} a_2 & c_2 \\ a_3 & b_3 \end{vmatrix} + c_1 \begin{vmatrix} a_2 & b_2 \\ a_3 & b_3 \end{vmatrix}$$

For example:

$$\begin{vmatrix} 2 & 5 & 3 \\ -3 & 0 & 1 \\ 2 & -7 & -11 \end{vmatrix} = 2 \begin{vmatrix} 0 & 1 \\ -7 & -11 \end{vmatrix} - 5 \begin{vmatrix} -3 & 1 \\ 2 & -11 \end{vmatrix} + 3 \begin{vmatrix} -3 & 0 \\ 2 & -7 \end{vmatrix}$$

$$= 2(0 + 7) - 5(33 - 2) + 3(21 - 0)$$

$$= 2(7) - 5(31) + 3(21)$$

$$= 14 - 155 + 63$$

$$= -78$$

Solution of (3 × 3) Systems of Linear Equations via Determinants

Just as we showed that the solution of two linear equations in two unknowns can be solved using second-order determinants, we could show that the general system

$$a_1 x + b_1 y + c_1 z = d_1$$
$$a_2 x + b_2 y + c_2 z = d_2$$
$$a_3 x + b_3 y + c_3 z = d_3$$

can be solved as follows:

$$x = \frac{\begin{vmatrix} d_1 & b_1 & c_1 \\ d_2 & b_2 \cdot c_2 \\ d_3 & b_3 & c_3 \end{vmatrix}}{D} \qquad y = \frac{\begin{vmatrix} a_1 & d_1 & c_1 \\ a_2 & d_2 & c_2 \\ a_3 & d_3 & c_3 \end{vmatrix}}{D} \qquad z = \frac{\begin{vmatrix} a_1 & b_1 & d_1 \\ a_2 & b_2 & d_2 \\ a_3 & b_3 & d_3 \end{vmatrix}}{D}$$

where

$$D = \begin{vmatrix} a_1 & b_1 & c_1 \\ a_2 & b_2 & c_2 \\ a_3 & b_3 & c_3 \end{vmatrix} \neq 0$$

if a unique common solution exists. If $D = 0$, then there is either no common solution or an infinite number of common solutions.

Let us solve the previously solved system

$$\begin{aligned} x + y - z &= 9 \\ 2x + y + 2z &= 15 \\ 3x - 2y + z &= 4 \end{aligned}$$

via determinants. We have

$$x = \frac{\begin{vmatrix} 9 & 1 & -1 \\ 15 & 1 & 2 \\ 4 & -2 & 1 \end{vmatrix}}{D} \qquad y = \frac{\begin{vmatrix} 1 & 9 & -1 \\ 2 & 15 & 2 \\ 3 & 4 & 1 \end{vmatrix}}{D} \qquad z = \frac{\begin{vmatrix} 1 & 1 & 9 \\ 2 & 1 & 15 \\ 3 & -2 & 4 \end{vmatrix}}{D}$$

where

$$D = \begin{vmatrix} 1 & 1 & -1 \\ 2 & 1 & 2 \\ 3 & -2 & 1 \end{vmatrix}$$

or

$$D = \begin{vmatrix} 1 & 1 & -1 \\ 2 & 1 & 2 \\ 3 & -2 & 1 \end{vmatrix}$$

$$= 1 \begin{vmatrix} 1 & 2 \\ -2 & 1 \end{vmatrix} - 1 \begin{vmatrix} 2 & 2 \\ 3 & 1 \end{vmatrix} + (-1) \begin{vmatrix} 2 & 1 \\ 3 & -2 \end{vmatrix}$$

$$= 1(1 + 4) - 1(2 - 6) - 1(-4 - 3)$$

$$= 1(5) - 1(-4) - 1(-7)$$

$$= 5 + 4 + 7$$

$$= 16 \neq 0$$

Therefore, a unique solution does exist.

$$x = \frac{\begin{vmatrix} 9 & 1 & -1 \\ 15 & 1 & 2 \\ 4 & -2 & 1 \end{vmatrix}}{16}$$

$$= \frac{9\begin{vmatrix} 1 & 2 \\ -2 & 1 \end{vmatrix} - 1\begin{vmatrix} 15 & 2 \\ 4 & 1 \end{vmatrix} + (-1)\begin{vmatrix} 15 & 1 \\ 4 & -2 \end{vmatrix}}{16}$$

$$= \frac{9(1 + 4) - 1(15 - 8) - 1(-30 - 4)}{16}$$

$$= (45 - 7 + 34)/16$$

or

$$x = 72/16 = 9/2 = 4.5$$

$$y = \frac{\begin{vmatrix} 1 & 9 & -1 \\ 2 & 15 & 2 \\ 3 & 4 & 1 \end{vmatrix}}{16}$$

$$= \frac{1\begin{vmatrix} 15 & 2 \\ 4 & 1 \end{vmatrix} - 9\begin{vmatrix} 2 & 2 \\ 3 & 1 \end{vmatrix} + (-1)\begin{vmatrix} 2 & 15 \\ 3 & 4 \end{vmatrix}}{16}$$

$$= (1(15 - 8) - 9(2 - 6) - 1(8 - 45))/16$$

$$= (7 + 36 + 37)/16$$

or

$$y = 80/16 = 5$$

$$z = \frac{\begin{vmatrix} 1 & 1 & 9 \\ 2 & 1 & 15 \\ 3 & -2 & 4 \end{vmatrix}}{16}$$

$$= \frac{1\begin{vmatrix} 1 & 15 \\ -2 & 4 \end{vmatrix} - 1\begin{vmatrix} 2 & 15 \\ 3 & 4 \end{vmatrix} + 9\begin{vmatrix} 2 & 1 \\ 3 & -2 \end{vmatrix}}{16}$$

$$= (1(4 + 30) - 1(8 - 45) + 9(-4 - 3))/16$$

$$= (34 + 37 - 63)/16$$

or

$$z = 8/16 = 0.5$$

Therefore, our common solution is at (4.5, 5, 0.5).

The preceding method may be used to solve any system of n linear equations in n unknowns by means of determinants, and is sometimes referred to as *Cramer's rule,* named for Gabriel Cramer, a Swiss mathematician of the eighteenth century.

The flowchart for solving any system of three linear equations in three unknowns via determinants is similar to the previously constructed flowchart (Figure 3.4) for solving any (2×2) system of linear equations. However, the coding is quite long, owing to the work involved in evaluating a third-order determinant and the difficulty of deciding whether the system is inconsistent or dependent if $D = 0$.

Let us construct an abbreviated flowchart (Figure 3.5) for solving any (3×3) system of linear equations:

$$(A1)X + (B1)Y + (C1)Z = D1$$
$$(A2)X + (B2)Y + (C2)Z = D2$$
$$(A3)X + (B3)Y + (C3)Z = D3$$

$$X = \frac{\begin{vmatrix} D1 & B1 & C1 \\ D2 & B2 & C2 \\ D3 & B3 & C3 \end{vmatrix}}{D}$$

$$Y = \frac{\begin{vmatrix} A1 & D1 & C1 \\ A2 & D2 & C2 \\ A3 & D3 & C3 \end{vmatrix}}{D}$$

$$Z = \frac{\begin{vmatrix} A1 & B1 & D1 \\ A2 & B2 & D2 \\ A3 & B3 & D3 \end{vmatrix}}{D}$$

where

$$D = \begin{vmatrix} A1 & B1 & C1 \\ A2 & B2 & C2 \\ A3 & B3 & C3 \end{vmatrix} \neq 0$$

Notice that we required separate computer programs for (2×2), (3×3), $(4 \times 4), \ldots, (m \times m)$ systems of linear equations, and the coding becomes more difficult as the number of equations and unknowns increase.

In Article 3.4 we will discuss matrix algebra, which will lead to one elementary program that can be used to solve m linear equations in m unknowns.

Figure 3.5

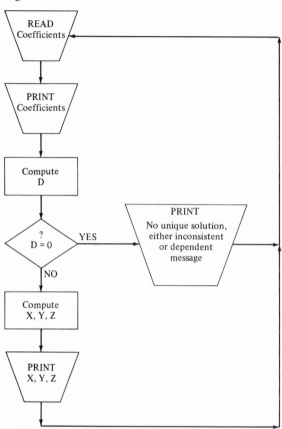

Problem Set 3.2

1. Use the elimination method to solve the following systems of linear equations:

(a)
$x + y + z = 4$
$2x - y - 2z = -1$
$x - 2y - z = 1$

(b)
$x + y + z = 0$
$2x - y + 5z = 3$
$-x - 2y + z = 0$

(c)
$w + t + r = 9$
$-w + 3t = 7$
$3t - r = 9$

(d)
$a + b + c = 1$
$2a + 2b + 2c = 2$
$3a + 3b + 3c = 3$

2. Evaluate the following determinants:

(a) $\begin{vmatrix} 2 & -3 & 0 \\ 1 & 5 & 3 \\ 3 & -1 & 3 \end{vmatrix}$
(b) $\begin{vmatrix} 0 & -7 & -0.5 \\ 2 & -1 & -5 \\ 3 & 0 & 0 \end{vmatrix}$
(c) $\begin{vmatrix} a & b & c \\ d & e & f \\ g & h & i \end{vmatrix}$

3. Solve for t:

$$\begin{vmatrix} 2 & -7 & t \\ 3 & 2 & 1 \\ 5 & 9 & 4 \end{vmatrix} = -3$$

4. Write a BASIC program to evaluate any third-order determinant.

5. Test your program in Problem 4 by using the determinants in Problem 2 as sample data.

6. Code the flowchart in Figure 3.5 for deciding whether a (3×3) system of linear equation has a unique solution—and for printing the unique solution if it exists— in the BASIC language.

7. Run the program in Problem 6, using the systems in Problem 1 as sample data.

8. Given a (4×4) square array of elements, we can compute the corresponding *determinant* for the square array as follows:

$$\begin{vmatrix} a_1 & b_1 & c_1 & d_1 \\ a_2 & b_2 & c_2 & d_2 \\ a_3 & b_3 & c_3 & d_3 \\ a_4 & b_4 & c_4 & d_4 \end{vmatrix} = a_1 \begin{vmatrix} b_2 & c_2 & d_2 \\ b_3 & c_3 & d_3 \\ b_4 & c_4 & d_4 \end{vmatrix} - b_1 \begin{vmatrix} a_2 & c_2 & d_2 \\ a_3 & c_3 & d_3 \\ a_4 & c_4 & d_4 \end{vmatrix}$$

$$+ c_1 \begin{vmatrix} a_2 & b_2 & d_2 \\ a_3 & b_3 & d_3 \\ a_4 & b_4 & d_4 \end{vmatrix} - d_1 \begin{vmatrix} a_2 & b_2 & c_2 \\ a_3 & b_3 & c_3 \\ a_4 & b_4 & c_4 \end{vmatrix}$$

Evaluate the determinant for the following (4×4) array of numbers:

$$\begin{vmatrix} 2 & 0 & -3 & 0 \\ 1 & 2 & 4 & 5 \\ 0 & 3 & 1 & 5 \\ -1 & -3 & 0 & 1 \end{vmatrix}$$

3.4

Solving *m* Linear Equations in *m* Unknowns via Matrix Methods

Matrices in General: Definition and Operations

A *matrix* is a rectangular array of elements. For example,

$$A = \begin{bmatrix} 2 & 3 \\ 0 & -1 \end{bmatrix}, \quad B = \begin{bmatrix} 2 & 3 & 4 \\ 0 & -1 & 2 \end{bmatrix}, \quad C = \begin{bmatrix} c_{11} & c_{12} & c_{12} \\ c_{21} & c_{22} & c_{23} \\ c_{31} & c_{32} & c_{33} \end{bmatrix}$$

We will use the notation $A = (a_{22})$ to indicate that A is a 2×2 matrix, or contains two rows and two columns of elements; $B = (b_{23})$ to indicate B is a 2×3 matrix, or contains two rows and three columns of elements; $C = (c_{33})$ to indicate that C is a 3×3 matrix, or contains three rows and three columns of elements. Notice in these three examples of matrices that the *expression* $C = (c_{33})$ indicates that C is a 3×3 matrix, while the *symbol* c_{33} represents the *particular element* of matrix C which is in the third row and third column.

Thus, $B = (b_{23})$ indicates that B is a 2×3 matrix, while $b_{23} = 2$ indicates that the particular element in the second row and third column of matrix B is 2. Also, $A = (a_{22})$, while $a_{11} = 2$, $a_{12} = 3$, $a_{21} = 0$, and $a_{22} = -1$.

A matrix A is said to be *equal* to a matrix B, denoted by $A = B$, if and only if *all corresponding elements are equal.* If $A = (a_{ij})$ and $B = (b_{ij})$ and $a_{ij} = b_{ij}$ for all i and j, then $A = B$. For example, if

$$A = \begin{bmatrix} 2 & 3 \\ 4 & 1 \end{bmatrix}, \qquad B = \begin{bmatrix} 2 & 3 \\ 4 & -1 \end{bmatrix},$$

$$C = \begin{bmatrix} 2 & 3 \\ 4 & 5/5 \end{bmatrix}, \qquad D = \begin{bmatrix} 2 & 3 & 4 \\ 4 & 1 & 7 \end{bmatrix}$$

then $A \neq B$ because $a_{22} \neq b_{22}$, $A = C$, and $B \neq C$. Matrix D cannot possibly be equal to any of the matrices A, B, or C because D is a 2×3 matrix, while A, B, and C are all 2×2 matrices. The elements $d_{13} = 4$ and $d_{23} = 7$ do not therefore correspond to any elements in A, B, or C. Observe that two matrices cannot possibly be equal unless they first contain the same numbers of rows and columns.

If matrix $A = (a_{ij})$ and matrix $B = (b_{ij})$ (that is, both matrices have the same number of rows and columns), then the *sum* of A and B, denoted by $A + B$, is computed as follows:

$$C = A + B = (c_{ij}) = (a_{ij} + b_{ij})$$

That is, we add all *corresponding elements.* The *difference* of A and B, denoted by $A - B$, is also computed similarly: $D = A - B = (d_{ij}) = (a_{ij} - b_{ij})$. If

$$A = \begin{bmatrix} 2 & 3 & 4 \\ 5 & 6 & -7 \end{bmatrix}, \qquad B = \begin{bmatrix} 1 & 0 & 2 \\ 5 & 1 & 3 \end{bmatrix}, \qquad C = \begin{bmatrix} 2 & 7 \\ -3 & 4 \end{bmatrix}$$

then

$$A + B = B + A = \begin{bmatrix} 3 & 3 & 6 \\ 10 & 7 & -4 \end{bmatrix}, \qquad A - B = \begin{bmatrix} 1 & 3 & 2 \\ 0 & 5 & -10 \end{bmatrix},$$

$$B - A = \begin{bmatrix} -1 & -3 & -2 \\ 0 & -5 & 10 \end{bmatrix}$$

Why is it impossible to add matrix C to either matrix A or matrix B?

If $A = (a_{ij})$ and r is any real number, then $rA = (a'_{ij})$, where $a'_{ij} = ra_{ij}$ for all i and j. For example, if

$$A = \begin{bmatrix} 2 & 3 & 4 \\ 5 & 6 & -1 \end{bmatrix}$$

then

$$-7A = \begin{bmatrix} -14 & -21 & -28 \\ -35 & -42 & 7 \end{bmatrix}$$

If $A = (a_{ij})$ and $B = (b_{jk})$ (that is, the number of columns in A is the same as the number of rows in B), then the *product* of A and B, denoted by AB, is computed as follows: $C = AB = (c_{ik})$, where $c_{ik} =$ *the sum of all possible*, $a_{ij} \cdot b_{jk}$. For example, if

$$A = \begin{bmatrix} 2 & 3 \\ 4 & -1 \end{bmatrix} = (a_{22}), \qquad B = \begin{bmatrix} 5 & 6 \\ 1 & 0 \end{bmatrix} = (b_{22}),$$

$$C = \begin{bmatrix} 2 & -1 & 5 \\ 0 & 1 & 10 \end{bmatrix} = (c_{23})$$

then

$$AB = \begin{bmatrix} (2 \cdot 5 + 3 \cdot 1) & (2 \cdot 6 + 3 \cdot 0) \\ (4 \cdot 5 + (-1)(1)) & (4 \cdot 6 + (-1)(0)) \end{bmatrix} = \begin{bmatrix} 13 & 12 \\ 19 & 24 \end{bmatrix}$$

$$BA = \begin{bmatrix} (5 \cdot 2 + 6 \cdot 4) & (5 \cdot 3 + 6(-1)) \\ (1 \cdot 2 + 0 \cdot 4) & (1 \cdot 3 + 0(-1)) \end{bmatrix} = \begin{bmatrix} 34 & 9 \\ 2 & 3 \end{bmatrix}$$

(Is $A \times B$ equal to $B \times A$?)

$$AC = \begin{bmatrix} (2 \cdot 2 + 3 \cdot 0) & (2(-1) + 3 \cdot 1) & (2 \cdot 5 + 3 \cdot 10) \\ (4 \cdot 2 + (-1)(0)) & (4(-1) + (-1)(1)) & (4 \cdot 5 + (-1)(10)) \end{bmatrix}$$

$$= \begin{bmatrix} 4 & 1 & 40 \\ 8 & -5 & 10 \end{bmatrix}$$

Why is it impossible to perform the multiplications CA and CB?

Problem Set 3.3

Given the matrices

$$A = \begin{bmatrix} 2 & 7 & 3 \\ 4 & 5 & -1 \end{bmatrix}, \qquad B = \begin{bmatrix} 2 \\ -3 \\ 1 \end{bmatrix},$$

$$C = \begin{bmatrix} 0 & 1 & 12 \\ 3 & 5 & -1 \\ 1 & 0 & 2 \end{bmatrix}, \qquad D = \begin{bmatrix} 5 & 7 & 8 \\ 0 & -9 & 2 \\ 1 & 1 & -5 \end{bmatrix}$$

1. State the number of rows and columns for each of the matrices A, B, C, and D. Use the notation $A = (a_{ij})$, $B = (b_{mn})$, and so on.

2. Perform the following operations if possible:
   (a) AB
   (b) BA
   (c) $C + D$
   (d) $D - C$
   (e) CD
   (f) DC
   (g) $-9B$
   (h) $7D + 3C$

The Algebra of Square Matrices

A *square matrix* $A = (a_{mm})$ is a matrix that contains the same number of rows and columns ($A = (a_{mm})$ is said to be a matrix of order m). For example,

$$A = \begin{bmatrix} 2 & 3 \\ -4 & 1 \end{bmatrix} = (a_{22}), \qquad B = \begin{bmatrix} 2 & 5 & -3 \\ 4 & 0.2 & 1 \\ -7 & 8 & 19 \end{bmatrix} = (b_{33})$$

If

$$A = \begin{bmatrix} 2 & 3 \\ -4 & 1 \end{bmatrix} = (a_{22}), \qquad B = \begin{bmatrix} 7 & 3 \\ 0 & -1 \end{bmatrix} = (b_{22})$$

then

$$A + B = B + A = \begin{bmatrix} 9 & 6 \\ -4 & 0 \end{bmatrix}$$

$$A - B = \begin{bmatrix} -5 & 0 \\ -4 & 2 \end{bmatrix}, \qquad B - A = \begin{bmatrix} 5 & 0 \\ 4 & -2 \end{bmatrix}$$

$$A \times B = \begin{bmatrix} 14 & 3 \\ -28 & -13 \end{bmatrix}, \qquad B \times A = \begin{bmatrix} 2 & 24 \\ 4 & -1 \end{bmatrix}$$

$$-7A = \begin{bmatrix} -14 & -21 \\ 28 & -7 \end{bmatrix}, \qquad 3B = \begin{bmatrix} 21 & 9 \\ 0 & -3 \end{bmatrix}$$

All previously described operations can be performed with two matrices of order 2, with two matrices of order 3, . . . , with two matrices of order m.

In square matrices, such as

$$A = \begin{bmatrix} a_{11} & a_{12} \\ a_{21} & a_{22} \end{bmatrix} \quad \text{and} \quad B = \begin{bmatrix} b_{11} & b_{12} & b_{13} \\ b_{21} & b_{22} & b_{23} \\ b_{31} & b_{32} & b_{33} \end{bmatrix},$$

the *main diagonal* is the diagonal consisting of all elements a_{xx} or b_{xx}. For example, in the given square matrix B, notice that b_{11}, b_{22}, and b_{33} are the elements of the main diagonal of B.

The *identity matrix* for a matrix of order m is a matrix containing 1's in the main diagonal and 0's elsewhere. We will denote the identity matrix of order m by I_m.

Look at these three examples of identity matrices:

$$I_2 = \begin{bmatrix} 1 & 0 \\ 0 & 1 \end{bmatrix}, \qquad I_3 = \begin{bmatrix} 1 & 0 & 0 \\ 0 & 1 & 0 \\ 0 & 0 & 1 \end{bmatrix}, \qquad I_4 = \begin{bmatrix} 1 & 0 & 0 & 0 \\ 0 & 1 & 0 & 0 \\ 0 & 0 & 1 & 0 \\ 0 & 0 & 0 & 1 \end{bmatrix} \cdots$$

If $A = (a_{mm})$, then $AI_m = I_mA = A$. If

$$A = \begin{bmatrix} 2 & 3 \\ 4 & 5 \end{bmatrix}, \qquad I_2 = \begin{bmatrix} 1 & 0 \\ 0 & 1 \end{bmatrix},$$

$$B = \begin{bmatrix} 2 & 3 & 4 \\ 5 & 6 & 7 \\ 8 & 9 & 10 \end{bmatrix}, \qquad I_3 = \begin{bmatrix} 1 & 0 & 0 \\ 0 & 1 & 0 \\ 0 & 0 & 1 \end{bmatrix},$$

then $AI_2 = I_2A = A$ and $BI_3 = I_3B = B$.

The *determinant* of a square matrix $A = (a_{mm})$, denoted by $\det(A)$, is the *numerical value* computed for the determinant of order m. For example, if

$$A = \begin{bmatrix} 2 & 3 \\ 4 & 5 \end{bmatrix}, \qquad B = \begin{bmatrix} 2 & 0 & 1 \\ 3 & 0 & -1 \\ 2 & 1 & 3 \end{bmatrix}$$

then

$$\det(A) = \begin{vmatrix} 2 & 3 \\ 4 & 5 \end{vmatrix} = 10 - 12 = -2$$

and

$$\det(B) = 2\begin{vmatrix} 0 & -1 \\ 1 & 3 \end{vmatrix} - 0\begin{vmatrix} 3 & -1 \\ 2 & 3 \end{vmatrix} + 1\begin{vmatrix} 3 & 0 \\ 2 & 1 \end{vmatrix}$$

$$= 2(0 + 1) - 0 + 1(3 - 0) = 2 + 3 = 5$$

A *singular matrix* is a square matrix whose determinant is *equal* to 0, and a *nonsingular matrix* is a square matrix whose determinant is *not equal* to 0. If

$$A = \begin{bmatrix} 2 & 3 \\ 4 & 5 \end{bmatrix} \quad \text{and} \quad B = \begin{bmatrix} 4 & 14 \\ 2 & 7 \end{bmatrix}$$

then A is nonsingular because

$$\det(A) = \begin{vmatrix} 2 & 3 \\ 4 & 5 \end{vmatrix} = 10 - 12 = -2 \neq 0$$

and B is singular because

$$\det(B) = \begin{vmatrix} 4 & 14 \\ 2 & 7 \end{vmatrix} = 28 - 28 = 0$$

The inverse of an mth-order matrix A, is an mth-order matrix $\bar{A}$, such that $A\bar{A} = \bar{A}A = I_m$. The manual computation of the inverse of a matrix is complicated, but we will use a BASIC matrix command to compute the inverse of any nonsingular matrix.

In order to illustrate the manual computation of the inverse of a nonsingular matrix, we must first take a closer look at determinants. Say that

$$\det(A) = \begin{vmatrix} a_{11} & a_{12} & a_{13} \\ a_{21} & a_{22} & a_{23} \\ a_{31} & a_{32} & a_{33} \end{vmatrix}$$

Then we must consider the following two definitions:

1. The *minor* of the element a_{ij} of $\det(A)$ is the determinant consisting of all elements in $\det(A)$ that are *not* in the ith row and jth column. For example, in $\det(A)$ above:

$$\text{minor of } a_{11} = \begin{vmatrix} a_{22} & a_{23} \\ a_{32} & a_{33} \end{vmatrix}$$

$$\text{minor of } a_{21} = \begin{vmatrix} a_{12} & a_{13} \\ a_{32} & a_{33} \end{vmatrix}$$

$$\text{minor of } a_{22} = \begin{vmatrix} a_{11} & a_{13} \\ a_{31} & a_{33} \end{vmatrix}$$

The listing of the minors of a_{12}, a_{31}, a_{32}, a_{13}, a_{23}, and a_{33} is left as an exercise for the reader.

2. The *cofactor* of an element a_{ij} of $\det(A)$ is the minor of a_{ij} if $i + j$ is an *even number*, and $-$ (the minor of a_{ij}) if $i + j$ is an *odd number*.

For example, in $\det(A)$ above the cofactor of

$$a_{11} = \text{minor of } a_{11} \ (1 + 1 = 2 \text{ is even})$$

$$a_{21} = \text{minus minor of } a_{21} \ (2 + 1 = 3 \text{ is odd})$$

$$a_{22} = \text{minor of } a_{22} \ (2 + 2 = 4 \text{ is even})$$

Now, if $A = (a_{mm})$ is a nonsingular matrix of order m (that is, $\det(A) \neq 0$), then the inverse of matrix A is denoted by $\bar{A} = (1/\det(A))(C)$, where $C = (c_{ij}) = $ (cofactor of a_{ji}) for all i and j. (*Note:* If A is a singular matrix, then $\bar{A}$ does not exist.) Consider the following sample problem. If

$$A = \begin{bmatrix} 1 & 3 & 4 \\ -2 & 4 & 5 \\ 3 & 1 & 6 \end{bmatrix}$$

$$\det(A) = 1 \begin{vmatrix} 4 & 5 \\ 1 & 6 \end{vmatrix} - 3 \begin{vmatrix} -2 & 5 \\ 3 & 6 \end{vmatrix} + 4 \begin{vmatrix} -2 & 4 \\ 3 & 1 \end{vmatrix}$$

$$= 1(24 - 5) - 3(-12 - 15) + 4(-2 - 12)$$

$$= 1(19) - 3(-27) + 4(-14) = 19 + 81 - 56$$

$$= 44 \neq 0$$

Therefore, A is nonsingular and A exists. Let

$$C_{11} = \text{cofactor of } a_{11} = \begin{vmatrix} 4 & 5 \\ 1 & 6 \end{vmatrix} = 19$$

$$C_{21} = \text{cofactor of } a_{12} = -\begin{vmatrix} -2 & 5 \\ 3 & 6 \end{vmatrix} = 27$$

$$C_{31} = \text{cofactor of } a_{13} = \begin{vmatrix} -2 & 4 \\ 3 & 1 \end{vmatrix} = -14$$

$$C_{12} = \text{cofactor of } a_{21} = -\begin{vmatrix} 3 & 4 \\ 1 & 6 \end{vmatrix} = -14$$

$$C_{22} = \text{cofactor of } a_{22} = \begin{vmatrix} 1 & 4 \\ 3 & 6 \end{vmatrix} = -6$$

$$C_{32} = \text{cofactor of } a_{23} = -\begin{vmatrix} 1 & 3 \\ 3 & 1 \end{vmatrix} = 8$$

$$C_{13} = \text{cofactor of } a_{31} = \begin{vmatrix} 3 & 4 \\ 4 & 5 \end{vmatrix} = -1$$

$$C_{23} = \text{cofactor of } a_{32} = -\begin{vmatrix} 1 & 4 \\ -2 & 5 \end{vmatrix} = -13$$

$$C_{33} = \text{cofactor of } a_{33} = \begin{vmatrix} 1 & 3 \\ -2 & 4 \end{vmatrix} = 10$$

Then

$$\bar{A} = (1/44) \begin{bmatrix} 19 & -14 & -1 \\ 27 & -6 & -13 \\ -14 & 8 & 10 \end{bmatrix}$$

and

$$A\bar{A} = \bar{A}A = I_3 = \begin{bmatrix} 1 & 0 & 0 \\ 0 & 1 & 0 \\ 0 & 0 & 1 \end{bmatrix}$$

Using the Algebra of Matrices to Solve an m × m System of Linear Equations

Using matrices, we can convert the following system of linear equations:

$$\begin{aligned} x + 3y + 4z &= 2 \\ -2x + 4y + 5z &= 0 \\ 3x + y + 6z &= -1 \end{aligned}$$

to the following matrix equation:

$$\begin{bmatrix} 1 & 3 & 4 \\ -2 & 4 & 5 \\ 3 & 1 & 6 \end{bmatrix} \begin{bmatrix} x \\ y \\ z \end{bmatrix} = \begin{bmatrix} 2 \\ 0 \\ -1 \end{bmatrix}$$

This matrix equation is of the form $AX = B$, where

$$A = \begin{bmatrix} 1 & 3 & 4 \\ -2 & 4 & 5 \\ 3 & 1 & 6 \end{bmatrix}, \quad X = \begin{bmatrix} x \\ y \\ z \end{bmatrix}, \quad B = \begin{bmatrix} 2 \\ 0 \\ -1 \end{bmatrix}$$

In elementary algebra we solve $2x = 7$ as follows:

$$2x = 7$$

$$(1/2)2x = (1/2)7$$

$$1x = 7/2$$

$$x = 7/2$$

Similarly, we can solve $AX = B$ as follows:

$$AX = B$$

$$(\bar{A}A)X = \bar{A}B$$

$$IX = C$$

$$X = C$$

where $C = \bar{A}B$, provided A is nonsingular. That is,

$$AX = B, \text{ or } \begin{bmatrix} 1 & 3 & 4 \\ -2 & 4 & 5 \\ 3 & 1 & 6 \end{bmatrix} \begin{bmatrix} x \\ y \\ z \end{bmatrix} = \begin{bmatrix} 2 \\ 0 \\ -1 \end{bmatrix}$$

We previously saw that $\det(A) = 44 \neq 0$ and

$$\bar{A} = (1/44) \begin{bmatrix} 19 & -14 & -1 \\ 27 & -6 & -13 \\ -14 & 8 & 10 \end{bmatrix}.$$

therefore $\quad (1/44) \begin{bmatrix} 19 & -14 & -1 \\ 27 & -6 & -13 \\ -14 & 8 & 10 \end{bmatrix} \begin{bmatrix} 1 & 3 & 4 \\ -2 & 4 & 5 \\ 3 & 1 & 6 \end{bmatrix} \begin{bmatrix} x \\ y \\ z \end{bmatrix}$

$$= (1/44) \begin{bmatrix} 19 & -14 & -1 \\ 27 & -6 & -13 \\ -14 & 8 & 10 \end{bmatrix} \begin{bmatrix} 2 \\ 0 \\ -1 \end{bmatrix}$$

and

$$\begin{bmatrix} 1 & 0 & 0 \\ 0 & 1 & 0 \\ 0 & 0 & 1 \end{bmatrix} \begin{bmatrix} x \\ y \\ z \end{bmatrix} = (1/44) \begin{bmatrix} 39 \\ 67 \\ -38 \end{bmatrix}$$

$$\begin{bmatrix} x \\ y \\ z \end{bmatrix} = \begin{bmatrix} 39/44 \\ 67/44 \\ -38/44 \end{bmatrix}$$

or $x = 39/44$, $y = 67/44$, and $z = -38/44$, by the definition of equality of matrices. This matrix solution of a 3×3 system of linear equations will provide a method for writing one computer program to solve an $m \times m$ system of linear equations.

BASIC Matrix Commands

Most BASIC language compilers contain a list of matrix commands which are similar to the internal functions. Actually, there are a number of prepackaged programs related to matrix operations stored in the BASIC compiler. Some of the common matrix commands are as follows:

(1) line number MAT READ A,B

This statement commands the computer to read in the elements of matrices A and B row-wise, provided they have been predimensioned to their exact dimensions (that is, you cannot overdimension the number of rows or columns).

Note: A programmer can use

line number MAT INPUT A,B.

The user has to type in the elements of A, then the elements of B row-wise.

(2) line number MAT PRINT X,Y,Z

This statement commands the computer to print out the elements of matrix X row by row, then the elements of matrix Y row by row, and finally the elements of matrix Z row by row, provided X, Y, and Z have been predimensioned to their exact dimensions.

(3) line number MAT C=A+B

This statement commands the computer to find the sum of matrices $A = (a_{ij})$ and $B = (b_{ij})$, and store the resulting elements in a matrix called C, provided A, B, and C have been predimensioned to their exact dimensions.

(4) line number MAT D=A−B

This statement commands the computer to subtract matrix $B = (b_{ij})$ from matrix $A = (a_{ij})$ and store the resulting elements in matrix D, provided A, B, and D have been predimensioned to their exact values.

(5) line number MAT E=(K)∗A

This statement commands the computer to multiply each element in matrix A by the real number K and store the resulting elements in matrix E, provided A and E have been predimensioned to their exact dimensions.

(6) line number MAT F=A∗B

This statement commands the computer to multiply matrix $A = (a_{ij})$ times matrix $B = (b_{jk})$ and store the resulting elements in matrix F, provided A, B, and F have been predimensioned to their exact dimensions.

(7)   line number MAT G=INV(A)

This statement commands the computer to find the inverse of any square matrix A and store the resulting elements in matrix G, provided A and G have been predimensioned to their exact values. (If A is a singular matrix, that is, det(A) = 0, the computer will print out an error message.)

(8)   line number LET T=DET

This statement, which does not exist in many earlier BASIC compilers, commands the computer to store the determinant value of the last matrix whose inverse was computed in a location called T.

(9)   line number MAT H=TRN(A)

This statement commands the computer to construct a new matrix H in the following manner: Interchange the rows and columns of matrix A, provided A and H have been predimensioned to their exact dimensions. For example, if

$$A = \begin{bmatrix} 2 & 3 & 4 \\ 5 & 6 & 7 \end{bmatrix} = (a_{23})$$

then

$$H = \begin{bmatrix} 2 & 5 \\ 3 & 6 \\ 4 & 7 \end{bmatrix} = (h_{32})$$

(10)   line number MAT R=IDN

If matrix R is any previously dimensioned square matrix, statement (10) converts matrix R to the identity matrix.

(11)   line number MAT S=ZER

If matrix S is any previously dimensioned matrix, statement (11) converts matrix S to the zero matrix (that is, a matrix containing all zeros).

Note: Not every BASIC compiler contains each of the matrix statements listed above. You must consult the user's manual before using any one of the commands (1) through (11).

SAMPLE PROBLEM

Given:

$$A = \begin{bmatrix} 5 & 6 & 7 \\ 2 & 3 & 4 \\ -1 & 2 & 1 \end{bmatrix}, \quad B = \begin{bmatrix} -2 & 6 & 8 \\ -3 & 2 & 1 \\ 0 & 1 & 5 \end{bmatrix}, \quad C = \begin{bmatrix} 5 & 6 \\ 7 & 8 \\ 9 & 1 \end{bmatrix}$$

Wanted: A BASIC program to compute and print out $A+B, B-A, -17C$, $BC, \bar{A}, \bar{A}C$.

Solution:

```
5 DIM A(3,3),B(3,3),C(3,2),D(3,3),E(3,3),F(3,2),G(3,2),X(3,3),Y(3,3)
10 MAT READ A,B,C
15 MAT D=A+B
20 MAT E=B-A
25 MAT F=(-17)*C
30 MAT G=B*C
35 MAT X=INV(A)
40 MAT Y=X*A
45 MAT PRINT A,B,C,D,E,F,G,X,Y
50 DATA 5,6,7,2,3,4,-1,2,1,-2,6,8,-3,2,1,0,1,5,5,6,7,8,9,1
55 END
RUN
```

16:54   08/06/75

```
 5    6    7
 2    3    4
-1    2    1

-2    6    8
-3    2    1
 0    1    5
```

15
5
6

1
-3
4

6
8
1

12
5
3

0
-1
-1

-102
-136
-17

5
7
9

3
-1
-1

-7
-5
1

-85
-119
-153

104   44

8   -1

52   13

.416667   -.666667   -.25

.5   -1.   .5

-.583334   1.33333   -.25

1   0   -9.53674E-07

-4.76837E-07   1.   -4.76837E-07

1.78814E-07   -3.57628E-07   1.

TIME 0.0 SECS.

Note: The last matrix in the computer printout should be the 3 × 3 identity matrix, which is

$$\begin{bmatrix} 1 & 0 & 0 \\ 0 & 1 & 0 \\ 0 & 0 & 1 \end{bmatrix}$$

Because of computer "roundoff errors," the printout shows numbers such as $-4.76837E-07 \approx 0$.

Problem Set 3.4

1. Give the output for the following programs:

(a)
```
10   DIM A(11)
20   FOR I=1 TO 11
30      READ A(I)
40   NEXT I
50   PRINT A(11)
60   PRINT (A(4)−A(6))/6
70   DATA 1,2,3,4,5,6,7,8,9,10,11
80   END
```

(b)
```
10   DIM A(11,1)
20   MAT READ A
30   PRINT A(11,1),(A(4,1)−A(6,1))/6
40   DATA 1,2,3,4,5,6,7,8,9,10,11
50   END
```

(c)
```
10   DIM A(2,2),B(2,2),C(2,3),X(2,2),Y(2,2),Z(2,3)
20   MAT READ A,B,C
30   MAT X=(−5)*B
40   MAT Y=X−A
50   MAT Z=B*C
60   MAT PRINT A,B,X,Y,Z
70   DATA 5,2,−1,3,0,1,7,8,1,2,3,5,−6,−7
80   END
```

2. Write a BASIC program to compute and print the inverses of the following matrices:

$$A = \begin{bmatrix} 2 & 3 \\ 7 & 9 \end{bmatrix}, \qquad B = \begin{bmatrix} 5 & 2 & 1 \\ 3 & 0 & 2 \\ -1 & 7 & 19 \end{bmatrix}$$

3. *Given*:

$$A = \begin{bmatrix} 2 & 3 \\ 4 & -11 \end{bmatrix}, \qquad B = \begin{bmatrix} 1 & 7 & 8 \\ 9 & -11 & 2 \end{bmatrix}$$

$$C = \begin{bmatrix} 3 & 4 & 5 & 16 \\ -1 & 10 & 9 & -11 \end{bmatrix}, \qquad F = \begin{bmatrix} 8 & 0 \\ -1 & 3 \end{bmatrix}$$

Wanted: A BASIC program to compute and print out $A - F$, AB, AC, $\bar{A}$, $\bar{F}$, $\overline{AF}$, $A\bar{A}$, $F\bar{F}$.

4. We have shown that a 3×3 system of linear equations can be solved using matrix algebra. The system

$$a_{11}x + a_{12}y + a_{13}z = b_{11}$$
$$a_{21}x + a_{22}y + a_{23}z = b_{21}$$
$$a_{31}x + a_{32}y + a_{33}z = b_{31}$$

can be written in the matrix form $AX = B$, where

$$A = \begin{bmatrix} a_{11} & a_{12} & a_{13} \\ a_{21} & a_{22} & a_{23} \\ a_{31} & a_{32} & a_{33} \end{bmatrix}, \quad X = \begin{bmatrix} x \\ y \\ z \end{bmatrix}, \quad B = \begin{bmatrix} b_{11} \\ b_{21} \\ b_{31} \end{bmatrix}$$

We can solve the system as follows:

$$AX = B$$
$$(\bar{A}A)X = \bar{A}B$$
$$IX = C$$
$$X = C$$

where $C = \bar{A}B$. Code the flowchart (Figure 3.6) in the BASIC language (make use of the matrix commands).

Figure 3.6

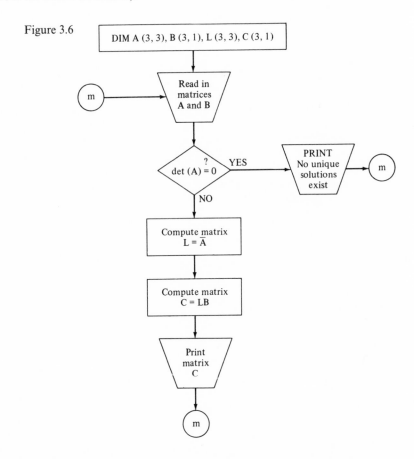

5. The flowchart illustrated in Problem 4 (Figure 3.6) represents the matrix solution to three linear equations in three unknowns. Which single statement in the program would have to be changed to use the matrix commands to solve a 4×4 linear system, a 5×5 linear system, ..., and an $m \times m$ linear system?

6. *Given*: Any square matrix A of order 3.
   Wanted: A BASIC program to compute and print out
       (a) $C = \bar{A}$
       (b) $I = CA$
       (c) $F = (f_{ij}) = ((a_{ij})^2 - 27)$ for all i and j
       (d) the comment:
           THE ELEMENTS IN THE PRINCIPAL DIAGONAL (a_{11}, a_{22}, a_{33}) ARE (or ARE NOT) ALL EQUAL TO 1.
       (e) THE ELEMENTS NOT IN THE PRINCIPAL DIAGONAL ARE (or ARE NOT) ALL EQUAL TO 0.
   Sample Data: 5,6,2,−3,2,1,2,4,5
           1,6,2,−3,1,1,2,4,1
           5,0,0,0,2,0,0,0,5
           1,0,0,0,1,0,0,0,1

7. If
$$F = \begin{bmatrix} 5 & 0 & 2 \\ 0 & -2 & 1 \\ 1 & 2 & 3 \end{bmatrix}$$
   find:
   (a) $\det(F)$
   (b) the cofactors of $f_{11}, f_{12}, f_{13}, f_{21}, f_{22}, f_{23}, f_{31}, f_{32}, f_{33}$
   (c) $\bar{F}$
   (d) Show that
$$F\bar{F} = I_3 = \begin{bmatrix} 1 & 0 & 0 \\ 0 & 1 & 0 \\ 0 & 0 & 1 \end{bmatrix}$$

3.5

Solving an $m \times n$ System of Linear Equations

The term "$m \times n$ system of linear equations" means m linear equations containing n unknowns. The three different possibilities are $m = n$, $m > n$, or $m < n$. We have already discussed the case where $m = n$.

Let us take another look at systems of linear equations where the number of equations is *the same as* the number of unknowns. An $m \times m$ system of linear equations may have a unique common solution (consistent system), no common solutions (inconsistent system), or an infinite number of common solutions (dependent system). We want to show especially how we can write a particular solution when an infinite number of solutions exist. Let us consider the following 3×3 systems of linear equations (Systems 1, 2, 3):

(1)
$$t + r + s = 4$$
$$2t - r + s = 3$$
$$t - 2r + 3s = 5$$

Subtract second equation from first equation:

$$-t + 2r = 1$$

Multiply first equation by 3 and subtract third equation:

$$2t + 5r = 7$$

Then

$$-t + 2r = 1$$
$$2t + 5r = 7$$

Multiply first equation by 2:

$$-2t + 4r = 2$$
$$2t + 5r = 7$$
$$9r = 9$$

or
$$r = 1.$$

If $-t + 2r = 1$, then $-t + 2(1) = 1$, $-t = -1$; or $t = 1$. Since $t + r + s = 4$, then $1 + 1 + s = 4$, or $s = 2$. Therefore the unique common solution is the ordered pair (1,1,2).

(2)
$$2x - y + 3z = 5$$
$$x + 2y - z = 6$$
$$3x + y + 2z = 8$$

Add first equation to three times second equation:

$$5x + 5y = 23$$

Multiply second equation by 2, and add result to third equation:

$$5x + 5y = 20$$

Subtract the two resulting equations:

$$0 = 3$$

This subtraction results in a contradiction; therefore there are *no common solutions*.

(3) $$a - 3b + c = 4$$
$$a - b - c = 2$$
$$2a - 5b + c = 7$$

Add first equation to second equation:

$$2a - 4b = 6$$
or $\quad a - 2b = 3.$

Add second equation to third equation:

$$3a - 6b = 9$$
or $\quad a - 2b = 3.$

Thus following 2×2 system of linear equations is obtained:

$$a - 2b = 3$$
$$a - 2b = 3$$
$$0 = 0$$

(Subtract the two resulting equations.) Thus, this 2×2 system of linear equations has an *infinite number of common solutions.* Therefore, the original 3×3 system of linear equations *also has an infinite number of common solutions.*

In order to find some of the common solutions, we take one of the resulting equations above and let one of the variables become an arbitrary value. If we choose $a - 2b = 3$, and let b be an arbitrary value, then $a - 2b = 3$, or $a = 3 + 2b$. Since $a - 3b + c = 4$, then

$$(3 + 2b) - 3b + c = 4$$

$$3 - b + c = 4$$

or $c = b + 1$. Therefore, the infinite number of common solutions of our original 3×3 system can be represented by:

b as an arbitrary value

$$a = 3 + 2b$$

$$c = b + 1.$$

That is, if we let $b = 1$, then $a = 5$, $c = 2$, and we have the common solution $(5,1,2)$. If we let $b = 2$, then $a = 7$, $c = 3$, and we have the common solution $(7,2,3)$. We could let $b = 0,1,2,3, \ldots$ to obtain any number of desired common solutions.

Now let us consider $m \times n$ systems of linear equations where $m > n$ (more equations than variables). Consider the following 3×2 linear system of equations:

$$t + r = 2$$
$$t - r = 1$$
$$-t + 3r = 5$$

If we look at a 2×2 system contained in the preceding system and find that it has no common solutions, then the 3×2 system will not have any common solution. If the 2×2 system selected has solutions, we must substitute in the remaining equation to see if the solutions pertain to the 3×2 system. Let us work with the first two equations:

$$t + r = 2$$
$$\underline{t - r = 1}$$
$$2t = 3$$

or $t = 3/2$. Then $3/2 + r = 2$, or $r = 1/2$.

We now check the common solution $(3/2, 1/2)$ in the remaining equation:

$$-t + 3r = 5$$
$$-3/2 + 3(1/2) \neq 5$$

Therefore, the 3×2 linear system does *not* have any common solution.

Let us now consider the following 4×3 linear system of equations:

$$x + 3y + z = 6$$
$$-x + y + z = 2$$
$$3x + y - z = 2$$
$$2x + 4y + z = 8$$

Consider the 3×3 linear system:

$$x + 3y + z = 6$$
$$-x + y + z = 2$$
$$3x + y - z = 2$$

Subtract second equation from first equation:

$$2x + 2y = 4$$

or $\qquad x + y = 2.$

Add second and third equations:

$$2x + 2y = 4$$

or $\qquad x + y = 2.$ Now subtracting:

$$x + y = 2$$
$$\underline{x + y = 2}$$
$$0 = 0$$

Therefore the 3×3 linear system has an *infinite* number of common solutions.

For $x + y = 2$, letting x be an arbitrary value, we have $y = 2 - x$. Then

$$x + 3y + z = 6$$
$$x + 3(2 - x) + z = 6 \qquad \text{(substitute } (2 - x) \text{ as value of } y\text{)}$$

$$x + 6 - 3x + z = 6$$

$$-2x + 6 + z = 6$$

or $z = 2x.$

The infinite number of solutions of the 3×3 linear system of equations can be represented by

$$y = 2 - x$$

$$z = 2x$$

where x is an arbitrary value.

We must now check this representation in the original 4×3 system of linear equations (Equation 4). Consider the fourth equation: $2x + 4y + z = 8$. Substituting $y = 2 - x$ and $z = 2x$ in this equation, we obtain

$$2x + 4(2 - x) + 2x = 8$$

$$2x + 8 - 4x + 2x = 8$$

$$8 = 8$$

Therefore, x as an arbitrary value ($y = 2 - x, z = 2x$) can represent the *infinite* number of solutions of this 4×3 linear system of equations.

Now let us look at $m \times n$ systems of linear equations where $m < n$ (fewer equations than variables). If $m < n$, the $m \times n$ linear system of equations will have either *no common solution* or *an infinite number of common solutions*.

For example, let us look at the following 2×3 system of linear equations:

$$4x - 2y + 6z = 6$$
$$-2x + y - 3z = -3$$

Multiply second equation by 2:

$$4x - 2y + 6z = 6$$
$$-4x + 2y - 6z = 6$$
$$0 = 0$$

Therefore, there are an *infinite number of common solutions*.

For $-2x + y - 3z = -3$, if we let x and z be arbitrary, we have $y = 2x + 3z - 3$. For example, if we let $x = 1$ and $z = 2$, then $y = 5$ indicates that $(1,5,2)$ is *one of the infinite number* of common solutions.

Consider the following 3×4 system of linear equations:

$$a + 2b - c + d = 5$$
$$a - 5b + 4c - 5d = 6$$
$$3a - b + 2c - 3d = 2$$

Subtract second equation from first equation, and subtract third equation from three times first equation:

$$7b - 5c + 6d = -1$$
$$\underline{7b - 5c + 6d = 13}$$
$$0 = -14$$

This is a contradiction; therefore, this 3×4 system of linear equations has *no common solutions.*

Problem Set 3.5

Solve the following systems of equations:

1. $\quad a + b + 3c = 11$
$\quad\ 3a + 2b + c = 1$
$\quad\ 2a + b - 5c = 11$

2. $\quad x - y = 1$
$\quad\ x + y = 6$
$\quad\ 2x + y = 10$

3. $t - r + 2s = 0$
$\quad t + 2r + s - 3w = 0$
$\quad t + r - 2w = 0$

4. $\quad a + 2b = 4$
$\quad\ 3a - 4b = 2$
$\quad -a + 5b = 2$
$\quad\ 2a - b = 3$

5. $\quad x + y + z + 2w = 7$
$\quad\ 2x - 3y + 2z - w = 8$
$\quad\ 3x + y + z - w = 1$
$\quad\ 2x - 3y + 5z + w = -3$

6. $\quad a - b - c = 7$
$\quad\ 2a - 3b + c = 7$
$\quad\ 3a - 7c = 9$

3.6

An Iterative Numerical Method for Solving an $m \times n$ System of Linear Equations

Consider the following 3×3 system of linear equations:

$$t + r + s = 4$$
$$2t - r + s = 3$$
$$t - 2r + 3s = 5$$

One method of *iteration* (step-by-step procedure) for solving a system of linear equations is to construct a matrix consisting of the coefficients of the unknowns and the numerical coefficients. The 3×3 system above can be represented by the following matrix:

$$\begin{bmatrix} 1 & 1 & 1 & 4 \\ 2 & -1 & 1 & 3 \\ 1 & -2 & 3 & 5 \end{bmatrix}$$

We now perform operations on the equations, using only the coefficients. We would like to have the resulting matrix contain exactly one variable in each equation with a coefficient of 1. This result is possible if we have an $n \times n$ system with a unique solution. Let us consider further this coefficient matrix

$$\begin{bmatrix} 1 & 1 & 1 & 4 \\ 2 & -1 & 1 & 3 \\ 1 & -2 & 3 & 5 \end{bmatrix}$$

and perform the following operations:

1. Take two times first equation minus the second equation; subtract the third equation from the first equation:

$$\begin{bmatrix} 1 & 1 & 1 & 4 \\ 0 & 3 & 1 & 5 \\ 0 & 3 & -2 & -1 \end{bmatrix}$$

2. Take first equation minus 1/3 times second equation; 1/3 times second equation; and subtract the third equation from the second equation:

$$\begin{bmatrix} 1 & 0 & 2/3 & 7/3 \\ 0 & 1 & 1/3 & 5/3 \\ 0 & 0 & 3 & 6 \end{bmatrix}$$

3. Take 1/3 times third equation:

$$\begin{bmatrix} 1 & 0 & 2/3 & 7/3 \\ 0 & 1 & 1/3 & 5/3 \\ 0 & 0 & 1 & 2 \end{bmatrix}$$

4. Take first equation minus 2/3 times third equation; and subtract 1/3 times third equation from the second equation:

$$\begin{bmatrix} 1 & 0 & 0 & 1 \\ 0 & 1 & 0 & 1 \\ 0 & 0 & 1 & 2 \end{bmatrix}$$

This final matrix represents the following equations:

$$t + 0 + 0 = 1$$
$$0 + r + 0 = 1$$
$$0 + 0 + s = 2$$

or the unique solution (1,1,2) to our original 3 × 3 system of linear equations (Equations 1, 2, and 3).

Let us look at another 3 × 3 system of linear equations:

$$2x - y + 3z = 5$$
$$x + 2y - z = 6$$
$$3x + y + 2z = 8$$

or

$$\begin{bmatrix} 2 & -1 & 3 & 5 \\ 1 & 2 & -1 & 6 \\ 3 & 1 & 2 & 8 \end{bmatrix}$$

Perform the following operations:

1. One-half times first equation; first equation minus two times second equation; three times second equation minus third equation:

$$\begin{bmatrix} 1 & -1/2 & 3/2 & 5/2 \\ 0 & -5 & 5 & -7 \\ 0 & 5 & -5 & 10 \end{bmatrix}$$

2. $(-1/5)$ times second equation; $1/5$ times third equation:

$$\begin{bmatrix} 1 & -1/2 & 3/2 & 5/2 \\ 0 & 1 & -1 & 7/5 \\ 0 & 1 & -1 & 2 \end{bmatrix}$$

3. Second equation minus third equation:

$$\begin{bmatrix} 1 & -1/2 & 3/2 & 5/2 \\ 0 & 1 & -1 & 7/5 \\ 0 & 0 & 0 & -3/5 \end{bmatrix}$$

This matrix represents the following equations:

$$x - (y/2) + (3z/2) = 5/2$$
$$0 + y - z = 7/5$$
$$0 + 0 + 0 = -3/5$$

The last equation obviously leads to a contradiction, which indicates that the given 3 × 3 system of linear equations *does not have any common solutions*.

Let us consider a 3 × 3 linear system of equations which has an *infinite number* of common solutions.

$$a - 3b + c = 4$$
$$a - b - c = 2$$
$$2a - 5b + c = 7$$

or

$$\begin{bmatrix} 1 & -3 & 1 & 4 \\ 1 & -1 & -1 & 2 \\ 2 & -5 & 1 & 7 \end{bmatrix}$$

Do the following operations:

1. First equation minus second equation; two times first equation minus third equation:

$$\begin{bmatrix} 1 & -3 & 1 & 4 \\ 0 & -2 & 2 & 2 \\ 0 & -1 & 1 & 1 \end{bmatrix}$$

2. First equation minus three times third equation; $-1/2$ times second equation; second equation minus two times third equation:

$$\begin{bmatrix} 1 & 0 & -2 & 1 \\ 0 & 1 & -1 & -1 \\ 0 & 0 & 0 & 0 \end{bmatrix}$$

This matrix leads to the equations

$$a + 0 - 2c = 1$$
$$0 + b - c = -1$$
$$0 + 0 + 0 = 0$$

The last equation tells us that there are *an infinite number of common solutions*, and we can let c be the arbitrary variable. With c as an arbitrary value:

$$b = c - 1, \qquad a = 2c + 1$$

For example, if $c = 1$, then $b = 0$ and $a = 3$, which gives us one of the infinite number of common solutions, namely, (3,0,1).

We previously solved the following 2×3 system of linear equations:

$$4x - 2y + 6z = 6$$
$$-2x + y - 3z = -3$$

or

$$\begin{bmatrix} 4 & -2 & 6 & 6 \\ -2 & 1 & -3 & -3 \end{bmatrix}$$

We take $1/4$ times first equation; first equation plus two times second equation:

$$\begin{bmatrix} 1 & -1/2 & 3/2 & 3/2 \\ 0 & 0 & 0 & 0 \end{bmatrix}$$

This latter matrix represents the following equations:

$$x - (y/2) + (3z/2) = 3/2$$
$$0 + 0 + 0 = 0$$

The second equation indicates there are an *infinite number of common solutions.* If we multiply the first equation by 2 to obtain $2x - y + 3z = 3$, then let x and z be arbitrary values and $y = 2x + 3z - 3$, we will represent the infinite number of common solutions.

The iterative method illustrated in this article is sometimes referred to as the *Echelon solution* of linear systems of equations. This solution process is ideally suited for a prepackaged computer program.

3.7

A Prepackaged Program for Placing Solutions to Linear Systems of Equations in Echelon Form

Name: Echelon

Description: This program solves any system of linear equations by placing the solutions in *Echelon* form.

Instructions: The user of this program merely commands the computer to run the program and will receive the following query:

```
RUN

ECHELON        16:11     10/21/75

ENTER # OF ROWS AND COLUMNS INCLUDING RIGHT HAND SIDE
?3, 4
ENTER MATRIX ROWWISE -CARRIAGE RETURN AFTER EACH ROW
?1, 1, 1, 4

??2, -1, 1, 3

??1, -2, 3, 5


   1       1       1       4

   2      -1       1       3

   1      -2       3       5


   1       0       0       1.

   0       1.      0       1.

   0       0       1.      2.


TIME 0.0 SECS.
```

RUN

ECHELON   16:12   10/21/75

ENTER # OF ROWS AND COLUMNS INCLUDING RIGHT HAND SIDE
?3,4
ENTER MATRIX ROWWISE -CARRIAGE RETURN AFTER EACH ROW
?2,-1,3,5

??1,2,-1,6

??3,1,2,8

2	-1	3	5
1	2	-1	6
3	1	2	8

1	0	1	0
0	1.	1.	0
0	0	0	1.

TIME 0.0 SECS.

RUN

ECHELON   16:13   10/21/75

ENTER # OF ROWS AND COLUMNS INCLUDING RIGHT HAND SIDE
?3,4
ENTER MATRIX ROWWISE -CARRIAGE RETURN AFTER EACH ROW
?1,-3,1,4

??1,-1,-1,2

??2,-5,1,7

1	-3	1	4
1	-1	-1	2
2	-5	1	7

```
1        0       - 2        1

0        1       - 1       - 1

0        0        0         0
```

TIME 0.0 SECS.

RUN

ECHELON   16:15   10/21/75

ENTER # OF ROWS AND COLUMNS INCLUDING RIGHT HAND SIDE
? 3, 3
ENTER MATRIX ROWWISE - CARRIAGE RETURN AFTER EACH ROW
? 1, 1, 2

?? 1, - 1, 1

?? - 1, 3, 5


```
1        1        2

1       - 1       1

- 1       3        5
```

```
1        0        0

0        1        0

0        0       1 .
```


TIME 0.0 SE CS.

RUN

ECHELON   16:17   10/21/75

ENTER # OF ROWS AND COLUMNS INCLUDING RIGHT HAND SIDE
? 3, 5

ENTER MATRIX ROW WISE -CARRIAGE RETURN AFTER EACH ROW
? 1, 2, -1, 1, 5

?? 1, -5, 4, -5, 6

?? 3, -1, 2, -3, 2

1	2	-1	1	5
1	-5	4	-5	6
3	-1	2	-3	2

1	0	.423571	-.714285	0
0	1.	-.714286	.857143	0
0	0	0	0	.999999

TIME 0.0 SECS.

The first computer output indicates that the linear system

$$x + y + z = 4$$
$$2x - y + z = 3$$
$$x - 2y + 3z = 5$$

has a *unique* solution, namely, $x = 1$, $y = 1$, and $z = 2$. The second computer output illustrates that the linear system

$$2x - y + 3z = 5$$
$$x + 2y - z = 6$$
$$3x + y + 2z = 8$$

has *no* solutions. The third computer output indicates that the linear system

$$x - 3y + z = 4$$
$$x - y - z = 2$$
$$2x - 5y + z = 7$$

has an *infinite* number of solutions, and they can be written $y = -1 + z$, $x = 1 + 2z$, by letting z be arbitrary.

The interpretation of the fourth and fifth computer outputs are left as an exercise for the reader. The flowchart for ECHELON is given in Figure 3.7. The coding of ECHELON follows.

```
100 REM      ECHELON FORM OF M EQUATIONS IN N-1 UNKNOWNS
110 PRINT "ENTER # OF ROWS AND COLUMNS INCLUDING RIGHT HAND SIDE"
120 DIMA(10,10)
130 INPUT M,N
140 PRINT "ENTER MATRIX ROWWISE -CARRIAGE RETURN AFTER EACH ROW"
150 MAT INPUT A(M,N)
160 MATPRINTA;
170 LET K=1
180 REM K COUNTS ROW # IN WHICH WE'RE TRYING TO GET A PRIMARY 1
190 FOR I=1 TO N
200    LET B=A(K,I)
210    IF A(K,I)<>0 THEN  390
220    FOR J=K+1 TO M
230       IF A(J,I)<>0 THEN  260
240    NEXT J
250    GOTO 370
260    REM      WANT TO SWITCH J ROW WITH K ROW
270    FOR L=1 TO N
280 REM COULD HAVE USED I TO N SINCE FIRST I-1 ARE 0.
290       LET T=A(K,L)
300       LET A(K,L)=A(J,L)
310       LET A(J,L)=T
320    NEXT L
330    REM      NOW ROW K IS NICE
340 REM THAT IS, WE HAVE NON-ZERO ELEMENT IN ROW K,COL.I
350    LET B=A(K,I)
360 GOTO390
370 NEXT I
380 GOTO 610
```

147

```
390 FOR Z=1 TO N
400 REM DIVIDING ROW K BY A(K,I) TO GET PRIMARY ONE IN A(K,I)
410   LET A(K,Z)=1/B*A(K,Z)
420   LET X=K
430   LET Y=Z
440   GOSUB 630
450 NEXT Z
460 FOR L=1 TO M
470 IF L=K THEN 570
480 REM USING PRIMARY 1 TO GET ZEROES IN COLUMN I IN
490 REM ALL ROWS EXCEPT ROW K.
500   LET C=A(L,I)
510   FOR P=I TO N
520     LET A(L,P)=A(L,P)-C*A(K,P)
530     LET X=L
540     LET Y=P
550     GOSUB 630
560   NEXT P
570 NEXT L
580 LET K=K+1
590 IF K>M THEN 610
600 GOTO 190
610 MAT PRINT A;
620 GOTO 670
630 REM  TO PREVENT ROUND OFF ERRORS
640 IF ABS(A(X,Y))>10↑(-4) THEN 660
650 LET A(X,Y)=0
660 RETURN
670 END
```

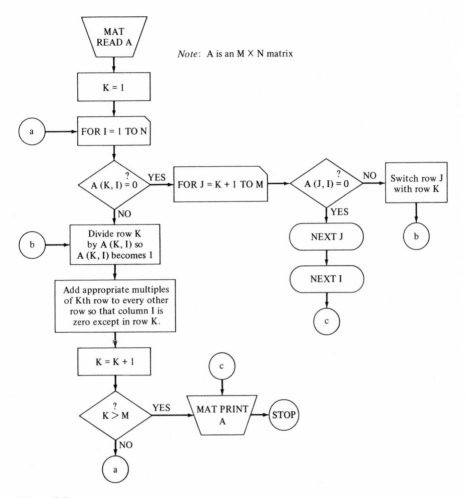

Figure 3.7

Problem Set 3.6

Use the prepackaged program ECHELON to solve each of the equations in Problem Set 3.5.

3.8

Systems of Linear Inequalities

The solution of problems in a linear programming course requires the solution of systems of linear inequalities as well as systems of linear equations. Any two real numbers x and y have exactly one of the following relationships: $x = y$

(that is, x is equal to y); $x > y$ (that is, x is greater than y); or $x < y$ (that is, x is less than y). The following definitions and *inequality properties* are true for any real numbers a, b, and c.

DEFINITIONS

1. $a < b$ if and only if $a + c = b$ for some positive number c.

2. $a > b$ if and only if $a = b + c$ for some positive number c.

INEQUALITY PROPERTIES

1. If $a > b$ and $b > c$, then $a > c$.

2. If $a < b$ and $b < c$, then $a < c$.

3. If $a > b$, then $a + c > b + c$.

4. If $a < b$, then $a + c < b + c$.

The following inequality properties are also true:

5. If $a > b$ and $c > 0$, then $ac > bc$.

6. If $a > b$ and $c < 0$, then $ac < bc$.

7. If $a < b$ and $c > 0$, then $ac < bc$.

8. If $a < b$ and $c < 0$, then $ac > bc$.

Linear Inequalities

In Chapter 2 we graphed equations such as $2x + 3y = 6$ and $2y = 7$. Let us now look at the graphs of $2x + 3y < 6$ and $2y \geq 7$. To graph $2x + 3y < 6$, we first locate and plot the graph of $2x + 3y = 6$ and decide which resulting region of the Cartesian plane will satisfy the statement $2x + 3y < 6$. (See Figure 3.8.) If

$$2x + 3y = 6$$

$$3y = 6 - 2x$$

$$y = 2 - (2x/3)$$

Notice that (3,0) and (0,2) lie on the graph of $2x + 3y = 6$, where the X-intercept $= 3$ and the Y-intercept $= 2$.

Any point *to the left of or below* the broken line representing the graph of $2x + 3y = 6$, such as (0,0), makes $2x + 3y < 6$ a true statement. Any point *to the right of or above* the broken line representing the graph of $2x + 3y = 6$, such as (5,5), makes $2x + 3y < 6$ a *false statement*. Therefore, we shade the

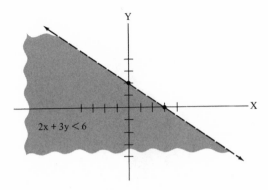

Figure 3.8

area *to the left of* the broken line. The line remains broken to indicate that $2x + 3y$ is strictly less than 6.

To graph $2y \geq 7$ (that is, $2y$ is greater than or equal to 7), we first locate and plot the graph of $2y = 7$ (Figure 3.9), or $y = 7/2$.

Any point *on* or *above* the line representing the graph of $2y = 7$, such as (1,9), makes $2y \geq 7$ a *true* statement. Any point *below* the line representing $2y = 7$, such as $(-1, -2)$ makes $2y \geq 7$ a *false* statement. Therefore, we shade the area *above* the solid line representing the graph of $2y = 7$ to indicate the region where $2y > 7$. The line remains solid to indicate that in $2y \geq 7$, $2y$ can be greater than or equal to 7.

Let us now graph the system of linear inequalities in which we are looking for common solutions. See Figure 3.10.

The solid line and light-shaded area represent the solutions to $x + y \leq 6$, and the broken line and the medium-shaded area represent the solution to

Figure 3.9

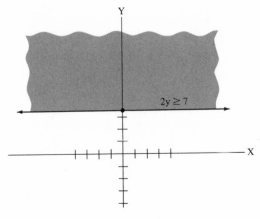

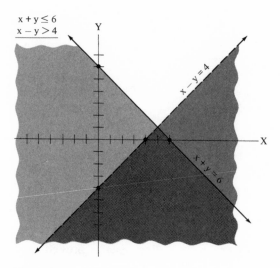

$x + y \leq 6$
$x - y > 4$

Figure 3.10

$x - y > 4$. The darkest-shaded area, where the lightest- and medium-shaded areas meet, represents *all the common solutions* to this given system of linear inequalities.

For example, let us assume a local hero sandwich shop offers two kinds of special heroes (h_1 and h_2). It takes 1 pound of provolone (cheese) and 2 pounds of salami to make a dozen h_1 heroes; and 1 pound of provolone and 1 pound of salami to make a dozen h_2 heroes. On Saturdays the employees of the hero shop make as many h_1 and h_2 heroes as they can before the lunch-hour rush. On one particular Saturday they have on hand 40 pounds of provolone and 60 pounds of salami for preparing h_1 and h_2 heroes. The owner of the hero shop would like to know how many dozen h_1 and h_2 heroes can be made. The problem above generates the following system of linear inequalities:

$$h_1 \geq 0$$
$$h_2 \geq 0$$

$$h_1 + h_2 \leq 40 \qquad \text{(provolone)}$$
$$\underline{2h_1 + h_2 \leq 60 \qquad \text{(salami)}}$$

$$h_1 + h_2 = 40 \qquad\qquad 2h_1 + h_2 = 60$$
$$h_2 = 40 - h_1 \qquad\qquad h_2 = 60 - 2h_1$$

We can now use the following values of the h_2 and h_1 intercepts for each equation and plot the two graphs, (0,40), (40,0) and (0,60), (30,0), as shown in Figure 3.11.

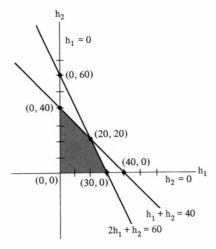

Figure 3.11

$$h_1 + h_2 \leq 40$$
$$2h_2 + h_2 \leq 60$$

Notice that *only the shaded area*, where both $h_1 \geq 0$ and $h_2 \geq 0$, *represents the common solutions* to the given system of linear equations. Furthermore, this shaded region represents the possible or feasible common solutions to the number of dozens of h_1 and h_2 heroes. If we had more information, we could determine the most profitable common solution. The various aspects of this problem represent some of the topics that would be covered in a linear programming course. Linear programming contains various matrix and iterative methods for solving complex systems of linear inequalities, which are similar to the methods we used for systems of linear equations.

Problem Set 3.7

1. Which of the following statements are true statements?
   (a) $2 + 3 < 5$
   (b) $2 + 3 \leq 5$
   (c) If $3 < 6$, then $3(-2) \overset{?}{<} 6(-2)$
   (d) $2 - 9 > -11$
   (e) $9 + 7 \geq 16 + 1$

2. What values of x would make the following inequalities true statements?
   (a) $x + 3 < 7$ (b) $x - 7 \leq 8$
   (c) $5x \leq 7$ (d) $-3x > 27 + x$

3. Graph the solution of each of the following systems of linear inequalities:

(a) $x - 3y > 3$
$x \qquad \geq 8$

(b) $x + 2y < 6$
$2x - y > 9$

(c) $x \qquad \geq 0$
$y \geq 0$
$3x - 2y \leq 6$
$x + y \geq 5$

(d) $x \geq 0$
$y \geq 0$
$x + y \leq 7$
$x - y \geq 5$

(e) $x \geq 0$
$y \leq 0$
$x - 3y \geq 7$
$x + y \leq 8$

(f) $x \geq 0$
$y \geq 0$
$4x - 2y + 6 \geq 0$
$3x + 5y - 5 \geq 0$

3.9

Introduction to Linear Programming: Maximum Solution (Two Variables)—Graphical Solutions

Again let us assume a local hero shop offers two kinds of special heroes (h_1 and h_2). It takes 1 pound of provolone (cheese) and 2 pounds of salami to make a dozen h_1 heroes; and 1 pound of provolone and 1 pound of salami to make a dozen h_2 heroes. On Saturdays the employees of the hero shop make as many h_1 heroes and h_2 heroes as they can before the lunch-hour rush. On one particular Saturday they have 40 pounds of provolone and 60 pounds of salami for preparing h_1 and h_2 heroes. In Article 3.8 we saw that the problem concerning the number of dozens of h_1 and h_2 heroes that can be made generates the following system of linear inequalities:

$$h_1 \geq 0$$
$$h_2 \geq 0$$

$$h_1 + h_2 \leq 40 \qquad \text{(provolone)}$$
$$2h_1 + h_2 \leq 60 \qquad \text{(salami)}$$

Furthermore, we found the common solutions to this system of linear inequalities to be in the shaded area shown in Figure 3.12. Suppose each dozen of h_1 heroes sold yields \$67 profit, and each dozen of h_2 heroes sold yields \$83 profit. We let $f = 67h_1$ and $83h_2$ represent the *profit function*, sometimes called the *objective function*, and try to find the *maximum value* of f or *maximum f*.

Each point in the shaded area of Figure 3.12 represents a solution to the given system of linear inequalities, and the value of f will vary from one point to another. For example, the ordered pair (10,10) lies in the shaded area, and at this

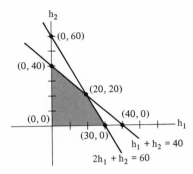

Figure 3.12

point

$$f = 67(10) + 83(10)$$

$$= 670 + 830$$

$$= \$1500$$

The ordered pair (10,30) lies in the common solution area, and at this point

$$f = 67h_1 + 83h_2$$

$$= 67(10) + 83(30)$$

$$= 670 + 2490$$

$$= \$3160$$

The *maximum value* of f will be found at one of the following boundaries, which are called the *corners* of the common solutions: (0,40), (20,20), or (30,0). At (0,40), $f = 67(0) + 83(40) = 0 + 3320 = \$3320$. At (20,20), $f = 67(20) + 83(20) = 1340 + 1660 = \$3000$. At (30,0), $f = 67(30) + 83(0) = 2010 + 0 = \$2010$. Therefore maximum $f = \$3320$ at (0,40); that is, the maximum profit would be obtained by making and selling no h_1 heroes and 40 dozen h_2 heroes.

In the previous linear programming problem, the system of linear inequalities is called the *restrictions*, or *constraints*, and the profit function $f = \$67h_1 + \$83h_2$ is called the *objective function*. That is,

$$\left. \begin{array}{l} h_1 \geq 0 \\ h_2 \geq 0 \\ \quad h_1 + h_2 \leq 40 \\ 2h_1 + h_2 \leq 60 \end{array} \right\} \quad \textit{restrictions or constraints}$$

$$f = \$67h_1 + \$83h_2 \qquad \textit{objective function}$$

Let us use the graphical procedure to solve the following linear programming problem:

$$x \geq 0$$
$$y \geq 0$$
$$2x + 3y \leq 6$$
$$\underline{4x + \; y \leq 8}$$
$$f = x + 2y$$

Find maximum f.

SOLUTION

1. Solve the system of linear inequalities (constraints) given graphically in Figure 3.13.

Figure 3.13

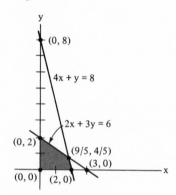

$$x \geq 0$$
$$y \geq 0$$
$$2x + 3y \leq \;\; 6$$
$$\underline{4x + \; y \leq \;\; 8}$$
$$2x + 3y = \;\; 6$$
$$\underline{4x + \; y = \;\; 8}$$
$$4x + 6y = \;\; 12$$
$$\underline{4x + \; y = \;\; 8}$$
$$5y = \;\; 4$$
$$y = 4/5$$

$$4x + 4/5 = 8$$
$$4x = 36/5$$
$$x = 9/5$$

2. Evaluate the objective function, $f = x + 2y$, at the following corner points of the common solution area:

At $(0,2)$, $f = 0 + 2(2) = 4$.

At $(9/5, 4/5)$, $f = 9/5 + 2(4/5) = 17/5 = 3\frac{2}{5}$.

At $(2,0)$, $f = 2 + 2(0) = 2$.

3. Therefore, maximum $f = 4$ at $(0,2)$.

Problem Set 3.8

Solve the following linear programming problems, using the graphical method:

1.

$$x \geq 0$$
$$y \geq 0$$
$$x + 2y \leq 40$$
$$3x + y \leq 45$$

$$f = 4x + y$$

Find maximum f.

2.

$$x \geq 0$$
$$y \geq 0$$
$$2x + y \leq 50$$
$$x + y \leq 40$$

$$f = 10x + 30y$$

Find maximum f.

3.

$$x \geq 0$$
$$y \geq 0$$
$$x - y \leq 0$$
$$2x + 3y \leq 60$$

$$f = 5x + 10y$$

Find maximum f.

4. Given the following data:

Product	No. of Units	Manufacturing Hours per Unit	Inspection Hours per Unit	Profit per Unit
A	x	2	1	$20
B	y	3	1	$30

If there are 100 manufacturing hours and 80 inspection hours available, how many units of A and B, respectively, would yield a maximum profit?

3.10

Maximum Solution (Three Variables)—Inspection of Corners Solutions

Let us consider the following linear programming problem: A manufacturer produces three products: A, B, and C. To manufacture one unit of A requires 1 hour in Department 1 and 2 hours in Department 2; one unit of B requires 2 hours in Department 1 and 2 hours in Department 2; and one unit of C requires 2 hours in Department 1 and 1 hour in Department 2. Department 1 has 40 hours available, and Department 2 has 60 hours available. Each unit of A, B, and C contributes respectively $10, $15, and $20 to profit. Find the number of units of A, B, and C which can be produced under the given restrictions to obtain a maximum profit.

SOLUTION

Product	Number of Units	Profit for Each Unit	Hours Needed in Department 1	Hours Needed in Department 2
A	x	$10	1	2
B	y	15	2	2
C	z	20	2	1

1. Determine the *constraints* and objective function:

$$x \geq 0$$
$$y \geq 0$$
$$z \geq 0$$

$$x + 2y + 2z \leq 40 \qquad \text{(40 hours available in Department 1)}$$
$$2x + 2y + z \leq 60 \qquad \text{(60 hours available in Department 2)}$$

$$f = \$10x + \$15y + \$20z$$

Now find maximum f.

2. Graphing is not practical when three variables are involved. We can obtain the number of corners for an $m \times n$ system by linear equation/inequalities via the formula

$$_mC_n = \frac{m!}{n!(m-n)!}$$

The constraints above represent a 5 × 3 system of linear inequalities. Thus,

$$_5C_3 = \frac{5!}{3!2!} = \frac{5(\overset{2}{\cancel{4}})(\overset{1}{\cancel{3}!})}{(\underset{1}{\cancel{3}!})(\underset{1}{\cancel{2}})} = 10$$

indicates that there are ten possible corners. In order to find maximum f, we evaluate the objective function only at corners that lie in the common solution area, excluding (0,0,0). Table 3.1 summarizes these evaluations.

3. Determine maximum f: maximum f = \$400 at (0,0,20) and (80/3,0,20/3). If fractional (partial) units of products A, B, and C are possible, we can obtain a maximum profit of \$400 profit by manufacturing 20 units of product C or by producing $26\frac{2}{3}$ units of product A and $6\frac{2}{3}$ units of product C. If fractional units are not possible, we can obtain a maximum profit of \$400 only by producing 20 units of product C.

Table 3.1. Ten possible corners of an $m \times n$ system

Coordinates of corner	In common solution area?	Value of objective function $f = \$10x + \$15y + \$20z$
1. (0,0,0)	Yes	————
2. (0,0,20)	Yes	$f = 0 + 0 + 20(20) = \$400$
3. (0,0,60)	No ($x + 2y + 2z \nleq 40$)	————
4. (0,20,0)	Yes	$f = 0 + 15(20) + 0 = \$300$
5. (0,30,0)	No ($x + 2y + 2z \nleq 40$)	————
6. (40,0,0)	No ($2x + 2y + z \nleq 60$)	————
7. (30,0,0)	Yes	$f = 10(30) + 0 + 0 = \$300$
8. (0,40, – 20)	No ($z \ngeq 0$)	————
$\quad$ Let $x = 0$		
$\quad$ Solve $2y + 2z = 40$		
$\qquad 2y + \;\; z = 60\quad$ for y and z		
9. (80/3,0,20/3)	Yes	$f = 10(80/3) + 0 + 20(20/3) = \$400$
$\quad$ Let $y = 0$		
$\quad$ Solve $x + 2z = 40$		
$\qquad 2x + \;\; z = 60\qquad$ for x and z		
10. (20,10,0)	Yes	$f = 10(20) + 15(10) + 0 = \$350$
$\quad$ Let $z = 0$		
$\quad$ Solve $x + 2y = 40$		
$\qquad 2x + 2y = 60\quad$ for x and y		

Consider the following linear programming problem:

$$\left.\begin{array}{l} x \geq 0 \\ y \geq 0 \\ z \geq 0 \\ 2x + y + z \leq 40 \\ x + y + 3z \leq 90 \end{array}\right\} \quad \textit{restrictions or constraints}$$

$$f = 10x + 20y + 30z \qquad \textit{objective function}$$

Find maximum f.

Step 1. Compute the number of possible corners for the given 5×3 system of inequalities (constraints).

$$_5C_3 = \frac{5!}{3!2!} = \frac{5(\overset{2}{\cancel{4}})(\overset{1}{\cancel{3!}})}{(\cancel{3!})(\underset{1}{\cancel{2}})} = 10 \text{ possible corners}$$

Table 3.2. Ten possible corners of a 5×3 system

Coordinates of corner	In common solution area?	Value of objective function $f = 10x + 20y + 30z$
1. $(0,0,0)$	Yes	———
2. $(0,0,40)$	No $(x + y + 3z \not\leq 90)$	———
3. $(0,0,30)$	Yes	$f = 0 + 0 + 30(30) = 900$
4. $(0,40,0)$	Yes	$f = 0 + 20(40) + 0 = 800$
5. $(0,90,0)$	No $(2x + y + z \not\leq 40)$	———
6. $(20,0,0)$	Yes	$f = 10(20) + 0 + 0 = 200$
7. $(90,0,0)$	No $(2x + y + z \not\leq 40)$	———
8. $(0,15,25)$	Yes	$f = 0 + 20(15) + 30(25) = 1050$

    Let $x = 0$

    Solve $y + z = 40$

           $y + 3z = 90$ *for* y *and* z

9. $(6,0,28)$	Yes	$f = 10(6) + 0 + 30(28) = 900$

    Let $y = 0$

    Solve $2x + z = 40$

           $x + 3z = 90$ *for* x *and* z

10. $(-50,140,0)$	No $(x \not\geq 0)$	———

    Let $z = 0$

    Solve $2x + y = 40$

           $x + y = 90$ *for* x *and* y

Step 2. Evaluate the objective function only at corners that lie in the common solution area, excluding (0,0,0). (See Table 3.2.)

Step 3. Determine the maximum value: maximum $f = 1050$ at (0,15,25).

Problem Set 3.9

Solve the following linear programming problems (use the inspection-of-corners method):

1. $x \geq 0, y \geq 0, z \geq 0$

$2x + 4y + z \leq 26$

$4x + 14y + 2z \leq 84$

$f = 2x + 5y + z$

Find maximum f.

2. $x \geq 0, y \geq 0, z \geq 0$

$x + 2y + z \leq 20$

$3x + y + z \leq 30$

$3x + 2y + 4z \leq 80$

$f = x + 5y + z$

Find minimum f.

3.11

Maximum Solutions: Simplex Method

The *simplex method* is an iterative numerical procedure used to solve any linear programming problem. This method is by no means "simple"; rather, it is quite complex. A prepackaged program called SIMPLEX will be provided in this section. However, one must be familiar with the basic mechanics of the simplex procedure in order to interpret the computer output after running SIMPLEX.

Consider our previous linear programming problem concerning two different types of heroes:

$$h_1 \geq 0$$
$$h_2 \geq 0$$
$$h_1 + h_2 \leq 40$$
$$2h_1 + h_2 \leq 60$$
$$f = \$67h_1 + \$83h_2$$

Find maximum f.

SOLUTION VIA SIMPLEX METHOD

Step 1. We must convert the system of inequalities to a system of equations. (We will assume all variables must be greater than or equal to 0); $f = \$67h_1 + \$83h_2$ has been given previously in Article 3.10, and $h_1 + h_2 \leq 40$ if and only if $h_1 + h_2 + r = 40$, where $r > 0$. (This is true because of the definition of $a < b$.)

Also, $2h_1 + h_2 \leq 60$ if and only if $2h_1 + h_2 + s = 60$, where $s > 0$. Therefore, we obtain the following system of equations:

$$f = \$67h_1 + \$83h_2$$

$$h_1 + h_2 + r = 40$$

$$2h_1 + h_2 + s = 60$$

The variables r and s are called *slack variables.*

Step 2. We solve the system of equations for the objective variable and slack variables:

$$f = \$67h_1 + \$83h_2 \quad \text{or} \quad f = 0 + \$67h_1 + \$83h_2$$

$$h_1 + h_2 + r = 40 \quad \text{or} \quad r = 40 - h_1 - h_2$$

$$2h_1 + h_2 + s = 60 \quad \text{or} \quad s = 60 - 2h_1 - h_2$$

Step 3. We write the system of equations

$$f = 0 + \$67h_1 + \$83h_2$$

$$r = 40 - h_1 - h_2$$

$$s = 60 - 2h_1 - h_2$$

in *matrix (tableau)* form as

		h_1	h_2
f	0	67	83
r	40	-1	-1
s	60	-2	-1

We can obtain a solution by letting the arbitrary variables (variables on the right side of the equation) be equal to 0. In the tableau above, if $h_1 = h_2 = 0$, then $f = 0$, $r = 40$, and $s = 60$; this solution is certainly not a maximum solution for f.

Step 4. In the simplex method we then switch arbitrary variables until a maximum solution is obtained. That is, in the tableau

		h_1	h_2
f	0	67	83
r	40	-1	-1^*
s	60	-2	-1

we would follow certain instructions to solve for h_1 or h_2 instead of r or s. The asterisk (*) above tells us we will solve for h_2 and s instead of r and s, and obtain the following tableau:

		h_1	r
f	3320	-16	-83
h_2	40	-1	-1
s	20	-1	1

or

$$f = 3320 - 16h_1 - 83r$$

$$h_2 = 40 - h_1 - r$$

$$s = 20 - h_1 + r$$

The tableau above represents the maximum solution. If we let $h_1 = r = 0$, then $f = \$3320$, $h_2 = 40$, $s = 20$. That is, maximum $f = \$3320$ at (0,40).

In a more complex linear programming problem we may have to switch arbitrary variables more than once until a maximum solution is obtained.

Simplex Procedure

1. We can obtain a *solution* at any step in the tableau by letting all arbitrary variables = 0.
2. A *solution is optimal* (a maximum or a minimum) if the numbers in the f row under the arbitrary variables are all zero or negative.
3. If you do not have an optimal solution, then select a pivotal element as follows:
    (a) Let the pivotal column be the one with the largest positive number in the f row (under an arbitrary variable).
    (b) Divide each element (except f element) in the first column by any negative pivotal column element; and let the pivotal row be the one whose quotient has the smallest absolute value.
4. Repeat steps 1 through 3 until an optimal solution is obtained.

3.12

A Prepackaged Program for Solving Maximum Linear Programming Problems

Name: SIMPLEX

Description: This program will find the maximum value of some objective function, given a system of linear inequalities (constraints).

Instructions: The user of this program must first construct the tableau for the linear programming problem, and then ask the computer to run SIMPLEX to receive the operating instructions.

Sample Problem:

$$h_1 \geq 0, h_2 \geq 0$$

$$h_1 + h_2 \leq 40$$

$$\underline{2h_1 + h_2 \leq 60}$$

$$f = \$67h_1 + \$83h_2$$

Find maximum f.

$$f = 67h_1 + 83h_2$$

$$h_1 + h_2 + r = 40 \qquad r > 0$$

$$\underline{2h_1 + h_2 + s = 60 \qquad s > 0}$$

$$f = \ 0 + 67h_1 + 83h_2$$

$$r = 40 - \quad h_1 - \quad h_2$$

$$\underline{s = 60 - \ 2h_1 - \quad h_2}$$

		h_1	h_2
f	0	67	83
r	40	-1	-1
s	60	-2	-1

RUN

```
SIMPLEX       10:49     06/16/76

ENTER NUMBER OF ROWS AND COLUMNS IN FIRST TABLEAU.
SEPARATE THE NUMBERS WITH A COMMA.   ?3,3
ENTER THE NUMBERS IN THE TABLEAU ONE ROW AT A TIME.
 SEPARATE THE NUMBERS BY COMMAS; DON'T FORGET THE MINUS
SIGNS.   PRESS 'RETURN' AFTER EACH ROW.
?0,67,83

??40,-1,-1

??60,-2,-1


0      67     83

40    -1     -1

60    -2     -1
```

PIVOT ELEMENT IS -1   IN ROW 2   COLUMN 3


```
3320    -16   -83

40    -1    -1

20    -1     1
```

THE LAST TABLEAU ABOVE IS THE FINAL TABLEAU.
NOW YOU MUST GO BACK TO THE BEGINNING OF THE
PROBLEM AND PUT IN THE VARIABLES IN THE PROPER
POSITIONS, I.E. ALONG THE LEFT SIDE AND ACROSS
THE TOP, FOR EACH TABLEAU STARTING WITH THE
FIRST ONE. WHEN YOU FINISH DOING THIS YOU WILL
BE ABLE TO READ YOUR ANSWER.

TIME 0.0 SECS.

Now the user of the prepackaged program SIMPLEX would have to
insert the variables in each tableau and write the final solution as shown in the
following printout.

RUN

SIMPLEX   10:51   06/16/76

ENTER NUMBER OF ROWS AND COLUMNS IN FIRST TABLEAU.
SEPARATE THE NUMBERS WITH A COMMA. ?3,3
ENTER THE NUMBERS IN THE TABLEAU ONE ROW AT A TIME.
 SEPARATE THE NUMBERS BY COMMAS; DON'T FORGET THE MINUS
SIGNS. PRESS 'RETURN' AFTER EACH ROW.
?0,67,83

?>40,-1,-1

??60,-2,-1

```
         h₁   h₂
f  0    67    83
l  40   -1    -1*
l  60   -2    -1
```

```
    PIVOT ELEMENT IS -1      IN ROW 2      COLUMN 3
```

$$
\begin{array}{c|ccc}
f & 3320 & \overset{h_1}{-16} & \overset{n}{-83} \\
h_2 & 40 & -1 & -1 \\
a & 20 & -1 & 1 \\
\end{array}
$$

maximum $f = \$3320$ *when* $h_1 = 0$ *and* $h_2 = 40.$

```
THE LAST TABLEAU ABOVE IS THE FINAL TABLEAU.
NOW YOU MUST GO BACK TO THE BEGINNING OF THE
PROBLEM AND PUT IN THE VARIABLES IN THE PROPER
POSITIONS, I.E. ALONG THE LEFT SIDE AND ACROSS
THE TOP, FOR EACH TABLEAU STARTING WITH THE
FIRST ONE.   WHEN YOU FINISH DOING THIS YOU WILL
BE ABLE TO READ YOUR ANSWER.
```

```
TIME 0.1 SECS.
```

Because of its length and complexities, the flowcharting of SIMPLEX is not included here. Let us use SIMPLEX to solve the following linear programming problem:

$$x \geq 0, y \geq 0, z \geq 0$$

$$x + 2y + 2z \leq 40$$

$$\underline{2x + 2y + z \leq 60}$$

$$f = \$10x + \$15y + \$20z$$

Find maximum f.

Step 1. Convert the system of inequalities to a system of equations:

$$f = 10x + 15y + 20z$$

$$x + 2y + 2z + r = 40, \qquad r > 0$$

$$\underline{2x + 2y + z + s = 60, \qquad s > 0.}$$

Step 2. Solve for the objective variable and the slack variables:

$$f = 0 + 10x + 15y + 20z$$

$$r = 40 - x - 2y - 2z$$

$$s = 60 - 2x - 2y - z$$

Step 3. Construct the tableau for the linear programming problem:

		x	y	z
f	0	10	15	20
r	40	-1	-2	-2
s	60	-2	-2	-1

Step 4. Use the following prepackaged program SIMPLEX to solve the linear programming problem.

```
RUN

SIMPLEX      10:54    06/16/76

ENTER NUMBER OF ROWS AND COLUMNS IN FIRST TABLEAU.
SEPARATE THE NUMBERS WITH A COMMA.    ?3,4
ENTER THE NUMBERS IN THE TABLEAU ONE ROW AT A TIME.
  SEPARATE THE NUMBERS BY COMMAS; DON'T FORGET THE MINUS
SIGNS.   PRESS 'RETURN' AFTER EACH ROW.
?0,10,15,20

??40,-1,-2,-2

??60,-2,-2,-1
```

(handwritten labels: x, y, z above columns; f, r, s at left)

```
f  0      10    15    20

r  40    -1    -2    -2*

s  60    -2    -2    -1


PIVOT ELEMENT IS -2    IN ROW 2    COLUMN 4
```

(handwritten labels: u, y, r above columns; f, z, s at left)

```
f  400    0    -5    -10

z  20    -.5    -1    -.5

s  40    -1.5    -1     .5
```

Therefore maximum $f = \$400$ when $x = 0$, $y = 0$, and $z = 20$.

```
THE LAST TABLEAU ABOVE IS THE FINAL TABLEAU.
NOW YOU MUST GO BACK TO THE BEGINNING OF THE
POBLEM AND PUT IN THE VARIABLES IN THE PROPER
POSITIONS. I.E. ALONG THE LEFT SIDE AND ACROSS
THE TOP, FOR EACH TABLEAU STARTING WITH THE
FIRST ONE.   WHEN YOU FINISH DOING THIS YOU WILL
BE ABLE TO READ YOUR ANSWER.

TIME 0.0 SECS.
```

Problem Set 3.10

1. Use the prepackaged program SIMPLEX to solve each of the linear programming problems in Problem Set 3.8 and Problem Set 3.9.

2. Use the prepackaged program SIMPLEX to solve the following linear programming problems:

   (a) $x + 5y + 3z \leq 38$ · $(x \geq 0, y \geq 0, z \geq 0)$

   $2x + 12y + 5z \leq 98$

   $x + 2y + 3z \leq 42$

   $f = x + 5y + 3z$

   Find maximum f.

   (b) $x + 2y + 3z + 4w \leq 60$ $(x \geq 0, y \geq 0, w \geq 0)$

   $2x + y + z + 3w \leq 80$

   $2x + 2y + 6z + w \leq 100$

   $5x + y + 4z + 2w \leq 120$

   $f = 15x + 30y + 40z + 10w$

   Find maximum f.

3.13

Using the Prepackaged Program SIMPLEX to Minimize an Objective Function

In Article 3.12 we used SIMPLEX to solve linear programming problems that contained only $\leq$ constraints and found maximum f. One approach to finding minimum f subject to $\geq$ constraints is to note that minimizing f is the same as maximizing $-f$.

Consider the following linear programming problem:

$$x \geq 0, \ y \geq 0$$
$$2x + 3y \geq 12$$
$$5x + 3y \geq 45$$
$$f = 5x + 4y$$

Find minimum f.

We will attempt to use SIMPLEX to maximize $-f = -5x - 4y$.

SOLUTION

Step 1. Convert the system of inequalities to a system of equations:

$$f = 5x + 4y$$

$$2x + 3y = 12 + r, \qquad r > 0$$
$$5x + 3y = 45 + s, \qquad s > 0$$

Step 2. Solve for $-f$, r, and s:

$$-f = \quad 0 - 5x - 4y$$
$$r = -12 + 2x + 3y$$
$$s = -45 + 5x + 3y$$

Step 3. Construct the tableau for the linear programming problem:

		x	y
$-f$	0	-5	-4
r	-12	2	3
s	-45	5	3

Step 4. Use the prepackaged program SIMPLEX.

```
RUN

SIMPLEX      10:56    06/16/76


ENTER NUMBER OF ROWS AND COLUMNS IN FIRST TABLEAU.
SEPARATE THE NUMBERS WITH A COMMA.   ?3,3
ENTER THE NUMBERS IN THE TABLEAU ONE ROW AT A TIME.
 SEPARATE THE NUMBERS BY COMMAS; DON'T FORGET THE MINUS
SIGNS.  PRESS 'RETURN' AFTER EACH ROW.
?0,-5,-4

??-12,2,3

??-45,5,3



 0     -5    -4

-12    2     3

-45    5     3


PIVOT ELEMENT TO GET PROPER MATRIX IS 5     IN ROW 3
COLUMN 2

-45   -1    -1

 6    .4    1.8

 9    .2    -.6
```

```
THE LAST TABLEAU ABOVE IS THE FINAL TABLEAU.
NOW YOU MUST GO BACK TO THE BEGINNING OF THE
PROBLEM AND PUT IN THE VARIABLES IN THE PROPER
POSITIONS, I.E. ALONG THE LEFT SIDE AND ACROSS
THE TOP, FOR EACH TABLEAU STARTING WITH THE
FIRST ONE.  WHEN YOU FINISH DOING THIS YOU WILL
BE ABLE TO READ YOUR ANSWER.

TIME 0.0 SECS.
```

Step 5. Interpret the following computer output.

```
RUN

SIMPLEX      10:59      06/16/76

ENTER NUMBER OF ROWS AND COLUMNS IN FIRST TABLEAU.
SEPARATE THE NUMBERS WITH A COMMA.  ?3,3
ENTER THE NUMBERS IN THE TABLEAU ONE ROW AT A TIME.
  SEPARATE THE NUMBERS BY COMMAS; DON'T FORGET THE MINUS
SIGNS.  PRESS 'RETURN' AFTER EACH ROW.
?0,-5,-4

??-12,2,3

??-45,5,3
```

$$-f \quad 0 \quad \overset{x}{-5} \quad \overset{y}{-4}$$
$$r \quad -12 \quad 2 \quad 3$$
$$\lambda \quad -45 \quad 5^{*} \quad 3$$

```
PIVOT ELEMENT TO GET PROPER MATRIX IS 5    IN ROW 3
COLUMN 2
```

$$-f \quad \overset{\lambda}{-45} \quad \overset{y}{-1} \quad -1$$
$$r \quad 6 \quad .4 \quad 1.8$$
$$x \quad 9 \quad .2 \quad -.6$$

If $-f = -45$, then $f = 45$.
Therefore minimum $f = 45$, when $x = 9$ and $y = 0$.

```
THE LAST TABLEAU ABOVE IS THE FINAL TABLEAU.
NOW YOU MUST GO BACK TO THE BEGINNING OF THE
PROBLEM AND PUT IN THE VARIABLES IN THE PROPER
POSITIONS, I.E. ALONG THE LEFT SIDE AND ACROSS
THE TOP, FOR EACH TABLEAU STARTING WITH THE
FIRST ONE.  WHEN YOU FINISH DOING THIS YOU WILL
BE ABLE TO READ YOUR ANSWER.

TIME 0.0 SECS.
```

The coding of SIMPLEX in the BASIC language is as follows:

```
1 REM TO DELETE INSTRUCTIONS, TYPE THE FOLLOWING:
2 REM  129 GOTO 140;    159 GOTO 170;    1100 GOTO 1110
5 DIMA(10,10),B(10,10)
0010 REM  GENERALIZED SIMPLEX TO HANDLE PROBLEMS IN WHICH
0020 REM  CONSTRAINTS ARE NOT ALL<=.WE CAN HANDLE PROBS.
0030 REM  WHERE ALL ARE >=& IN WHICH SOME ELEMENT S IN
40 REM    FIRST COLUMN ARE NEGATIVE
0090 LET  T=0
0100 REM  IF T=0 MATRIX A IS OF NICE FORM WHERE FIRST COL IS
0110 REM  ALL POSITIVE BELOW ROW 1
0120 DIM A$(3)
130 PRINT "ENTER NUMBER OF ROWS AND COLUMNS IN FIRST TABLEAU."
131 PRINT "SEPARATE THE NUMBERS WITH A COMMA.  ";
0140 INPUT M,N
160 PRINT "ENTER THE NUMBERS IN THE TABLEAU ONE ROW AT A TIME."
161 PRINT" SEPARATE THE NUMBERS BY COMMAS; DON'T FORGET THE MINUS"
162 PRINT "SIGNS.   PRESS 'RETURN' AFTER EACH ROW."
170MATINPUTA(M,N)
0180 MAT   PRINT A:
185MATB=ZER(M,N)
0190 MAT B=A
0200 FOR S=2 TO M
0210   IF A(S,1)<0 GOTO 0240
0220 NEXT S
0230 GOTO 0430
0240 FOR V=2 TO M
0250   FOR U=2 TO N
```

```
0260     LET L=V
0270     LET K=U
0280     LET T=1
0290     IF A(L,K)=0 GOTO 0410
0300     GOSUB 0450
0310     FOR R=2 TO M
0320       IF B(R,1)<0 GOTO 0410
0330     NEXT R
0340     PRINT "PIVOT ELEMENT TO GET PROPER MATRIX IS"A(L,K);"IN ROW"L
0350     PRINT "COLUMN"K
0360     MAT  PRINT B;
0370     LET T=0
0380     MAT A=B
0400     GOTO 0430
0410   NEXT U
0420 NEXT V
0430 GOSUB 0990
0440 GOSUB 0820
0450 LET P=A(L,K)
0480 IF T=1 GOTO  0500
0490 PRINT "PIVOT ELEMENT IS "A(L,K);"IN ROW"L;"COLUMN"K
495  PRINT
0500 LET B(L,K)=1/P
0510 FOR I=1 TO L-1
0520   LET B(I,K)=A(I,K)/P
0530 NEXT I
0540 FOR I=L+1 TO M
0550   LET B(I,K)=A(I,K)/P
0560 NEXT I
```

172

```
0570 FOR I=1 TO K-1
0580     LET B(L,I)=-A(L,I)/P
0590 NEXT I
0600 FOR I=K+1 TO N
0610     LET B(L,I)=-A(L,I)/P
0620 NEXT I
0630 FOR I=1 TO M
0640     LET J=1
0650     IF I=L GOTO   0710
0660     IF J=K GOTO   0680
0670     LET B(I,J)=(P*A(I,J)-A(L,J)*A(I,K))/P
0680     LET J=J+1
0690     IF J>N GOTO   0710
0700     GOTO 0650
0710 NEXT I
0720 IF T=1 GOTO   0790
0750 MAT  PRINT B;
0760 PRINT
0770 PRINT
0780 IF T=0 GOTO   0800
0790 RETURN
0800 MAT A=B
0810 GOTO 0430
0820 FOR I=2 TO M
0830     REM   CANT ALL BE POSITIVE.FOR THEN NO LIMIT ON MAXIMUM
0840     REM   THAT IS WONT HAPPEN IN.A PHYSICAL PROBLEM
0850     IF A(I,K)>=0 GOTO   0960
0860     LET X=I
0870     LET Z=X+1
0880     IF Z>M GOTO   0940
```

```
0890    IF A(Z,K)>=0 GOTO  0920
0900    IF ABS(A(X,1)/A(X,K))<=ABS(A(Z,1)/A(Z,K)) GOTO  0920
0910    LET X=Z
0920    LET Z=Z+1
0930 IFZ<=MTHEN890
0940    LET L=X
0950    GOTO 0970
0960 NEXT I
0970 RETURN
0980 REM     FIND COL OF MAX POS ELEM IN FIST ROW -NOT COL.
0990 LET I=2
1000 FOR J=3 TO N
1010    IF A(1,J)<0 GOTO 1040
1020    IF A(1,I)>=A(1,J) GOTO 1040
1030LETI=J
1040 NEXT J
1050LETK=I
1060 IF A(1,K)<=0 GOTO  1100
1070 REM  IFA(1,K)<=0THEN REALLY DONE EXCEPTFOR FINAL
1080 REM    PRINT OUT OF A
1090 RETURN
1100 PRINT "THE LAST TABLEAU ABOVE IS THE FINAL TABLEAU."
1101 PRINT "NOW YOU MUST GO BACK TO THE BEGINNING OF THE"
1102 PRINT "PROBLEM AND PUT IN THE VARIABLES IN THE PROPER"
1103 PRINT "POSITIONS, I.E. ALONG THE LEFT SIDE AND ACROSS"
1104 PRINT "THE TOP, FOR EACH TABLEAU STARTING WITH THE"
1105 PRINT "FIRST ONE.  WHEN YOU FINISH DOING THIS YOU WILL"
1106 PRINT 'BE ABLE TO READ YOUR ANSWER."
1110 END
```

174

Problem Set 3.11

Solve the following linear programming problems by using the prepackaged program SIMPLEX to maximize $-f$.

1. $x \geq 0, y \geq 0$

$2x + 4y \geq 20$

$\underline{y + 6x \geq 10}$

$f = 2x + 5y$

Find minimum f.

2. $x \geq 0, y \geq 0, z \geq 0$

$x + y + z \geq 15$

$2x + y + 3z \geq 25$

$\underline{x + 2y + z \geq 40}$

$f = 5x + 10y + 15z$

Find minimum f.

3. $x \geq 0, y \geq 0, z \geq 0$

$2x + 2y + z \geq 4$

$2x \qquad + z \geq 6$

$\underline{4x + 2y + 4z \geq 10}$

$f = x + 2y + z$

Find minimum f.

4

Introduction to the Foundations of Mathematics

4.1

Introduction

The reasoning process which takes place in subjects such as algebra, geometry, probability, the calculus, and switching algebra can all be traced back to the rules of symbolic logic. The German philosopher and mathematician Gottfried Wilhelm von Leibniz (1646–1716) was the first to envision a set of symbols and laws by which the reasoning process could be reduced to a type of calculation. The English mathematician George Boole (1815–1864) developed a formal system of symbolic logic in which the basic operations were separated from the elements to be operated on.

4.2

Symbolic Logic

Basic Elements

In symbolic logic, variables such as p, q, r, and s are used as placeholders for *simple statements*. For example, p, q, r, and s may be used as placeholders for the following simple statements:

p: Elementary Algebra is a mathematics course.

q: Plane Geometry is a social studies course.

r: $2 + 7 = 9$ ($2 + 7$ is equal to 9).

s: $2 + 7 = 19$ ($2 + 7$ is equal to 19).

Basic Assumption

The *basic assumption* of symbolic logic is that each statement we use can be assigned *exactly one truth value*, either TRUE or FALSE. (Such a statement is said to be well defined.) For the previously given simple statements,

p: Elementary Algebra is a mathematics course.
p's truth value is TRUE.

q: Plane Geometry is a social studies course.
q's truth value is FALSE.

r: $2 + 7 = 9$.
r's truth value is TRUE.

s: $2 + 7 = 19$.
s's truth value is FALSE.

Note: Statements such as

m: Joe is an electrician, and
n: $2x + 7 = 29$ *cannot* be assigned exactly one truth value.

Compound Statements

The symbols in Table 4.1 are used to form *compound statements* (statements that relate two simple statements) in symbolic logic.

Table 4.1. Statement symbols

Symbol	Read as	Example	Type of statement formed
~	not	$\sim p$ (not p)	negation
∧	and	$p \wedge q$ (p and q)	conjunction
∨	"or"	$p \vee q$ (either p or q, perhaps both)	inclusive disjunction
⊻	"or"	$p \veebar q$ (either p or q, not both)	exclusive disjunction
→	if . . . then . . .	$p \rightarrow q$ (if p, then q)	conditional
↔	. . . if and only if . . .	$p \leftrightarrow q$ (p if and only if q)	biconditional

Note: In English grammar we use two types of *or*'s (the symbols ∨ and ⊻ in Table 4.1). The *inclusive or* is used in this example: I like to bowl or (∨) I like to golf. The *exclusive or* is used in the following statement: I will go golfing from 7 to 10 A.M. next Saturday or (⊻) I will wax my car from 7 to 10 A.M. next Saturday. In order to be consistent in this chapter, we will define and use *only one* "or," the *inclusive or* (∨).

Let us reconsider the previously illustrated simple statements:

 p: Elementary Algebra is a mathematics course.

 q: Plane Geometry is a social studies course.

 r: $2 + 7 = 9$.

 s: $2 + 7 = 19$.

From these we can form the following compound statements:

 p ∨ *q*: Elementary Algebra is a mathematics course or Plane Geometry is a social studies course.

 r ∧ *s*: $2 + 7 = 9$ and $2 + 7 = 19$.

 p → *s*: If Elementary Algebra is a mathematics course, then $2 + 7 = 19$.

 r ↔ *s*: $2 + 7 = 9$ if and only if $2 + 7 = 19$

 ~*q*: Plane Geometry is not a social studies course.

Basic Definitions

The following basic definitions are used to determine the *truth value* of compound statements, given that we can determine the truth value of the simple statements.

NEGATIONS

Generally, if *p* is any statement, then *not p* (the negation of *p*) is the denial of *p* and is true when *p* is false, and is false when *p* is true. These two logical possibilities for the truth value (truth or falsity) of *p* are expressed in the following *truth table*.

Negation

p	~*p*
T	F
F	T

For example: "Plane Geometry is a social studies course," (F); and ~*p*, "Plane Geometry is not a social studies course" (T).

CONJUNCTIONS

The word *and* placed between two statements p,q results in a new statement "p and q," called the *conjunction* of p and q. The four logical possibilities for the truth value (truth or falsity) of the conjunction of two statements p and q are expressed in the following truth table.

Conjunction

p	q	$p \wedge q$
T	T	T
T	F	F
F	T	F
F	F	F

Notice that $p \wedge q$ is true *only* when *both* p and q are true. For example: "r: $2 + 7 = 9$" (T), and "s: $2 + 7 = 19$" (F); therefore, "$r \wedge s$: $2 + 7 = 9$ and $2 + 7 = 19$" (F).

DISJUNCTIONS

The word *or* placed between two statements p and q produces a new statement p or q, called the *disjunction* of p and q. The four logical possibilities for the truth value of the disjunction of two statements p and q are listed in the following truth table.

Disjunction

p	q	$p \vee q$
T	T	T
T	F	T
F	T	T
F	F	F

You can see that $p \vee q$ is false *only* when both p and q are false.

For example: "p: Elementary Algebra is a mathematics course" (T); and "q: Plane Geometry is a social studies course" (F). Therefore, "$p \vee q$: Elementary Algebra is a mathematics course *or* Plane Geometry is a social studies course" (T).

CONDITIONAL STATEMENTS

The words *if* and *then* are frequently used to combine two statements, p and q, into the new statement "if p, then q," which is called the *conditional* of p and q. The four logical possibilities for the truth value of the conditional of two statements p and q (denoted by the symbol $p \rightarrow q$ and read "if p, then q" or "p implies q") are shown in the following truth table.

Conditional

p	q	$p \to q$
T	T	T
T	F	F
F	T	T
F	F	T

Note that $p \to q$ is false *only* when p is true and q is false.

For example: "p: Elementary Algebra is a mathematics course" (T); and "s: $2 + 7 = 19$" (F). Therefore, "$p \to s$: If Elementary Algebra is a mathematics course, then $2 + 7 = 19$" (F).

BICONDITIONAL STATEMENTS

Whenever both "if p, then q" and "if q, then p" statements are true, we can say that p and q are *biconditional* or *equivalent* statements. Such statements mean that p and q are *both true* or *both false* statements. The four logical possibilities for the truth value of the equivalence or biconditional statement comprising two statements p and q (denoted by the symbol $p \leftrightarrow q$ and read "p, if and only if q" or "if p, then q, and if q, then p") are expressed in the following truth table.

Biconditional

p	q	$p \leftrightarrow q$
T	T	T
T	F	F
F	T	F
F	F	T

Notice that $p \leftrightarrow q$ is true *only* when *both* p and q have the *same* truth values.

For example: "r: $2 + 7 = 9$" (T), and "s: $2 + 7 = 19$" (F). Therefore, "$r \leftrightarrow s$: $2 + 7 = 9$ if and only if $2 + 7 = 19$" (F).

Note that these stated definitions *must be* adhered to if the structure of symbolic logic is to be consistent. A person may choose to define negation, conjunction, disjunction, conditional, and biconditional statements in ways other than those given, but such a system will not be consistent with common usage and *cannot* be used readily to develop structures such as the existing set theory, switching algebra, probability, and other branches of mathematics.

More about Truth Tables

Truth tables are used to decide under what conditions a given *compound* statement is *true* and under what conditions it is *false*. Let us construct the truth table for each of the following statements:

1. $p \vee \sim p$

2. $p \wedge \sim p$

3. $(\sim p \vee q) \to (p \leftrightarrow q)$, where p and q are any *well-defined statements.*

(1)

p	$\sim p$	$p \vee \sim p$
T	F	T
F	T	T

Here, $p \vee \sim p$ is *true* under *all* logical possibilities for p. Such a statement is said to be a *logically true* one or a *tautology.*

(2)

p	$\sim p$	$p \wedge \sim p$
T	F	F
F	T	F

Here, $p \wedge \sim p$ is *false* under *all* logical possibilities for p. Such a statement is said to be a *logically false* one.

(3)

			$(\sim p \vee q) \to (p \leftrightarrow q)$			
p	q	$\sim p$	$(\sim p \vee q)$	$(p \leftrightarrow q)$	$(\sim p \vee q) \to (p \leftrightarrow q)$
T	T	F	T	T	T
T	F	F	F	F	T
F	T	T	T	F	F
F	F	T	T	T	T

Here, $(\sim p \vee q) \to (p \leftrightarrow q)$ is *false only* when p is *false* and q is *true.* A statement that is *true* under certain logical possibilities and *false* under the remaining logical possibilities is simply *neither a logically true nor logically false* statement, and is called a *contingency.*

Problem Set 4.1

1. If p and q represent well-defined simple *sentences,* such that p is *true* and q is *false,* then give the truth value for the following statements:
   (a) $\sim q$ (g) $p \to q$
   (b) $q \vee p$ (h) $p \leftrightarrow q$
   (c) $p \vee q$ (i) $p \to \sim q$
   (d) $q \wedge p$ (j) $p \wedge q$
   (e) $\sim p$ (k) $\sim p \wedge q$
   (f) $\sim p \vee q$ (l) $q \wedge \sim p$

2. Convert the following sentences to symbolic form (define clearly each variable you use):
   (a) John plays varsity football, and Joe plays varsity soccer.
   (b) If I pass the final exam, then I will pass the course.

(c) I will not attend the bowling party.

(d) I will try out for the baseball team or the football team.

(e) We will sell many Valentine's boxes of candy if and only if sugar prices decline.

3. Construct the truth table for *each* of the following compound statements, given that p and q are well defined:

(a) $\sim(p \lor \sim p)$

(b) $p \land \sim q$

(c) $\sim q \to p$

(d) $\sim p \leftrightarrow q$

(e) $(p \land q) \to \sim p$

(f) $(p \land q) \to \sim q$

(g) $(p \land \sim q) \leftrightarrow \sim p$

(h) $(p \lor q) \to \sim p$

4. In constructing a truth table for compound sentences containing *one* variable p, it is necessary to investigate these two logical possibilities:

p
T
F

For compound sentences containing *two* variables (p and q), it is necessary to investigate these four logical possibilities:

p	q
T	T
T	F
F	T
F	F

For compound sentences containing *three* variables (p, q, and r), it is necessary to investigate these eight logical possibilities:

p	q	r
T	T	T
T	T	F
T	F	T
T	F	F
F	T	T
F	T	F
F	F	T
F	F	F

Construct truth tables for *each* of the following compound sentences, given that p, q, and r are well defined:

(a) $(p \to q) \land r$

(b) $p \to (q \land r)$

(c) $\sim p \leftrightarrow (q \lor \sim r)$

5. (a) Prove $p \land (q \land r) \leftrightarrow (p \land q) \land r$ is logically true.

(b) Explain what the truth value of $p \land (q \land r) \leftrightarrow \sim((p \land q) \land r)$ would be, without making a truth table.

Logical Equivalence

A statement r is said to be *logically equivalent* to a statement s (both r and s can be *either simple* or *compound statements*) if and only if the statement $r \leftrightarrow s$ is logically true; that is, r and s must have the same truth values.

For example, let us decide which two of the following three statements are *logically equivalent*:

$$(1) \ \sim(p \lor q) \qquad (2) \ \sim p \lor \sim q \qquad (3) \ \sim p \land \sim q$$

SOLUTION

Let us construct the following truth table.

p	q	$\sim p$	$\sim q$	$p \lor q$	$\sim(p \lor q)$	$\sim p \lor \sim q$	$\sim p \land \sim q$
T	T	F	F	T	F	F	F
T	F	F	T	T	F	T	F
F	T	T	F	T	F	T	F
F	F	T	T	F	T	T	T

Therefore,

p	q	$\sim(p \lor q) \leftrightarrow (\sim p \lor \sim q)$	$\sim(p \lor q) \leftrightarrow (\sim p \land \sim q)$
T	T	F	T
T	F	F	T
F	T	F	T
F	F	T	T

Notice that $\sim(p \lor q) \leftrightarrow (\sim p \lor \sim q)$ is *not logically true*; therefore $\sim(p \lor q)$ and $\sim p \lor \sim q$ are *not logically equivalent*. However, $\sim(p \lor q) \leftrightarrow (\sim p \land \sim q)$ *is logically true*; therefore $\sim(p \lor q)$ and $(\sim p \land \sim q)$ *are logically equivalent*.

The definition of logical equivalence allows us to develop a number of laws that we can use in formal proofs. Some of the more common laws developed in an elementary symbolic logic course are given below.

COMMUTATIVE LAWS

$\quad\quad p \lor q \quad\quad$ is logically equivalent to $q \lor p$.

$\quad\quad p \land q \quad\quad$ is logically equivalent to $q \land p$.

ASSOCIATIVE LAWS

$\quad\quad (p \lor q) \lor r \quad\quad$ is logically equivalent to $p \lor (q \lor r)$.

$\quad\quad (p \land q) \land r \quad\quad$ is logically equivalent to $p \land (q \land r)$.

DISTRIBUTIVE LAWS

$p \vee (q \wedge r)$ is logically equivalent to $(p \vee q) \wedge (p \vee r)$.

$p \wedge (q \vee r)$ is logically equivalent to $(p \wedge q) \vee (p \wedge r)$.

IDEMPOTENT LAWS

$p \vee p$ is logically equivalent to p.

$p \wedge p$ is logically equivalent to p.

DE MORGAN'S LAWS

$\sim(p \vee q)$ is logically equivalent to $\sim p \wedge \sim q$.

$\sim(p \wedge q)$ is logically equivalent to $\sim p \vee \sim q$.

IDENTITY LAWS

$p \vee (\text{true})$ is logically equivalent to (true).

$p \wedge (\text{true})$ is logically equivalent to (p).

COMPLEMENT LAWS

$\sim(\sim p)$ is logically equivalent to p.

$p \vee \sim p$ is logically true.

$p \wedge \sim p$ is logically false.

Implication

A statement r logically *implies* a statement s (both r and s can be *either simple or compound* statements) *if and only if* s is *true* whenever r is *true*.

Given the definitions for $p \rightarrow q$ and $p \leftrightarrow q$, we construct the following truth table.

Logical Possibility	p	q	$p \rightarrow q$	$p \leftrightarrow q$
1	T	T	T	T
2	T	F	F	F
3	F	T	T	F
4	F	F	T	T

We can see that $p \rightarrow q$ does *not* imply $p \leftrightarrow q$ because there exists a logical possibility where $p \rightarrow q$ is *true* and $p \leftrightarrow q$ is *not true* (namely, logical possibility 3 in the table). However, $p \leftrightarrow q$ *does* imply $p \rightarrow q$ because $p \leftrightarrow q$ is true under logical possibilities 1 and 4, as is $p \rightarrow q$.

The definition of implication allows us to decide whether arguments (courtroom situations, mathematical proofs, and so on) are *valid*. An argument consists of a number of *premises* and a *conclusion*. For example, let us consider the following two arguments and their symbolic representations:

1.   If n is divisible by 4, then n is divisible by 2   (first premise)
     n is divisible by 4   (second premise)
     Therefore, n is divisible by 2   (conclusion)

   $p \rightarrow q$ where p: n is divisible by 4
   p q: n is divisible by 2
   $\therefore q$ $\therefore$ represents the word *therefore*.

2.   If n is divisible by 4, then n is divisible by 2   (first premise)
     n is divisible by 2   (second premise)
     Therefore, n is divisible by 4   (conclusion)

   $p \rightarrow q$ where p: n is divisible by 4
   q q: n is divisible by 2
   $\therefore p$ $\therefore$ represents the word *therefore*.

An *argument* is said to be *valid* if and only if the *conjunction* of the premises implies the *conclusion* (that is, whenever *all* premises are true, the conclusion *must be true*). Let us check the validity of the two sample logical arguments we have given above.

1. $p \rightarrow q$
     p
     q

Logical Possibility	p	q	$p \rightarrow q$	Conjunction of Premises $(p \rightarrow q) \wedge p$	Conclusion q
1	T	T	T	T	T
2	T	F	F	F	F
3	F	T	T	F	T
4	F	F	T	F	F

The *first argument is valid* because the *conjunction* of the premises is *true* under logical possibility 1 and so is the conclusion.

2. $p \to q$

   q
   _____
   $\therefore p$

Logical Possibility	p	q	$p \to q$	Conjunction of Premises $(p \to q) \wedge q$	Conclusion p
1	T	T	T	T	T
2	T	F	F	F	T
3	F	T	T	T	F
4	F	F	T	F	F

The *second argument is not valid* because there exists a logical possibility where the *conjunction* of the premises is *true* and the *conclusion* is *not true*, namely, logical possibility 3. The general argument:

   $p \to q$ (major premise)

   p (minor premise)
   _____
   $\therefore q$ (conclusion)

is *always* a *valid* argument. This method of proof is sometimes called the *law of modus ponens,* or *law of detachment,* reasoning by *assuming the antecedent,* or proof by *direct reasoning.* Two other methods of proof, which will not be discussed in this text, are (1) *modus tollens* (indirect reasoning)

   $p \to q$ (major premise)

   $\sim q$ (minor premise)
   _____
   $\therefore \sim p$ (conclusion)

and (2) the *transitive law*

   $p \to q$ (first premise)

   $q \to r$ (second premise)
   _____
   $\therefore p \to r$ (conclusion)

Problem Set 4.2

1. Prove that the following pairs of statements are logically equivalent:
(a) $p \vee q; q \vee p$
(b) $p \wedge q; q \wedge p$
(c) $(p \vee q) \vee r; p \vee (q \vee r)$
(d) $p \vee (q \wedge r); (p \vee q) \wedge (p \vee r)$
(e) $p \wedge (q \vee r); (p \wedge q) \vee (p \wedge r)$
(f) $\sim(p \wedge q); \sim p \vee \sim q$

2. Does the statement $((p \lor q) \land \sim p)$ imply the statement q? Why or why not?

3. Convert each of the following arguments to symbolic form (define clearly *each variable* you use):

   (a) If I go bowling, then I will not play tennis.
       I will play tennis.
       _____
       Therefore, I will not go bowling.

   (b) If I study for at least 5 hours, then I will pass the exam.
       If I do not study for at least 5 hours, then I cannot go bowling.
       _____
       Therefore, either I pass the exam or I can go bowling.

4. Prove the law of *modus tollens* (*indirect reasoning*) represents a *valid* argument.

$$p \to q$$
$$\sim q$$
$$\overline{\therefore \sim p}$$

5. Prove the *transitive law* represents a *valid* argument.

$$p \to q$$
$$q \to r$$
$$\overline{\therefore p \to r}$$

6. (a) Can anything be said about the validity of an argument when one of its premises is logically false?

   (b) Can anything be said about an argument when its conclusion is logically true?

4.3

Introduction to Sets

As a fundamental notion of mathematics, the concept of set is essential to the study of probability theory.

A *set* is a well-defined collection of objects; that is, it is clearly indicated whether a given object does or does not belong to a given set. We customarily use capital letters to denote sets and list the objects contained in a set within a pair of braces. For example:

Listing Method	*Verbal Description*
$A = \{1,2,3,4\}$	Set A contains the numbers 1, 2, 3, and 4.
$C = \{1,2,3 \cdots\}$	Set C contains all the counting numbers.
$F = \{1,8,27 \cdots\}$	Set F contains the cubes of all the counting numbers.
$G = \{P_1,P_2,P_3\}$	Set G contains the objects P_1, P_2, P_3, which may themselves also be sets.

The objects that belong to a set are called *elements*, or *members*, of the set and are denoted by lower-case letters with the following notation:

$a \in A$ is read: "*a* is an element of the set *A*," or "*a* belongs to the set *A*."

$b \notin B$ is read: "*b* is not an element of the set *B*," or "*b* does not belong to the set *B*."

The symbol "/" generally means "not" when it is drawn through, or slashes, another mathematical symbol. For example, $d \notin D$ (*d* is not an element of set *D*), $3 \neq 2$ (3 is not equal to 2).

Besides the listing and verbal methods of describing sets, we may indicate membership in a particular set by designating the elements in terms of one or more properties, or by giving a *rule for set-builder notation.* Consider the following examples.

1. $F = \{1,8,27 \cdots\}$ may be denoted

   $F = \{X^3 | X \text{ is a counting number}\}$

We read: "set *F* is the set of all X^3 such that (the meaning of the vertical line) *X* is a counting number."

2. $C = \{1,2,3 \cdots\}$ may be denoted by the rule

   $C = \{c | c \text{ is a counting number}\}$.

3. $E = \{2,4,6,8 \cdots\}$ may be written in set-builder notation as

   $E = \{e | e \text{ is an even positive integer}\}$.

4. $H = \{(1,2), (2,1), (2,2)\}$.

Notice that each element of this set consists not of numbers but of *ordered pairs* of numbers, where the order of the components of each element in set *H* is most significant. You know that the ordered pair (1,2) with the first component 1 and the second component 2 is distinct from the ordered pair (2,1). Set-builder notation is extremely helpful in defining set operations and set relationships.

A set may have a *finite* or an *infinite* number of elements. A set is called *finite* if the elements of the set can be counted, and the counting process comes to an end. In the *infinite* set, there are an unlimited number of elements. For example, the set of days in a week is certainly countable or finite, but the set of all points on a number line constitutes an infinite set. And set $A = \{1,2,3,4\}$, which has exactly four elements, is finite, while set $B = \{1,8,27 \cdots\}$, which has no last element, is an example of an infinite set.

When we speak of the *universal set*, or universe, we mean the set of all elements we are considering for a particular discussion, and denote it by *U*. When you are given a problem, it is important that you grasp clearly the particular universe with which you are dealing. Sometimes a universe *U* is a very small set; for example, $U = \{2\}$ may be our universe of discourse. Or it may be an infinite set, such as $U = \{1,2,3,4, \ldots\}$.

SUBSETS

Definition 1: A set X is said to be a *subset* of a set Y if and only if every element of X is also an element of Y. We write this relationship as $X \subset Y$ and read it as "X is a subset of Y," or "X is included in Y." For example, let E = the set of positive *even* integers and I = the set of positive integers. Then the set of positive even integers is a subset of the positive integers, and we write $E \subset I$. Can we say that the set of positive *odd* integers is a subset of the positive integers?

If we let

$$U = \{\text{married couples in the U.S.}\}$$

$$C = \{\text{married couples with one child in the U.S.}\}$$

$$T = \{\text{married couples with two children in the U.S.}\}$$

then C and T are subsets of U, and we write $C \subset U$ and $T \subset U$.

Definition 2: If two sets C and D have the same or *identical* elements, they are said to be *equal*. That is, $C = D$ if and only if $C \subset D$ and $D \subset C$. For example, let $C = \{1,2,3,4,5\}$ and $D = \{5,4,3,2,1\}$. Then, by our definition, $C \subset D$ and $D \subset C$ (every element of C is an element of D and every element of D is an element of C), and we write $C = D$.

Definition 3: If two sets A and B have the *same number* of elements, they are said to be *equivalent*. Thus, $A = \{\text{Monday, Wednesday, Friday}\}$ and $B = \{a,b,c\}$ are equivalent sets because each set has the same number of elements (in this case, three).

Definition 4: The *empty* set, or *null* set, is a set that contains no elements and is denoted by the symbol $\emptyset$ or $\{\ \}$. If we try to list the elements of the null set, we find that there are none. For example, can we list the members of the set consisting of all women who have served as president of the United States? Or can we list the members of the set of human beings with four eyes? We may say that the sets in these two examples are null, or empty, sets.

The null set is considered to be a subset of *every* set. For example, if we are given the set $E = \{2,4,6,8,10\}$, we might ask: What is $\{x \in E | x \text{ is odd}\}$; that is, what is the subset that contains all odd integers in E? Since E has no odd elements, this set must be the empty set $\emptyset$. We write $F = \{x \in E | x \text{ is odd}\} = \emptyset$.

Definition 5: Any subset of given set B which does not contain all the elements of B is called a *proper* subset of B. That is, A is a proper subset of B if and only if A is a subset of B and at least one element of B is not an element of A (and $A \neq \emptyset$). For example, if $A = \{2,3\}$ and $B = \{1,2,3,4\}$, then A is a proper subset of B. You can see that there is at least one element of B, say 4, such that $4 \in B$ and $4 \notin A$.

The universal set and the null set are referred to as *improper* subsets; the other subsets are referred to as *proper*. For example, if we list all the subsets of the set $U = \{a,b,c,\}$, we would find there are eight: $\{a\}$, $\{b\}$, $\{c\}$, $\{a,b\}$, $\{a,c\}$, $\{b,c\}$, $\{a,b,c\}$, and $\varnothing$. The set $\{a,b,c\}$, which is the entire set U, and $\varnothing$ are improper subsets of U; the other six subsets are proper subsets of U.

Definition 6: Two sets A and B are *disjoint* if they have no common elements. For example, the set of positive integers and the set of negative integers are disjoint because the elements in A are *mutually exclusive* of the elements in B. Would you say that the set of students studying French and the set of mathematics students in your school are disjoint?

OPERATIONS WITH SETS

Definition: The *complement* of a set A, denoted by A', is defined as follows: If A is a subset of a given universe U, then A' is another subset containing all the elements of the universe which are not in A. Thus,

$$A' = \{x | x \in U \text{ and } x \notin A\}$$

To determine A', we list all elements contained in the universal set that are *not* contained in set A. For example, if $U = \{1,2,3,\ldots\}$, $A = \{1,2,3,4,5\}$, and $B = \{6,8,9\}$, then $A' = \{6,7,8,9,\ldots\}$ and $B' = \{1,2,3,4,5,7,10,11,12,13,\ldots\}$.

Venn diagrams: A good way to show or illustrate the relationships between sets and operations with sets is to use sketches known as *Venn diagrams*. We usually represent the universe by the region within some plane geometric figure such as a rectangle, and indicate subsets of the universe by smaller regions within the rectangle. The Venn diagram in Figure 4.1 illustrates that $A \subset U$. Do you see that Figure 4.1 shows us that every element contained in A is also contained in U?

If we want to show that $A \subset B$ and $B \subset U$, we use the Venn diagram in Figure 4.2. We could illustrate by the Venn diagram in Figure 4.3 that A and B are *disjoint* subsets (have no elements in common) of U.

Figure 4.4 shows A' as the complement of A, where A and A' are subsets of U.

Figure 4.1

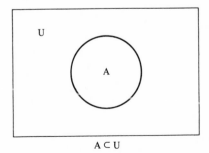

$A \subset U$

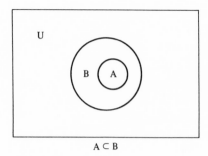

A ⊂ B

Figure 4.2

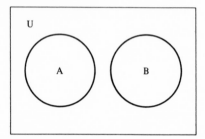

Figure 4.3

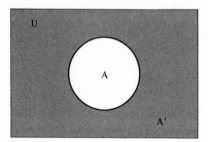

Figure 4.4

Definition: The *union* of two sets A and B, written $A \cup B$, is the *set of all elements* that belong to A or to B, or to both A and B. That is, $A \cup B = \{x|x \in A$ or $x \in B\}$. For example, if we are given that $U = \{1,2,3,4,\ldots,10\}$, $A = \{1,2,3\}$, and $B = \{4,5\}$, then $A \cup B = \{1,2,3,4,5\}$.

To illustrate this example of the union of A and B we use the Venn diagram in Figure 4.5 and shade the part that indicates the set whose elements are either in A or in B, or in both.

Note: Given sets $A = \{1,2,3\}$ and $C = \{3,7,8\}$, then $A \cup C = \{1,2,3,7,8\}$. Notice that the common element 3 is listed *only once* in the union of sets A and B.

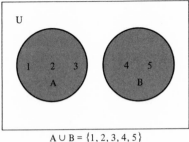

$A \cup B = \{1, 2, 3, 4, 5\}$

Figure 4.5

Definition: The *intersection* of two sets A and B, written $A \cap B$, is the set of elements that belong to both A and B. That is, $A \cap B = \{x | x \in A$ and $x \in B\}$. For example, if we are given that $U = \{1,2,3, \ldots ,10\}$, $A = \{1,2,3,4,5\}$, and $B = \{2,5,7,8,9\}$, then $A \cap B = \{2,5\}$.

We could illustrate this example of the intersection of A and B by shading the part of the Venn diagram, as in Figure 4.6, which indicates the set whose elements are in A and in B.

Definition: Two sets X and Y are said to be *mutually exclusive* if and only if $X \cap Y = \emptyset$ or $\{ \}$. That is, the two sets have no elements in common or, equivalently, their intersection contains no elements. For example, if A, B, and C are subsets of U, with $A = \{3,4,5\}$, $B = \{-2,7,8\}$, and $C = \{7,8,9\}$, then A and B are *mutually* exclusive because $A \cap B = \emptyset$. Notice that B and C are not mutually exclusive because $B \cap C = \{7,8\}$, a set that is not the empty set.

Figure 4.6

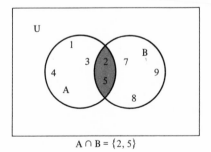

$A \cap B = \{2, 5\}$

MULTIPLE OPERATIONS WITH SETS

If we are given $U = \{1,2,3, \ldots , 10\}$, $A = \{1,2,3,7,5\}$, $B = \{1,5,3\}$, and $C = \{1,6\}$, we could perform the following operations.

1. If we wish to determine the complement of $(B \cup C)$, denoted by $(B \cup C)'$, we first find $B \cup C = \{1,3,5,6\}$. Then we determine the complement of $(B \cup C)$, or $(B \cup C)' = \{2,4,7,8,9,10\}$.

Note: In multiple set operations, the operation(s) inside parentheses are performed first.

2. To find $(C \cap B)'$, we first determine $C \cap B = \{1\}$, and then $(C \cap B)' = \{2,3,4,5,6,7,8,9,10\}$.

3. $C' \cap B' = \{2,3,4,5,7,8,9,10\} \cap \{2,4,6,7,8,9,10\}$
   $= \{2,4,7,8,9,10\}$

4. $C' \cup B' = \{2,3,4,5,7,8,9,10\} \cup \{2,4,6,7,8,9,10\}$
   $= \{2,3,4,5,6,7,8,9,10\}$

Note: In operations 2, 3, and 4, we can see that $(C \cap B)' \neq C' \cap B'$, but $(C \cap B)' = C' \cup B'$. We could also show that $(C \cup B)' = C' \cap B'$. In mathematics the general relationships

$$(X \cup Y)' = X' \cap Y' \quad \text{and} \quad (X \cap Y)' = X' \cup Y'$$

are known as *De Morgan's laws*.

5. $(A \cup B) \cup C = \{1,2,3,5,7\} \cup \{1,6\}$
   $= \{1,2,3,5,6,7\}$

6. $A \cup (B \cup C) = \{1,2,3,7,5\} \cup \{1,3,5,6\}$
   $= \{1,2,3,5,6,7\}$

7. $A \cup (B \cap C) = \{1,2,3,7,5\} \cup \{1\}$
   $= \{1,2,3,5,7\}$

8. $(A \cup B) \cap (A \cup C) = \{1,2,3,5,7\} \cap \{1,2,3,5,6,7\}$
   $= \{1,2,3,5,7\}$

Note: In operations 5, 6, 7, and 8,

$$(A \cup B) \cup C = A \cup (B \cup C)$$

and

$$A \cup (B \cap C) = (A \cup B) \cap (A \cup C)$$

In the algebra of sets, we can show that, given any universal set U and any subsets A, B, and C of U, the following operational laws are true:

1. Commutative Laws
   $A \cup B = B \cup A$
   $A \cap B = B \cap A$

2. Associative Laws
   $(A \cup B) \cup C = A \cup (B \cup C)$
   $(A \cap B) \cap C = A \cap (B \cap C)$

3. Distributive Laws
$$A \cup (B \cap C) = (A \cup B) \cap (A \cup C)$$
$$A \cap (B \cup C) = (A \cap B) \cup (A \cap C)$$

4. Identity Laws
$$A \cup U = U \qquad A \cup \emptyset = A$$
$$A \cap U = A \qquad A \cap \emptyset = \emptyset$$

5. Complement Laws
$$A \cup A' = U \qquad (A')' = A$$
$$A \cap A' = \emptyset$$

6. De Morgan's Laws
$$(A \cup B)' = A' \cap B'$$
$$(A \cap B)' = A' \cup B'$$

7. Idempotent Laws
$$A \cup A = A$$
$$A \cap A = A$$

Problem Set 4.3

1. List the elements of the following sets:
   (a) A = the set of all people in your immediate family.
   (b) B = the set of all odd counting numbers less than 10.
   (c) C = the set of all presidents of the United States since John F. Kennedy.

2. If $U = \{1,2,3,\ldots\}$, then list the elements of the following sets:
   (a) $E = \{x^2 | x \in U\}$
   (b) $F = \{x | x$ is divisible by 2 and $x \in U\}$
   (c) $G = \{x | x + 7 = 15$ and $x \in U\}$
   (d) $H = \{x | x + 7 = 8$ and $x \in U\}$
   (e) $I = \{x | x^2 = 4$ and $x \in U\}$
   (f) $J = \{x | x^2 = 2$ and $x \in U\}$

3. If $U = \{1,2,3,4,5\}$, $B = \{2,4\}$, $C = \{3,5\}$, $D = \{1,2,4\}$, $E = \{5,3\}$, $F = \{4,2\}$, $G = \{1\}$, $H = \{5,3,2,1\}$, find:
   (a) $B \cup C$
   (b) $B \cap C$
   (c) E'
   (d) G'
   (e) U'
   (f) $H' \cup B$
   (g) $(F \cup E)'$
   (h) $F' \cup E'$
   (i) $F' \cap E'$
   (j) $(E \cup H) \cup C$
   (k) $E \cup (H \cup C)$
   (l) $(F \cap H) \cap E$
   (m) $F \cap (H \cap E)$
   (n) $F \cup (H \cap E)$
   (o) $(F \cup H) \cap E$

4. For the sets given in Problem 2, is
   (a) $B \subset D?$
   (b) $D \subset B?$
   (c) $B \subset F?$
   (d) $F \subset B?$
   (e) $B \subset D?$
   (f) $D \subset B?$
   (g) $B \subset F?$
   (h) $F \subset B?$
   (i) $B = D?$
   (j) $D = B?$
   (k) $B = F?$
   (l) $F = B?$

5. Describe in words or symbols the shaded areas in the Venn diagrams (a) through (g) of Figure 4.7.

Figure 4.7

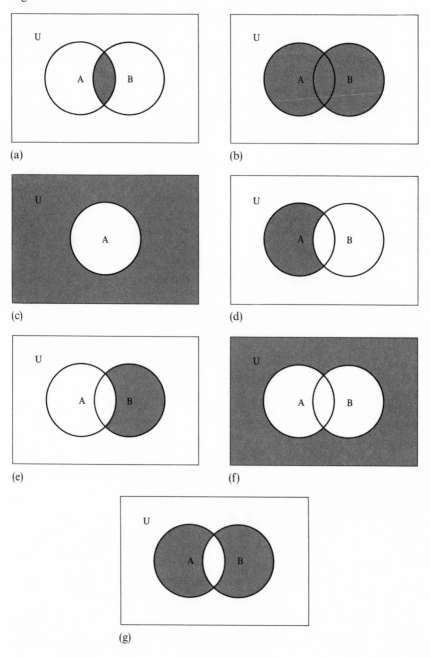

6. (a) Write all the subsets of $U = \{a,b,c,d\}$.

(b) Are there any disjoint subsets of U with one element each? If so, list these subsets.

(c) Are there any disjoint subsets of U with two elements each? If so, list them.

7. Given $U = \{2,4,6,8,10,12,14\}$

$\qquad A = \{4,8,10\}$

$\qquad B = \{6,10,14\}$

$\qquad C = \{2,12\}$

Show that

(a) $A \cup (B \cap C) = (A \cup B) \cap (A \cup C)$

(b) $A \cap (B \cup C) = (A \cap B) \cup (A \cap C)$

(c) $(A \cap B)' = A' \cup B'$

(d) $A \cap (B \cap C) = (A \cap B) \cap C$

(e) $(A')' = A$

(f) $A \cup \varnothing = A$

4.4

Relationships between Symbolic Logic and Set Theory

BASIC ELEMENTS

In symbolic logic the basic elements are *simple statements*, which are represented by variables such as p, q, r, and s. The basic elements in set theory are sets, which are represented by symbols such as A, B, C, and D.

BASIC ASSUMPTION

In symbolic logic the *basic assumption* is that each statement used is well defined (that is, each statement used can be assigned exactly *one* truth value, either true (T) or false (F). The basic assumption in set theory is that each set used is *well defined* (that is, it is clearly indicated whether a given object does ($\in$) or does not ($\notin$) belong to a given set).

BASIC OPERATIONS

The following list compares *basic operations* of symbolic logic and set theory, which are basically the *same* operations:

Symbolic Logic	Set Theory
1. negation ($\sim$)	1. complement ($'$)
2. conjunction ($\wedge$)	2. intersection ($\cap$)
3. disjunction ($\vee$)	3. union ($\cup$)
4. implication	4. subset
5. logical equivalence	5. equality of sets

Let us illustrate one pair of *equivalent* operations by comparing the definition for $p \vee q$ with the definition for $A \cup B$. We previously defined $p \vee q$ and listed the four logical possibilities of $p \vee q$ as follows:

p	q	$p \vee q$
T	T	T
T	F	T
F	T	T
F	F	F

We also defined

$$A \cup B = \{x | x \in A \text{ or } x \in B\}$$

However, we could define $A \cup B$ using an element ($\in$) table instead of a truth table. That is, if A and B are well-defined sets, there are the following definitions for $A \cup B$ under the given four logical possibilities:

A	B	$A \cup B$	
$\in$	$\in$	$\in$	(If $x \in A$ and $x \in B$, then $x \in (A \cup B)$).
$\in$	$\notin$	$\in$	(If $x \in A$ and $x \notin B$, then $x \in (A \cup B)$).
$\notin$	$\in$	$\in$	(If $x \notin A$ and $x \in B$, then $x \in (A \cup B)$).
$\notin$	$\notin$	$\notin$	(If $x \notin A$ and $x \notin B$, then $x \notin (A \cup B)$).

Notice that these table definitions for $p \vee q$ and $A \cup B$ are *equivalent* if we replace p and q with A and B, and replace T and F with $\in$ and $\notin$.

The following tables illustrate the *equivalent* definitions for $p \wedge q$ and $A \cap B$:

p	q	$p \wedge q$	A	B	$A \cap B$
T	T	T	$\in$	$\in$	$\in$
T	F	F	$\in$	$\notin$	$\notin$
F	T	F	$\notin$	$\in$	$\notin$
F	F	F	$\notin$	$\notin$	$\notin$

Without loss of generality we can obtain *equivalent definitions* and laws if we make the following substitutions:

Symbolic Logic Symbol/Symbols	*replaced by*	Set Theory Symbol/Symbols
p, q, r		A, B, C
$\vee$		$\cup$
$\wedge$		$\cap$
$\sim$		$'$

Note that a definition or law containing one statement p has *two* logical possibilities (T or F), while a definition or law containing one set A also has *two* logical possibilities ($\in$ or $\notin$). Definitions or laws containing two statements p and q require *four* logical possibilities (TT, TF, FT, FF), while definitions or laws containing two sets A and B also require *four* logical possibilities ($\in\in$, $\in\notin$, $\notin\in$, $\notin\notin$), and so on.

An *element table* can be used to prove the laws of set theory in the same way we can show logical equivalence for two statements in symbolic logic. For example, in Table 4.2 we prove that $A \cup (B \cap C) = (A \cup B) \cap (A \cup C)$.

Solution: See Table 4.2.

Table 4.2

Logical possibilities	A	B	C	$B \cap C$	$A \cup B$	$A \cup C$	$A \cup (B \cap C)$	$(A \cup B) \cap (A \cup C)$
1	$\in$	$\in$	$\in$	$\in$	$\in$	$\in$	$\in$	$\in$
2	$\in$	$\in$	$\notin$	$\notin$	$\in$	$\in$	$\in$	$\in$
3	$\in$	$\notin$	$\in$	$\notin$	$\in$	$\in$	$\in$	$\in$
4	$\in$	$\notin$	$\notin$	$\notin$	$\in$	$\in$	$\in$	$\in$
5	$\notin$	$\in$	$\in$	$\in$	$\in$	$\in$	$\in$	$\in$
6	$\notin$	$\in$	$\notin$	$\notin$	$\in$	$\notin$	$\notin$	$\notin$
7	$\notin$	$\notin$	$\in$	$\notin$	$\notin$	$\in$	$\notin$	$\notin$
8	$\notin$	$\notin$	$\notin$	$\notin$	$\notin$	$\notin$	$\notin$	$\notin$

We can see that both $A \cup (B \cap C)$ and $(A \cup B) \cap (A \cup C)$ obtain the *same results* for the same logical possibilities; therefore, it is clearly illustrated that $A \cup (B \cap C) = (A \cup B) \cap (A \cup C)$ for *all eight* logical possibilities.

Problem Set 4.4

1. Show that the definitions for $\sim p$ and A' are equivalent if we replace p with A, T with $\in$, and F with $\notin$.

2. Explain the relationship between the definition of an implication in symbolic logic and the definition of a subset in set theory.

3. Explain the relationship between logical equivalence of statements and equality of sets.

4. Use element tables to prove the following laws:
   (a) $(A \cap B) \cap C = A \cap (B \cap C)$
   (b) $A \cap (B \cup C) = (A \cap B) \cup (A \cap C)$
   (c) $(A')' = A$
   (d) $(A \cup B)' = A' \cap B'$
   (e) $(A \cap B)' = A' \cup B'$
   (f) $A \cup B = B \cup A$

4.5

Switching Algebra

Switching algebra, sometimes called the "algebra of the computer," is used in designing electric networks.

Basic Element: The basic element of switching algebra is an electronic switch denoted by

—o p o—

Basic Assumption: The basic assumption of switching algebra is that each switch in an electronic network is either *open* (current is *not* passing through the switch) or *closed* (current *is* passing through the switch) at a particular instance. Open switches are sometimes denoted by the numeral 0 and closed switches by the numeral 1.

Open Switch (0)   Closed Switch (1)

Basic definitions

If *p* and *q* are *any switches*, there are *three basic networks* that can be formed using one or both of them in order to develop more complex networks. The three basic networks are defined as follows:

Definition 1: A *parallel network* is denoted by $p \oplus q$ and wired as follows:

and is defined as

p	q	$p \oplus q$
1	1	1
1	0	1
0	1	1
0	0	0

Note that the *only time* current will *not* flow through a parallel network is when *both p* and *q* are open.

Definition 2: A *series network* is denoted by $p \odot q$ and wired as follows:

and is defined as

p	q	$p \odot q$
1	1	1
1	0	0
0	1	0
0	0	0

Observe that the *only* time current will flow through a series network is when *both* p and q are closed.

Definition 3: An *opposite network* is denoted by $\bar{p}$ and wired in such a way that if the switch p is *open*, the switch $\bar{p}$ is *closed*; and if the switch p is *closed*, the switch $\bar{p}$ is open. Thus,

p	$\bar{p}$
1	0
0	1

BASIC LAWS

Perhaps you have already noticed that if we *replace* true (T) with closed (1) and false (F) with open (0), the definitions for *parallel, series,* and *opposite switching* networks are *equivalent* respectively to some definitions in symbolic logic: *disjunction, conjunction,* and *negation.* Therefore, each of the laws we discussed in symbolic logic can be used in designing sophisticated switching networks. For example, in designing a complex switching network, we could use either the network $p \oplus (q \odot r)$ or $(p \oplus q) \odot (p \oplus r)$ to perform the same task.

Proof: Is $p \oplus (q \odot r)$

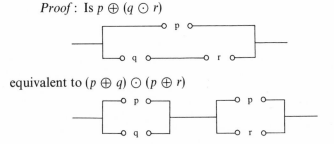

equivalent to $(p \oplus q) \odot (p \oplus r)$

(see Table 4.3)?

Table 4.3 illustrates the fact that the networks $p \oplus (q \odot r)$ and $(p \oplus q) \odot (p \oplus r)$ are open and closed under the *same conditions.* Therefore, the network $p \oplus (q \odot r)$ is *equivalent to* the network $(p \oplus q) \odot (p \oplus r)$. Note in the switching diagrams that $p \oplus (q \odot r)$ requires *three* switches, while $(p \oplus q) \odot (p \oplus r)$ requires *four* switches. Therefore, the first network would be less expensive to produce.

Table 4.3

p	q	r	$q \odot r$	$p \oplus q$	$p \oplus r$	$p \oplus (q \odot r)$	$(p \oplus q) \odot (p \oplus r)$
1	1	1	1	1	1	1	1
1	1	0	0	1	1	1	1
1	0	1	0	1	1	1	1
1	0	0	0	1	1	1	1
0	1	1	1	1	1	1	1
0	1	0	0	1	0	0	0
0	0	1	0	0	1	0	0
0	0	0	0	0	0	0	0

Problem Set 4.5

1. Draw the switching network for each of the following switching algebra statements:
   (a) $p \odot q$
   (b) $p \odot (q \oplus r)$
   (c) $(p \odot q) \oplus (p \odot r)$
   (d) $(p \oplus q) \odot r$

2. Convert the following networks to switching algebra statements:

(a)

(b)

(c)
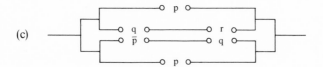

(d)

(e)

3. Show that the network $\bar{p} \odot \bar{q}$ is equivalent to the network $\overline{(p \oplus q)}$.

4. Show that the network $p \odot (q \oplus r)$ is equivalent to the network $(p \odot q) \oplus (p \odot r)$.

5. Show that the network $(\overline{p \odot q})$ is equivalent to the network $\bar{p} \oplus \bar{q}$.

6. Show that the network $p \oplus \bar{p}$ *always* has current flowing through it, and the network $p \odot \bar{p}$ *never* has current flowing through it.

7. (a) Find the switching algebra statement corresponding to the following network:

(b) Show that the network in (a) has current flowing if and only if switches p and q are closed.

4.6

Number Systems with Bases Other Than Ten

The *decimal number* system is an additive *positional* number system with a base of ten. It utilizes the ten numerals 0, 1, 2, 3, 4, 5, 6, 7, 8, 9, and is compatible with the way we *count*. It is therefore widely used in arithmetic and algebra. In this section we will also consider number systems with bases two, eight, and sixteen.

The Binary (Base Two) Number System

The binary number system is an additive positional number system with a base of *two*. It utilizes *only* the symbols 0 and 1, and is compatible with switching algebra.

COMPARISON BETWEEN THE DECIMAL (BASE TEN) AND
BINARY (BASE TWO) NUMBER SYSTEMS

The decimal (base ten) number system uses the symbols 0, 1, 2, 3, 4, 5, 6, 7, 8, 9; while the binary (base two) number system uses *only* the symbols 0, 1. Both the decimal and binary systems are positional, or place value, number systems. In the decimal number system each position has a value of *ten times as much* as the position to the *right* of it. Look at the following table of place values in base ten.

Base ten place values

10^3	10^2	10^1	10^0	10^{-1}	10^{-2}	10^{-3}
1000	100	10	1	1/10	1/100	1/1000
1000	100	10	1	0.1	0.01	0.001

In the binary number system each position has a value of *twice as much* as the position to the *right* of it. You can observe this relationship of values in the following table of place value in base two:

Base two place values

2^3	2^2	2^1	2^0	2^{-1}	2^{-2}	2^{-3}
8	4	2	1	1/2	1/4	1/8
8	4	2	1	0.5	0.25	0.125

CONVERTING FROM BASE TWO TO BASE TEN

To convert a base two number to a base ten number, we simply multiply each face value (0 or 1) by the corresponding place value and add these products. For example, let us convert 101.011_{two} to a number in base ten:

$$101.011_{two} = 1(2^2) + 0(2^1) + 1(2^0) + 0(2^{-1}) + 1(2^{-2}) + 1(2^{-3})$$
$$= 1(4) + 0(2) + 1(1) + 0(0.5) + 1(0.25) + 1(0.125)$$
$$= 4 + 0 + 1 + 0 + 0.25 + 0.125$$
$$= 5.375_{ten}$$

CONVERTING FROM BASE TEN TO BASE TWO

One way to convert a number like 53_{ten} to a base two number is to use *repetitive subtractions*. First we decide how many places in base two we need:

32	16	8	4	2	1

How many 32's in   53?
$$\frac{-32}{21} \quad \textit{Ans. (1)}$$

How many 16's in 21?
$$\frac{-16}{5} \quad \textit{Ans. (1)}$$

How many 8's in 5?   *Ans.* (0)

How many 4's in   5?
$$\frac{-4}{1} \quad \textit{Ans. (1)}$$

How many 2's in 1?   *Ans.* (0)

How many 1's in   1?

$$\frac{-1}{0} \qquad Ans.\ (1)$$

Therefore, $53_{ten} = 110101_{two}$

This procedure can become quite tedious if we want to convert a number like $52,131_{ten}$ to base two. Another method for converting from base ten to base two is to use an *algorithm*, which tells us to continue dividing the base ten number and partial quotients obtained by 2, and keep the remainders. The *first* remainder will represent the number of 1's in the base two number; the *second* remainder will represent the number of 2's in the base two number; the *third* remainder will represent the number of 4's in the base two number, and so on. For example, let us use this algorithm to convert 53_{ten} to a base two number:

$$\begin{array}{r} 26 \\ 2\overline{)53} \end{array} \qquad \text{remainder of 1} \quad (1\text{'s})$$

$$\begin{array}{r} 13 \\ 2\overline{)26} \end{array} \qquad \text{remainder of 0} \quad (2\text{'s})$$

$$\begin{array}{r} 6 \\ 2\overline{)13} \end{array} \qquad \text{remainder of 1} \quad (4\text{'s})$$

$$\begin{array}{r} 3 \\ 2\overline{)6} \end{array} \qquad \text{remainder of 0} \quad (8\text{'s})$$

$$\begin{array}{r} 1 \\ 2\overline{)3} \end{array} \qquad \text{remainder of 1} \quad (16\text{'s})$$

$$\begin{array}{r} 0 \\ 2\overline{)1} \end{array} \qquad \text{remainder of 1} \quad (32\text{'s})$$

Therefore, $53_{ten} = 110101_{two}$, which is the same result we obtained using the repetitive subtraction method.

The Octal (Base Eight) Number System

The binary (base two) number system is used in writing binary (machine) language programs. However, the coding of binary language programs is sometimes initially written in the *octal* (base eight) or *hexadecimal* (base sixteen) number system because of the increased number of symbols and the relationship to the binary (base two) number system. Consider the following summary of the octal (base eight) number system:

1. *Symbols.* The symbols used in the octal number system are 0, 1, 2, 3, 4, 5, 6, 7.

2. *Place Value.* Study the following table of base eight place values.

Base eight place values

8^3	8^2	8^1	8^0	8^{-1}	8^{-2}	8^{-3}
512	64	8	1	1/8	1/64	1/512
512	64	8	1	0.125	0.015625	0.001953125

3. *Converting from Base Eight to Base Ten.* For example, let us convert 571.2_{eight} to a number in base ten:

$$571.2_{eight} = 5(8^2) + 7(8^1) + 1(8^0) + 2(8^{-1})$$
$$= 5(64) + 7(8) + 1(1) + 2(0.125)$$
$$= 320 + 56 + 1 + 0.250$$
$$= 377.250_{ten}$$

4. *Converting from Base Ten to Base Eight.* To convert 53_{ten} to base eight, we will use the same algorithm discussed previously, except we use repetitive divisions by 8.

$$\frac{6}{8)\,53} \quad \text{remainder of 5} \quad (1\text{'s})$$

$$\frac{0}{8)\,6} \quad \text{remainder of 6} \quad (8\text{'s})$$

Therefore, $53_{ten} = 65_{eight}$.

RELATIONSHIP BETWEEN BASE EIGHT AND BASE TWO

The *largest single digit* we can write in base eight is $7_{eight} = 111_{two}$. Therefore, if the *largest* digit in base eight can be written using the *fours twos ones* places in base two, then so can *each* of the *smaller* digits be written using these three places. This means that if we want to convert any base eight number to an equivalent base two number, all we need do is *replace each* base eight digit with its equivalent base two representation, using the *fours twos ones* places. For example,

$$53_{ten} = \quad 6|5_{eight}$$
$$= 110|101_{two}$$

Now let us convert 1200_{ten} to base eight and then convert the base 8 number to the equivalent base 2 number:

$$\frac{150}{8)\,1200} \quad \text{remainder of 0} \quad (1\text{'s})$$

$$\frac{18}{8)\,150} \quad \text{remainder of 6} \quad (8\text{'s})$$

$$\frac{2}{8\overline{)18}} \qquad \text{remainder of 2 \quad (64's)}$$

$$\frac{0}{8\overline{)2}} \qquad \text{remainder of 2 \quad (512's)}$$

Therefore, $1200_{ten} = 2 \mid 2 \mid 6 \mid 0_{eight}$

$\qquad\qquad\qquad\; = 010 \mid 010 \mid 110 \mid 000_{two}$

$\qquad\qquad\qquad\; = 10010110000_{two}$

The Hexadecimal (Base Sixteen) Number System

Consider the following summary of the hexadecimal (base sixteen) number system, which is sometimes used initially to code binary (machine) language programs:

SYMBOLS

The symbols commonly used in the hexadecimal number system are: 0,1,2,3,4,5,6,7,8,9, A (ten of some place value), B (eleven of some place value), C (twelve of some place value), D (thirteen of some place value), E (fourteen of some place value, F (fifteen of some place value).

PLACE VALUE

Look at the following table of place values in base sixteen.

Base sixteen place values

16^3	16^2	16^1	16^0	16^{-1}	16^{-2}	16^{-3}
4096	256	16	1	1/16	$1/16^2$	$1/16^3$
4096	256	16	1	0.0625	0.00390625	0.0002441406

CONVERTING FROM BASE SIXTEEN TO BASE TEN

Study the following example:

$$\begin{aligned} AE2.1_{sixteen} &= 10(16^2) + 14(16^1) + 2(16^0) + 1(16^{-1}) \\ &= 10(256) + 14(16) + 2(1) + 1(0.0625) \\ &= 2560 + 224 + 2 + 0.0625 \\ &= 2786.0625_{ten} \end{aligned}$$

CONVERTING FROM BASE TEN TO BASE SIXTEEN

To convert 53_{ten} to base sixteen, we use the algorithm of repetitive divisions (using 16 as the divisor):

$$16\overline{)53} \quad \frac{3}{}$$

$16\overline{)53}$ remainder of 5   (1's)

$$16\overline{)3} \quad \frac{0}{}$$

$16\overline{)3}$ remainder of 3   (16's)

Therefore, $53_{ten} = 35_{sixteen}$.

RELATIONSHIP BETWEEN BASE SIXTEEN AND BASE TWO

The largest single digit in base sixteen is $F_{sixteen} = 1111_{two}$. Therefore, if the *largest* digit in base sixteen can be written by using the places *eights fours twos ones* in base two, then so can each of the *smaller* digits be written, using these four places. This means that if we want to convert *any* base sixteen number to an equivalent base two number, all we need to do is replace *each* base sixteen digit with its equivalent base two representation, using the *eights fours twos ones* places. Study this conversion in the following example:

$$53_{ten} = 3|5_{sixteen}$$
$$= 0011|0101_{two}$$
$$= 110101_{two}$$

Now let us convert 1200_{ten} to base sixteen and then convert the base sixteen number to the *equivalent* base two number:

$$16\overline{)1200} \quad \frac{75}{}$$

$16\overline{)1200}$ remainder of 0   (1's)

$$16\overline{)75} \quad \frac{4}{}$$

$16\overline{)75}$ remainder of B (eleven), (16's)

$$16\overline{)4} \quad \frac{0}{}$$

$16\overline{)4}$ remainder of 4   (256's)

Therefore $1200_{ten} = 4| \quad B|0_{sixteen}$
$$= 0100|1011|0000_{two}$$
$$= 10010110000_{two}$$

Problem Set 4.6

1. Convert the following numbers to equivalent decimal (base ten) numbers:
    (a) 213.7_{eight} (d) 101101.011_{two}

    (b) 524_{eight} (e) $200F_{sixteen}$

    (c) $82B.1_{sixteen}$ (f) 231_{seven}

2. Convert the following decimal (base ten) numbers to equivalent base eight numbers:

    (a) 231   (b) 401   (c) 1524   (d) 2300

3. Convert the decimal (base ten) numbers in Problem 2 to equivalent hexadecimal (base sixteen) numbers.

4. Convert the decimal (base ten) numbers in Problem 2 to equivalent base five numbers.

5. Convert the following numbers to equivalent base two numbers.

    (a) 472_{eight} (c) $AB7_{sixteen}$

    (b) 3017_{eight} (d) $30C9_{sixteen}$

4.7

A Binary (Machine) Language

Figure 4.8 is a simplified representation of the internal operation of a computer. In the binary (machine) language programming each operation, command, and piece of data must be entered into the computer using binary (base two) numbers. Furthermore, each instruction and each piece of data must have a memory address (location), which is also a binary number.

Figure 4.8

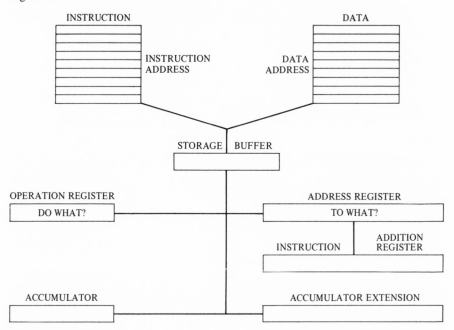

Table 4.4

Command	Binary code	Function of command
1. Clear and add	10000001	Clear the accumulator and add the contents of some data address to the accumulator.
2. Add	10000010	Add the contents of some data address.
3. Subtract	10000011	Subtract the contents of some data address from the contents of the accumulator.
4. Multiply	10000100	Multiply the contents of the accumulator by the contents of some data address.
5. Divide	10000101	Divide the contents of the accumulator by the contents of some data address.
6. Stop	10001000	End of program.
7. Read	10010000	Read the contents of some data address.
8. Print	10010001	Print the contents of some data address.
9. Transfer—unconditionally	11000000	Transfer unconditionally to some instructional address.
10. Transfer on negative	11000001	If the contents of the accumulator is negative, transfer to some instructional address.
11. Transfer on positive	11000010	If the contents of the accumulator is positive, transfer to some instructional address.
12. Store	11100000	Store the contents of the accumulator in some data address.

Each instruction in a machine language program must tell the computer two things: (1) what to do (add, subtract, print, and so on); and (2) on or with what piece of data (at some address or memory location) must the instruction be performed.

The instructional addresses of a machine language program must be separated by *increments of 1*. The instructional address register feeds the instructions, one at a time (in numerical order via their address or location) into the storage buffer.

The storage buffer breaks the instruction into two parts (Do what? *and* To what?), which are fed to the operation register and address register, respectively.

All work is done or operations performed in a place in the computer called the *accumulator* and/or one of the accumulator extensions. However, information can be printed from memory *only*; that is, if there is something in the accumulator to be printed, it must be stored in some memory address before it can be printed.

Figure 4.8 and the explanation of the internal parts of a computer, given above, are oversimplified for reasons of clarity and brevity. Modern computers contain large memories, many storage buffers, and many accumulators.

In order to illustrate binary (machine) language programming, let us assume that our binary language consists of the binary commands listed in Table 4.4.

Writing a binary language program can become quite confusing because of the use of binary numbers for instructions as well as for data. Therefore, a computer programmer may write the program using hexadecimal (base 16) numbers and convert the program to base 2 when entering it into the computer (Article 4.6 demonstrates this procedure).

Table 4.5 is included here for the purpose of writing our binary commands in hexadecimal notation.

Table 4.5

Command	Binary code	Hexadecimal code
Clear and add	10000001	81
Add	10000010	82
Subtract	10000011	83
Multiply	10000100	84
Divide	10000101	85
Stop	10001000	88
Read	10010000	90
Print	10010001	91
Transfer, unconditionally	11000000	C0
Transfer, −	11000001	C1
Transfer, +	11000011	C2
Store	11100000	E0

Now let us consider the machine language program on page 212 to print out the value of $Y = (A - B)/(A + B)$, given the values of A and B.

As you can see, programming in machine language can be quite tedious. Although most computer programs are written in compiler language such as BASIC, it should be noted that the compiler itself (the program which changes your BASIC program into a machine language program) is written in machine language.

	Address	Contents (Do what? To what?)	Comments
START	A1	· · ·	Enter value of A
	A2	· · ·	Enter value of B
	A3	81 A1	Clear and add A to accumulator
	A4	82 A2	Add B (A + B in accumulator)
	A5	E0 F1	Store A + B in location F1
	A6	81 A1	Clear and add A to accumulator
	A7	83 A2	Subtract B (A − B in accumulator)
	A8	85 F1	Divide by (A + B)
	A9	E0 F1	Store (A − B)/(A + B) in location F1
	AA	91 F1	Print the contents of location F1((A − B)/(A + B))
	AB	C0 A3	Transfer to start, enter new A and B
	AC	88	End of program

Problem Set 4.7

Given: A,B,C for $Ax^2 + Bx + C = 0$, where $A \neq 0$.

Wanted: A machine language program to compute $D = B^2 - 4AC$ and print either A,B,C, and D if $D \geq 0$, or D if $D < 0$.

5

Sophisticated Counting, Probability, and Related Prepackaged Computer Programs

5.1

Introduction

One direct application of set theory is the development of probability theory. Sophisticated counting techniques, such as permutation and combination formulas, are extremely useful in the solution of probability problems.

5.2

Sophisticated Counting

The Cartesian Product

The Cartesian product of two sets A and B, denoted by $A \times B$, is defined as follows:

$$A \times B = \{(x,y) | x \in A \text{ and } y \in B\}$$

For example, if $A = \{1,2,3\}$, $B = \{5,6\}$, then

$$A \times B = \{(1,5), (1,6), (2,5), (2,6), (3,5), (3,6)\}$$

and

$$B \times A = \{(5,1), (5,2), (5,3), (6,1), (6,2), (6,3)\}$$

Is $A \times B$ equal to $B \times A$? Why not?

Fundamental Principle of Counting

If a task can be performed in any number of n_1 ways, and after it is completed another task can be performed in any number of n_2 ways, then the number of ways the two tasks can be performed in succession is $n_1 \cdot n_2$ ways.

In general, if $1,2,3,\ldots,k$ tasks can be performed in $n_1,n_2,\ldots,n_k$ ways, respectively, then the k tasks can be performed in succession in $n_1 \cdot n_2 \cdot \ldots \cdot n_k$ ways.

EXAMPLES

1. A class is to select a president first, then a vice-president, from five possible candidates named A, B, C, D, and E. In how many possible ways can the selection be made?

President	Vice-president	
5	· 4	= 20 possible selections

What are these 20 possible selections? Let us look at a *tree diagram* (Figure 5.1) of the possible selections. We see that

$$U = \{(A,B), (A,C), (A,D), (A,E), (B,A), (B,C), (B,D), (B,E), (C,A),$$
$$(C,B), (C,D), (C,E), (D,A), (D,B), (D,C), (D,E), (E,A), (E,B),$$
$$(E,C), (E,D)\}$$

or

$$U = \{(x, y) | x \in T, y \in T, x \text{ is president}, y \text{ is vice-president}\}$$

where $T = \{A,B,C,D,E\}$.

Note: The order of selection (selecting a president before selecting a vice-president) makes a difference.

2. If two tires are tested and labeled "G" for good or "D" for defective, how many possibilities of labeling are there? What are they?

For Tire 1	For Tire 2	
2	· 2	= 4 possibilities

Examine the tree diagram in Figure 5.2, which shows us these four possibilities. Thus,

$$U = \{(G,G), (G,D), (D,G), (D,D)\}$$

or

$$U = \{(x,y) | x \in C \text{ and } y \in C\}$$

where $C = \{G,D\}$.

3. How many different three-digit numbers may be formed using the digits 7,8,9 if repetitions of digits are allowed?

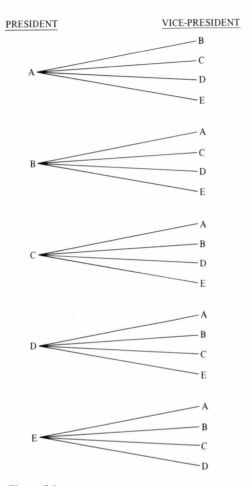

Figure 5.1

Figure 5.2

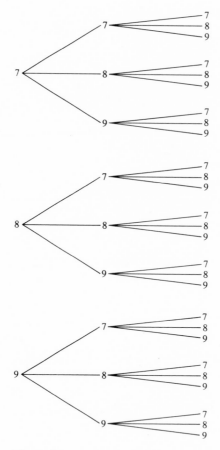

Figure 5.3

Figure 5.4

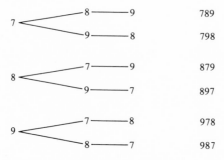

For Hundreds' Digit		For Tens' Digit		For Ones' Digit	
3	·	3	·	3	= 27 three-digit numbers

We illustrate these 27 possibilities of numbers with the tree diagram in Figure 5.3.

4. How many different three-digit numbers may be formed using the digits 7,8,9 if repetitions of digits are *not* allowed? Again we list all the possible three-digit numbers:

For Hundreds' Digit		For Tens' Digit		For Ones' Digit	
3	·	2	·	1	= 6

Our tree diagram in Figure 5.4 illustrates the composition of these six numbers.

Problem Set 5.1

1. Three batteries are to be tested and labeled A (accepted) or R (rejected).
   (a) How many different possibilities are there?
   (b) List all the different possibilities.

2. Three students are asked which of two candidates (A or B) for class president they are supporting. These possible responses from each of the students are A, B, or U (undecided).
   (a) How many different possible responses from the group of three students are there?
   (b) What are these possibilities?

3. Twenty students' names are written on different pieces of paper and placed in a box. Two names are to be selected from the box and awarded first and second prizes.
   (a) How many different possibilities of selection are there?
   (b) If we know that John was awarded first place, in how many different ways can the second prize winner be selected?

4. A patient has contracted pneumonia. His physician decides to prescribe 3 of 15 possible antibiotics. How many possible prescriptions can the doctor write?

5. A subscriber to a theater club has the choice of selecting in some order 4 of 9 possible play productions. In how many different ways can the selection be made?

5.3

Order versus No Order

Let us discuss briefly the selection of *r* objects from *n* objects. In one type of selection the *order* of selection will make a difference. For example, if we are to select a president and then a vice-president from five candidates (A, B, C, D, or

E), the selection (A,B) will be different from the selection (B,A). Why? This type of selection is called a *permutation* of two objects selected from five objects.

However, if we are to select a committee of any two people from the five candidates (A, B, C, D, or E), the selection (A,B) will not be different from the selection (B,A). Why not? This type of selection is called a *combination* of two objects selected from five objects.

5.4

Factorial Notation

Factorial notation allows us to express the product of consecutive integers in a simple form. The symbol $X!$ is read as "x factorial." By definition, $x! = x(x - 1)(X - 2) \cdots (1)$. For example,

$$1! = 1$$
$$2! = 2 \cdot 1 = 2$$
$$3! = 3 \cdot 2 \cdot 1 = 6$$
$$4! = 4 \cdot 3 \cdot 2 \cdot 1 = 24$$
$$5! = 5 \cdot 4 \cdot 3 \cdot 2 \cdot 1 = 120$$

Note that

$$n! = n(n - 1)!$$
$$6! = 6(5!) = 6(120) = 720$$
$$7! = 7(6!) = 7(720) = 5040$$

and so on. Also note that $0! = 1$ by definition.

We will use factorial notation in our formulas for counting the number of permutations and the number of combinations of r objects selected from n objects. Therefore, we must be able to evaluate different expressions involving factorials, such as:

$$4! - 2! = 4 \cdot 3 \cdot 2 \cdot 1 - 2 \cdot 1 = 24 - 2 = 22$$
$$(4 - 2)! = 2! = 2$$

$$\frac{10!}{8!} = \frac{10 \cdot 9 \cdot \overset{1}{\cancel{8!}}}{\underset{1}{\cancel{8!}}} = 90$$

$$\frac{10!}{3!7!} = \frac{10 \cdot \overset{3}{\cancel{9}} \cdot \overset{4}{\cancel{8}} \cdot \overset{1}{\cancel{7!}}}{\underset{1}{\cancel{3}} \cdot \underset{1}{\cancel{2}} \cdot 1 \cdot \underset{1}{\cancel{7!}}} = 120$$

(See Table 2 in Appendix H.)

5.5

Permutations

When asked to select r objects from n distinct objects, where the order of selection makes a difference, we are computing the number of permutations of n distinct objects taken r at a time. For example, if we are asked how many different ways we can select a president, then a vice-president, and then a treasurer from among five candidates, we are selecting three people from among five people where order makes a difference, and we write

$$_5P_3 = 5 \cdot 4 \cdot 3 = 60 \text{ possible selections}$$

This computation is a direct application of the fundamental principle of counting.

In general, the number of permutations of r objects selected from n distinct objects is denoted by

$$_nP_r = n(n-1)(n-2) \cdots (n-(r-1))$$

or

$$_nP_r = n(n-1)(n-2) \cdots (n-r+1)$$

We may also write

$$_8P_8 = 8 \cdot 7 \cdot 6 \cdot 5 \cdot 4 \cdot 3 \cdot 2 \cdot 1 = \frac{8!}{(8-8)!} = \frac{8!}{0!} = 8!$$

$$_8P_7 = 8 \cdot 7 \cdot 6 \cdot 5 \cdot 4 \cdot 3 \cdot 2 = \frac{8!}{(8-7)!} = \frac{8!}{1!} = 8!$$

$$_8P_6 = 8 \cdot 7 \cdot 6 \cdot 5 \cdot 4 \cdot 3 = \frac{8!}{(8-6)!} = \frac{8!}{2!}$$

$$_8P_5 = 8 \cdot 7 \cdot 6 \cdot 5 \cdot 4 = \frac{8!}{(8-5)!} = \frac{8!}{3!}$$

$$_8P_4 = 8 \cdot 7 \cdot 6 \cdot 5 = \frac{8!}{(8-4)!} = \frac{8!}{4!}$$

$$_8P_3 = 8 \cdot 7 \cdot 6 = \frac{8!}{(8-3)!} = \frac{8!}{5!}$$

$$_8P_2 = 8 \cdot 7 = \frac{8!}{(8-2)!} = \frac{8!}{6!}$$

$$_8P_1 = 8 = \frac{8!}{(8-1)!} = \frac{8!}{7!}$$

$$_8P_0 = 1 = \frac{8!}{(8-0)!} = \frac{8!}{8!}$$

(There is only one way we can select 0 objects from 8 objects.)
Thus, *in general,*

$$_nP_r = n(n - 1)(n - 2) \cdots (n - r + 1)$$

or equivalently

$$_nP_r = \frac{n!}{(n - r)!}$$

In the sample problem where we selected a president, then a vice-president, and then a treasurer from among five people, we compute

$$_5P_3 = \frac{5!}{(5 - 3)!} = \frac{5!}{2!} = \frac{5 \cdot 4 \cdot 3 \cdot \overset{1}{\cancel{2}} \cdot \overset{1}{\cancel{1}}}{\underset{1}{\cancel{2}} \cdot \underset{1}{\cancel{1}}} = 60$$

Now suppose we were asked how many different arrangements could be made of all the letters in the word SIT. We could write

$$_3P_3 = \frac{3!}{(3 - 3)!} = \frac{3!}{0!} = 3! = 6$$

The tree diagram in Figure 5.5 illustrates the six different arrangements.

Figure 5.5

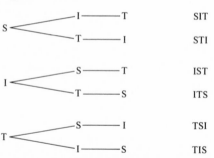

However, if we were asked how many different arrangements could be made of all the letters in the word TOO, there would *not* be six different arrangements, as the tree diagram in Figure 5.6 shows.

In the word SIT, which contains three different letters, any two of the different letters can be arranged in $2 \cdot 1$ or 2! ways, which are included in the arrangement of all three different letters as $3 \cdot 2 \cdot 1$, or $_3P_3$. However, in the word TOO, the two letters O and O can be arranged in *only* one different way. Therefore, the *different* arrangements of all the letters in the word TOO are expressed as

$$\frac{_3P_3}{2!} = \frac{3!}{2!} = 3$$

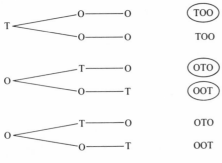

Figure 5.6

Note: We must cancel out the 2! arrangements of two different objects in $_3P_3$ ways because the two O's are *not* different and can be arranged *only* in one way.

Thus, *in general*, the number of permutations of n objects—where a_1 are alike, a_2 are alike, . . . , a_m are alike—is

$$\frac{_nP_n}{a_1!a_2!\cdots a_m!} = \frac{n!}{a_1!a_2!\cdots a_m!}$$

For example, if a comedian is to make ten appearances during a particular month and has three different routines—of which he wants to use the first routine five times, the second routine three times, and the third routine two times—these routines can be done in

$$\frac{10!}{5!3!2!} = \frac{10\cdot 9\cdot \overset{4}{8}\cdot 7\cdot \overset{1}{6}\cdot \overset{1}{5}!}{\underset{1}{5}!\underset{1}{3}!\underset{1}{2}!} = 2520 \text{ different ways}$$

Problem Set 5.2

1. Compute:
   (a) 5!   (c) 6! + 3!   (e) $_nP_n$
   (b) (6!)(3!)   (d) 6!/3!   (f) $_nP_0$

2. A disc jockey has five time slots left in his broadcast in which to play five new songs that he can select from 12 new songs on file. How many different ways can this be done?

3. If the disc jockey in Problem 2 has 12 time slots in which to play the 12 new songs, how many ways could this be done?

4. A student must include one language course, one mathematics course, one science course, one general education course, and one physical education course in his/her program for next semester. The student may select these required courses from a list of three language, two mathematics, two science, five general education, and

six physical education courses. In how many different ways can the student select his/her program for next semester?

5. An oil company has 13 salesmen's positions to fill. Twenty-five men apply for the 13 positions. Twelve of the 25 applicants have previous sales experience.
   (a) In how many different ways can the 13 positions be filled, choosing from among all the 25 applicants?
   (b) In how many different ways can the 13 positions be filled, choosing only applicants with previous sales experience?
   (c) In how many different ways can the 13 positions be filled from among the 25 applicants if five of the positions require previous sales experience and the remaining eight positions do not require previous sales experience?

6. How many different arrangements can be made of all the letters:
   (a) in the word HOME?
   (b) in the word NINE?
   (c) in the word LETTERS?
   (d) in the word TOGETHERNESS?

7. A TV producer wishes to place five different taped TV programs into five different time slots. In how many different ways can this arrangement be done?

5.6

Combinations

When asked to select r objects from n distinct objects, where the order of selection does *not* make a difference, we are computing the number of combinations of n distinct objects taken r at a time. For example, if we are asked to select a committee of any three people from five people (A,B,C,D, or E), the order in which we select the committee does not make a difference. That is, the committee consisting of persons A,B, and C would be the same as the committee consisting of persons A,C, and B.

In the preceding article, when we were to select a president, then a vice-president, and then a treasurer from five people (A,B,C,D, or E), the order *did* make a difference. We could select these three people in $_5P_3$ ways $= 5!/(5 - 3)!$, or 60 ways.

Let us consider the different committees of any three people selected from persons A,B,C,D, and E. We can list these groups as: (A,B,C), (A,B,D), (A,B,E), (A,C,D), (A,C,E), (A,D,E), (B,C,D), (B,C,E), (B,D,E), (C,D,E). As you can see, there are ten possible committees of three members selected from five different people, and we write $_5C_3 = 10$. *Note*:

$$_5C_3 = \frac{_5P_3}{3!} = \frac{5!/(5-3)!}{3!} = \frac{5!}{3!(5-3)!} = \frac{5!}{3!2!} = 10$$

(See Table 3 in Appendix H.)

Thus, *in general*, the number of combinations of r objects selected from n distinct objects is denoted by

$$_nC_r = \frac{_nP_r}{r!} \quad \text{or} \quad _nC_r = \frac{n!}{r!(n-r)!}$$

Consider the following problem: In how many different ways can a committee of five be selected from among five men and four women if this committee is to contain at least three women? Notice that the committee selected may include three women or four women: (3 women, 2 men) or (4 women, 1 man). Then

$$(_4C_3 \cdot {_5C_2}) + (_4C_4 \cdot {_5C_1})$$
$$= (4 \cdot 10) + (1 \cdot 5)$$
$$= 40 + 5 = 45 \text{ different ways}$$

5.7

The Binomial Theorem

In Article 6.9 we will have use for the binomial theorem, which is usually presented in an intermediate algebra course. By using the binomial theorem, we can raise the sum of two terms or the difference between two terms to an indicated power. Thus:

$$(g + d)^1 = g + d$$
$$(g + d)^2 = (g + d)(g + d)$$
$$= g^2 + 2gd + d^2$$
$$(g + d)^3 = (g + d)(g + d)(g + d)$$
$$= g^3 + 3g^2d + 3gd^2 + d^3$$

In general, the binomial theorem states

$$(g + d)^n = g^n + \frac{n}{1}g^{n-1}d + \frac{n(n-1)}{1(2)}g^{n-2}d^2 + \cdots + d^n$$

where $n \in \{1,2,3,\ldots\}$; or

$$(g + d)^n = {_nC_n}g^n + {_nC_{n-1}}g^{n-1}d + {_nC_{n-2}}g^{n-2}d^2 + \cdots + {_nC_0}d^n$$

where $n \in \{1,2,3,\ldots\}$.

EXAMPLES

1. $$(a + b)^4 = {_4C_4}a^4 + {_4C_3}a^3b + {_4C_2}a^2b^2 + {_4C_1}ab^3 + {_4C_0}b^4$$
$$= a^4 + 4a^3b + 6a^2b^2 + 4ab^3 + b^4$$

2. $(x - y)^3 = {}_3C_3x^3 + {}_3C_2x^2(-y)^1 + {}_3C_1x(-y)^2 + {}_3C_0(-y)^3$

$= x^3 - 3x^2y + 3xy^2 - y^3.$

3. $(2x + y)^5 = {}_5C_5(2x)^5 + {}_5C_4(2x)^4y + {}_5C_3(2x)^3y^2 + {}_5C_2(2x)^2y^3$

$+ {}_5C_1(2x)^1y^4 + {}_5C_0y^5$

$= (1)(32x^5) + 5(16x^4)y + 10(8x^3)y^2 + 10(4x^2)y^3$

$+ 5(2x)y^4 + (1)y^5$

$= 32x^5 + 80x^4y + 80x^3y^2 + 40x^2y^3 + 10xy^4 + y^5$

Again, consider the general statement of the binomial theorem:

$$(g + d)^n = {}_nC_ng^n + {}_nC_{n-1}g^{n-1}d + {}_nC_{n-2}g^{n-2}d^2 + \cdots + {}_nC_0d^n$$

where $n \in \{1,2,3,\ldots\}$.

Note: The term containing g^r in the expansion of $(g + d)^n$ is equal to ${}_nC_{n-r}g^rd^{n-r} = {}_nC_rg^rd^{n-r}$. Thus,

(a) The term containing g^7 in $(g + d)^{11}$

$= {}_{11}C_7g^7d^{11-7} = 330g^7d^4.$

(b) The term containing a^9 in $(a + r)^{20}$

$= {}_{20}C_9a^9r^{20-9} = 167,960a^9r^{11}.$

(c) The term containing s^8 in $(s + f)^{10}$

$= {}_{10}C_8s^8f^{10-8} = 45s^8f^2.$

(d) The term containing $(0.8)^4$ in $(0.8 + 0.2)^5$

$= {}_5C_4(0.8)^4(0.2)^{5-4} = 5(0.4096)(0.2) = 0.4096.$

(See Table 3 in Appendix H.)

Problem Set 5.3

1. Compute
   (a) ${}_6C_3$
   (b) ${}_6C_3 + {}_6C_4$
   (c) ${}_nC_n$
   (d) ${}_nC_0$

2. Show that ${}_6C_4 = {}_5C_3 + {}_5C_4$.

3. How many different five-card hands may be formed using a standard deck of 52 playing cards?

4. How many different five-card hands dealt from a standard deck of 52 playing cards contain:
   (a) exactly three aces?
   (b) at least three aces?
   (c) at most three aces?

5. (a) How many different committees of six people may be chosen from seven women and five men?
   (b) How many of these committees of six people will contain exactly four men?
   (c) At least four men?
   (d) Exactly four women?

6. A true-false test consists of ten questions. In how many different ways can a student get
   (a) three questions wrong?
   (b) at least eight questions right?
   (c) two questions right?

7. Use the binomial theorem to
   (a) Expand $(a + b)^5$.
   (b) Expand $(2a - b)^4$.
   (c) Expand $(x - y)^3$.
   (d) Find the term containing a^3 in $(a + r)^7$.
   (e) Find the term containing g^9 in $(g + d)^{13}$.
   (f) Find the term containing $(0.9)^3$ in $(0.9 + 0.1)^6$.
   (g) Find the term containing $(0.99)^2$ in $(0.99 + 0.01)^3$.

8. Lillian's teacher stated to her class that the term "combination lock" is actually a misnomer or wrong name. She added that such a lock should be more accurately termed "a lock of permutations." Do you agree or disagree with her teacher? Why?

5.8

A Prepackaged Counting Program

Name: STAT1

Description: This program computes the number of permutations of r objects selected from n distinct objects, or the number of combinations of r objects selected from n distinct objects.

Instructions: Enter the data beginning in line 150 as follows:

$$150 \quad \text{DATA N,R,D}$$

where:

N = total number of distinct objects

R = number of objects to be selected from N distinct objects

$$D = \begin{cases} 0 & \text{if we want } _nP_r \\ 1 & \text{if we want } _nC_r \end{cases}$$

Note: Line 200 is the END statement. STAT1 will not compute $_nC_0 = 1$.

SAMPLE PROBLEM

Find $_8P_3$ and $_8C_3$.

User's Input:

```
GET-STAT1
150 DATA 8,3,0
151 DATA 8,3,1
RUN
```

Computer Output:

```
P( 8    , 3    )= 336
C( 8    , 3    )= 56

LINE     5:   END OF DATA

TIME 0.0 SECS.
```

The flowchart for STAT1 is shown in Figure 5.7. The coding for STAT1 is as follows:

```
5  READ N, R, D
10 LET P= 1
15 FOR X= N- R+ 1  TO N
20    LET P= P*X
25 NEXT X
30 IF D= 1 THEN 45
35 PRINT "P("N; ", "R; ")= "P
40 GOTO 5
45 LET H= 1
50 FOR X= 1 TO R
55    LET H= H*X
60 NEXT X
65 LET C= P/H
70 PRINT "C("N; ", "R; ")= "C
75 GOTO 5
200 END
```

Problem Set 5.4

1. Use STAT1 to compute the following:

(a) $_{11}P_3$ (d) $_{10}C_7$
(b) $_9C_5$ (e) $_{11}C_7$
(c) $_{12}P_4$ (f) $_8P_5$

2. Use STAT1 to show that $_{10}C_5 = {_9C_4} + {_9C_5}$.

Figure 5.7

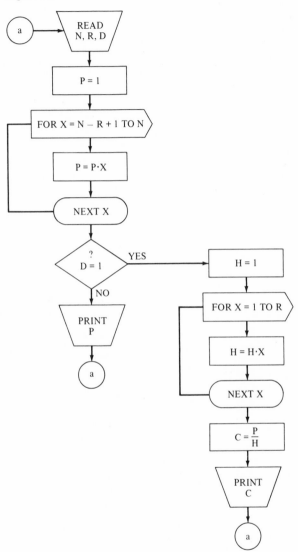

5.9

The Sample Space, Sample Point, and Event

Definitions

SAMPLE SPACE

A *sample space* associated with an experiment or well-defined course of action is the set of all possible outcomes for the experiment. For example,

1. If we were to select two fenders from a lot of five fenders, and then test each of the fenders and classify it as *G* (good) or *D* (defective), the sample space $S = \{(G,G), (G,D), (D,G), (D,D)\}$.

2. If the names of four different people (A,B,C, or D) were written on separate sheets of paper and placed in a box, and we were to select two names to serve on a committee, the sample space $S = \{(A,B), (A,C), (A,D), (B,C), (B,D), (C,D)\}$.

SAMPLE POINT

A *sample point* is an element of a sample space set and represents a possible outcome. A sample point may have any number of components. For example, if we test three dry cell batteries to determine if each is good (g) or defective (d), each sample point would consist of three components, such as (g,g,g) or (d,d,d). If we test only one battery, each sample point would consist of only one component, such as (g) or (d).

EVENT

An *event* associated with a sample space is any subset of the sample space. We give two examples:

1. In the experiment where we select and test two fenders and label them *G* (good) or *D* (defective), the sample space $S = \{(G,G), (G,D), (D,G), (D,D)\}$. Consider the following events:

   (a) *E*: Exactly one fender is defective.

   $$E = \{(G,D), (D,G)\}$$

   (b) *F*: The first fender tested is defective.

   $$F = \{(D,G), (D,D)\}$$

   (c) $E \cup F$: Exactly one fender is defective, or the first fender tested is defective, or both.

   $$E \cup F = \{(G,D), (D,G), (D,D)\}$$

   (d) $E \cap F$: Exactly one fender is defective and the first fender tested is defective.

   $$E \cap F = \{(D,G)\}$$

   (e) *F'*: The first fender tested *is not* defective.

   $$F' = \{(G,G), (G,D)\}$$

2. In the experiment where we select a committee of two from four persons (A,B,C, or D), the sample space $S = \{(A,B), (A,C), (A,D), (B,C), (B,D), (C,D)\}$. Consider the following events:

   (a) *E*: Person A is on the committee.

   $$E = \{(A,B), (A,C), (A,D)\}$$

(b) F: Person C is on the committee.

$F = \{(A,C), (B,C), (C,D)\}$

(c) $E \cup F$: Person A *or* person C is on the committee.

$E \cup F = \{(A,B), (A,C), (A,D), (B,C), (C,D)\}$

(d) $E \cap F$: Person A *and* person C are on the committee.

$E \cap F = \{(A,C)\}$

(e) E': Person A *is not* on the committee.

$E' = \{(B,C), (B,D), (C,D)\}$

5.10

Acceptable Assignment of Probabilities

If $S = \{e_1, e_2, e_3, \ldots, e_n\}$ is a sample space associated with some experiment, and we assign each possible outcome (e_j) of the experiment a number called the *probability* of e_j, denoted by $p(e_j)$, where $j = 1, 2, \ldots, n$ such that:

(1) $o \leq p(e_j) \leq 1$ for $j = 1, 2, \ldots, n$

(the probability of each outcome must be between o and 1 inclusive) *and*

(2) $p(e_1) + p(e_2) + p(e_3) + \cdots + p(e_n) = 1$

(the sum of the probabilities of all the outcomes in S must equal 1), then we are said to have an *acceptable assignment of probabilities*.

Note: Recall that the outcomes of the sample space $e_1, e_2, e_3, \ldots, e_n$ are called *sample points*.

5.11

Probability of an Event

Given a sample space $S = \{e_1, e_2, e_3, \ldots, e_n\}$ associated with some experiment and some event $E = \{o_1, o_2, o_3, \ldots, o_m\}$ such that $E \subset S$, then the *probability* of event E is denoted by

$$P(E) = p(o_1) + p(o_2) + p(o_3) + \cdots + p(o_m)$$

Note: If each of the sample points in S has the same probability, that is, $p(e_1) = p(e_2) = \cdots = p(e_n)$, then $P(E) = m/n$, where $m =$ the number of sample points in event E and $n =$ the number of sample points in the sample space S.

EXAMPLES

1. In the experiment where we select two fenders and classify them as G (good) or D (defective), we saw that

$$S = \{e_1, e_2, e_3, e_4\}$$

where $e_1 = (G,G)$, $e_2 = (G,D)$, $e_3 = (D,G)$, and $e_4 = (D,D)$.

Now suppose we are told that the probability of selecting a defective fender on any one trial is 0.1. That is, $p(D) = 0.1$ and $p(G) = 0.9$. We can assign probabilities to each of the sample points in S as follows:

$$p(e_1) = (0.9)(0.9) = 0.81$$

$$p(e_2) = (0.9)(0.1) = 0.09$$

$$p(e_3) = (0.1)(0.9) = 0.09$$

$$p(e_4) = (0.1)(0.1) = 0.01$$

Note: $p(e_1) + p(e_2) + p(e_3) + p(e_4) = 1$. Previously, we were given the following events:

$$E = \{(G,D), (D,G)\} = \{e_2, e_3\}$$

$$F = \{(D,G), (D,D)\} = \{e_3, e_4\}$$

$$E \cup F = \{(G,D), (D,G), (D,D)\} = \{e_2, e_3, e_4\}$$

$$E \cap F = \{(D,G)\} = \{e_3\}$$

Therefore,

$$P(E) = p(e_2) + p(e_3) = 0.09 + 0.09 = 0.18$$

$$P(F) = p(e_3) + p(e_4) = 0.09 + 0.01 = 0.10$$

$$P(E \cup F) = p(e_2) + p(e_3) + p(e_4) = 0.09 + 0.09 + 0.01 = 0.19$$

$$P(E \cap F) = p(e_3) = 0.09$$

2. In the experiment where we select a committee of two from persons (A,B,C, or D), we saw $S = \{e_1, e_2, e_3, e_4, e_5, e_6\}$, where $e_1 = (A,B)$, $e_2 = (A,C)$, $e_3 = (A,D)$, $e_4 = (B,C)$, $e_5 = (B,D)$, $e_6 = (C,D)$.

We assume that each of the sample points in S have the same probability of occurring, and therefore we assign:

$$p(e_1) = p(e_2) = p(e_3) = p(e_4)$$

$$= p(e_5) = p(e_6) = \frac{1}{6}$$

Previously we were given the following events:

$$E = \{(A,B), (A,C), (A,D)\} = \{e_1, e_2, e_3\}$$

$$F = \{(A,C), (B,C), (C,D)\} = \{e_2, e_4, e_6\}$$
$$E \cup F = \{(A,B), (A,C), (A,D), (B,C), (C,D)\}$$
$$= \{e_1, e_2, e_3, e_4, e_6\}$$
$$E \cap F = \{(A,C)\} = \{e_2\}$$

Since each of the sample points in S have the same probability, we write

$$P(E) = 3/6 = 1/2$$
$$P(F) = 3/6 = 1/2$$
$$P(E \cup F) = 5/6 \qquad Note: \ P(E \cup F) \neq P(E) + P(F)$$
$$P(E \cap F) = 1/6$$

3. A task consists of selecting a committee of five people from five men and six women. What is the probability that exactly three men will be on the committee of five?

We assume that each of the possible committees has an equal chance of occurring, and we are told that for event E, exactly three men are on the committee of five. Therefore,

$$P(E) = \frac{\text{number of elements in } E}{\text{number of elements in sample space } S}$$

$$= \frac{\left(\begin{array}{c}\text{number of different}\\ \text{ways to select 3 men}\end{array}\right) \cdot \left(\begin{array}{c}\text{number of different}\\ \text{ways to select 2 women}\end{array}\right)}{\text{number of different ways to select committee of 5}}$$

or

$$p(E) = \frac{{}_5C_3 \cdot {}_6C_2}{{}_{11}C_5}$$

$$= \frac{(10)(15)}{462} = \frac{150}{462}$$

$$= \frac{25}{77} \approx 0.32.$$

Problem Set 5.5

1. A fair pair of dice are rolled (each die consists of six faces labeled 1, 2, 3, 4, 5, and 6, respectively). Events E, F, and G are as follows:
   E: The sum of the upper faces read is 5.
   F: The sum of the upper faces read is less than 8.
   G: The sum of the upper faces read is 7.
   (a) List the elements in the sample space S.
   (b) Assign probabilities to each of the sample points in S.

(c) List the elements in events E, F, and G.

(d) Find $P(E)$, $P(F)$, and $P(G)$.

2. Three batteries are selected from a large lot of batteries, then tested and classified A (accepted) or R (rejected). The probability that a battery is accepted on any one try is (0.99), (that is, $p(A) = 0.99$ and $p(R) = 0.01$).

(a) List the eight elements in the sample space S associated with this experiment.

(b) Assign probabilities to each of the sample points in S.

(c) Find the probability that exactly two of the three batteries tested are accepted.

(d) Find the probability that at least two of the three batteries tested are accepted.

3. A TV producer has five different hour-long time slots to be filled with five rerun programs. He has seven comedy reruns, five drama reruns, and eight variety reruns to choose from. If each of the reruns has an equal chance of being chosen,

(a) How many different ways can he fill the five time slots?

(b) What is the probability that he will choose exactly two comedy reruns and exactly two variety reruns?

(c) What is the probability that he will choose five drama reruns?

4. The probability that a rug salesman makes a sale when he calls on a prospective customer is 0.3. If he calls on two prospective customers in one day, what is the probability that he will make at least one sale?

5. Three cards are drawn at random from a standard deck of 52 playing cards. What is the probability of selecting

(a) exactly two queens?

(b) at most two queens?

(c) three hearts?

(d) a heart, a spade, and a club?

6. Ten separate pieces of paper are marked with the digits 0, 1, 2, 3, 4, 5, 6, 7, 8, 9, and placed in a bowl. One piece of paper is drawn for the unit's digit of a five-digit lottery number, and then placed back in the bowl. A second piece of paper is drawn for the tens' digit and placed back in the bowl, and so on until the fifth digit for the ten thousands' place of the five-digit lottery number is selected. (Notice that repetitions of digits are possible.)

(a) How many different five-digit lottery numbers can be drawn?

(b) What is the probability that the lottery number selected is an even number?

(c) What is the probability that the lottery number selected ends in 6?

(d) What is the probability that the lottery number selected begins with a 3 and ends with a 6?

(e) What is the probability that the lottery number selected is 12345?

7. Given a sample space $S = \{e_1, e_2, e_3, e_4, e_5\}$, where $p(e_1) = 0.2$, $p(e_2) = 0.1$, $p(e_3) = 0.2$, $p(e_4) = 0.4$, find:

(a) $p(e_5)$.

(b) the probability of event E, where $E = \{e_2, e_3, e_4\}$.

(c) the probability of event F, where $F = \{e_1, e_3, e_5\}$.

(d) $P(E \cup F)$.

(e) $P(E \cap F)$.

(f) $P(E')$.

(g) $P(F')$.

8. The probability that a salesman makes a sale on any one visit to a prospective customer is 0.3. If he makes three calls on a certain day and we represent a sale by s and no sale by f, we may list the sample space as follows: $S = \{(s,s,s), (s,s,f), (s,f,s), (s,f,f), (f,s,s), (f,s,f), (f,f,s), (f,f,f)\}$.
   (a) Assign probabilities to each of the sample points in S.
   (b) Find the probability that at most two sales are made.
   (c) Find the probability that no sales were made.

5.12

Three Probability Theorems

If $S = \{e_1, e_2, e_3, \ldots, e_n\}$ is a sample space for some experiment, and E and F are events in S, then the following theorems are true.

THEOREM 1. $P(S) = 1$

This theorem is a direct consequence of the fact that in an acceptable assignment of probability, the sum of the probabilities of all the sample points in S must be 1.

THEOREM 2. $P(E') = 1 - P(E)$ and $P(E) = 1 - P(E')$

These theorems follow since $E \cup E' = S$, $E \cap E' = \emptyset$, and $P(S) = 1$.

Example: Suppose five fenders are selected at random from a lot of fenders, then tested and classified G (good) or D (defective). We know the $p(G) = 0.95$ on any one trial. What is the probability of getting at least one good fender of the five tested?

Let E be at least one good fender and E' equal not any or zero good fenders $= \{(D,D,D,D,D)\}$.

$$P(E) = 1 - P(E')$$
$$= 1 - P\{(D,D,D,D,D)\}$$
$$= 1 - (0.05)(0.05)(0.05)(0.05)(0.05)$$
$$= 1 - 0.0000003125$$
$$= 0.9999996875$$

THEOREM 3. $P(E \cup F) = P(E) + P(F) - P(E \cap F)$

Note: $P(E \cup F) = P(E) + P(F)$ if and only if E and F are *mutually exclusive* (that is, $E \cap F = \emptyset$).
   If $E \cap F \neq \emptyset$, then $P(E \cup F) \neq P(E) + P(F)$ because $P(E) + P(F)$ in Figure 5.8 would add in twice the probability of region 2 in Figure 5.8.

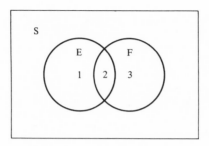

Figure 5.8

Example: The probability that a person who receives a certain flu vaccine and does not contract a virus is 0.8. If three patients are inoculated with the vaccine, what is the probability that at least two of the three will contract a virus, or that the second person inoculated contracts a virus?

Let $p(s) = 0.8$ and $p(f) = 0.2$, where s represents an inoculated person who does not contract a virus; f represents an inoculated person who does contract a virus; and E = at least two who contract a virus; F = the second person inoculated who contracts a virus. Then

$$S = \{(s,s,s), (s,s,f), (s,f,s), (s,f,f), (f,s,s), (f,s,f), (f,f,s), (f,f,f)\}$$

and

$$E = \{(s,f,f), (f,s,f), (f,f,s), (f,f,f)\}$$

Therefore,

$$P(E) = 0.032 + 0.032 + 0.032 + 0.008 = 0.104$$

and

$$F = \{(s,f,s), (s,f,f), (f,f,s), (f,f,f)\}$$

Therefore

$$P(F) = 0.128 + 0.032 + 0.032 + 0.008 = 0.200$$

Now

$$E \cap F = \{(s,f,f), (f,f,s), (f,f,f)\}$$

Therefore

$$P(E \cap F) = 0.032 + 0.032 + 0.008 = 0.072$$

Then

$$P(E \cup F) = P(E) + P(F) - P(E \cap F)$$

$$= 0.104 + 0.200 - 0.072$$

$$= 0.232$$

Note: The Venn diagram in Figure 5.9 clearly shows that we cannot count $P(E \cap F)$ twice to obtain $P(E \cup F)$.

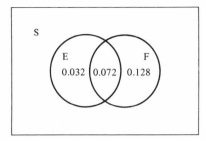

Figure 5.9

Problem Set 5.6

1. The Hudson Railroad reports that 90% of its trains arrive on time. If we randomly record the arrival of six Hudson Railroad trains, what is the probability that
   (a) At least one of the six trains will not be on time?
   (b) Exactly one of the six trains will be on time?

2. Given that events E and F in a sample space S have the following probabilities: $P(E) = 0.4$, $P(F) = 0.3$, $P(E \cap F) = 0.1$. Find $P(E \cup F)$.

3. Given that events E and F in a sample space S are mutually exclusive and $P(E) = 0.4$, $P(F) = 0.3$. Find $P(E \cup F)$.

4. A small publishing company publishes two magazines, *Pictorial* and *Today*. One-third of the company's customers subscribe to *Pictorial*, one-sixth subscribe to *Today*, and one-eighteenth subscribe to both magazines. If a customer is selected at random, what is the probability that he/she subscribes to either *Pictorial* magazine or *Today* magazine, or both?

5.13

Conditional Probability

If E and F are events in some sample space S, then *the probability of event E occurring, given event F has already occurred*, is denoted by

$$P(E|F) = \frac{P(E \cap F)}{P(F)}$$

(We are actually reducing the sample space to event F.) Also, the probability of event F occurring, *given event E has already occurred*, is denoted by

$$P(F|E) = \frac{P(F \cap E)}{P(E)}$$

(We are actually reducing our sample space to event E.)

Example: Consider the testing of three fenders, where $p(G) = 0.9$ and $p(D) = 0.1$ on any one try. Let event E: Exactly two of the fenders are defective; and event F: The second fender tested is defective. Find $P(E|F)$ and $P(F|E)$.

$$S = \{(G,G,G), (G,G,D), (G,D,G), (G,D,D), (D,G,G), (D,G,D), (D,D,G),$$
$$(D,D,D)\}$$

and

$$E = \{(G,D,D), (D,G,D), (D,D,G)\}$$

Therefore

$$P(E) = 0.009 + 0.009 + 0.009 = 0.027$$

and

$$F = \{(G,D,G), (G,D,D), (D,D,G), (D,D,D)\}$$

Therefore

$$P(F) = 0.081 + 0.009 + 0.009 + 0.001 = 0.100$$

Now

$$E \cap F = \{(G,D,D), (D,D,G)\}$$

Therefore

$$P(E \cap F) = 0.009 + 0.009 = 0.018$$

Then

$$P(E|F) = \frac{P(E \cap F)}{P(F)} = \frac{0.018}{0.100} = \frac{18}{100} = \frac{9}{50} = 0.18$$

$$P(F|E) = \frac{P(E \cap F)}{P(E)} = \frac{0.018}{0.027} = \frac{18}{27} = \frac{2}{3} \approx 0.67$$

Events E and F are said to be *independent* if and only if $P(E|F) = P(E)$ and $P(F|E) = P(F)$. Are the events E and F in the sample problem above independent? Why or why not?

5.14

Bayes' Theorem

Bayes' theorem defines the probability of any one of several mutually exclusive events E_n, conditioned by any event D.

Given a sample space S and events $E_1, E_2, \ldots, E_n, D$ in S, such that $E_1 \cup E_2 \cup \cdots \cup E_n = S$ and $E_i \cap E_j = \emptyset$, if $i \neq j$, then

$$P(E_i|D) = \frac{P(E_i)P(D|E_i)}{P(E_1)P(D|E_1) + P(E_2)P(D|E_2) + \cdots + P(E_n)P(D|E_n)}$$

for any $i = 1,2,3,\ldots,n$.

Example: Machines E_1, E_2 and E_3 all produce the same 20¢ candy bars for the Chewy Chocolate Candy Corporation. Machines E_1, E_2, and E_3 produce 20%, 30%, and 50%, respectively, of the total output of this candy bar. The probability that machine E_1 produces a defective candy bar is 0.02; the probability that machine E_2 produces a defective candy bar is 0.01; and the probability that machine E_3 produces a defective candy bar is 0.03. If one 20¢ candy bar is selected at random and is found to be defective, what is the probability that it was produced by machine E_2?

E_1: Produced by machine E_1.

E_2: Produced by machine E_2.

E_3: Produced by machine E_3.

D: Candy bar is found to be defective.

Note: $E_i \cap E_j = \emptyset$ if $i \neq j$, $E_1 \cup E_2 \cup E_3 = S$, and $P(E_1) = 0.2$; $P(E_2) = 0.3$; $P(E_3) = 0.5$. Therefore

$$P(D|E_1) = 0.02; \quad P(D|E_2) = 0.01; \quad P(D|E_3) = 0.03$$

$$P(E_2|D) = \frac{P(E_2)P(D|E_2)}{P(E_1)P(D|E_1) + P(E_2)P(D|E_2) + P(E_3)P(D|E_3)}$$

$$= \frac{(0.3)(0.01)}{(0.2)(0.02) + (0.3)(0.01) + (0.5)(0.03)}$$

$$= \frac{3}{4 + 3 + 15}$$

$$= \frac{3}{22} \approx 0.14$$

SAMPLE PROBLEM

For the preceding example, find $P(E_1|D)$ and $P(E_3|D)$.

5.15

Proof for Bayes' Theorem for Three Events E_1, E_2, E_3

Given a sample space S and events E_1, E_2, E_3, and any event D in S such that $E_i \cap E_j = \emptyset$ if $i \neq j$, $E_1 \cup E_2 \cup E_3 = S$. Then

$$D = S \cap D$$

$$= (E_1 \cup E_2 \cup E_3) \cap D$$

$$= (E_1 \cap D) \cup (E_2 \cap D) \cup (E_3 \cap D)$$

Therefore,

$$P(D) = P(E_1 \cap D) + P(E_2 \cap D) + P(E_3 \cap D)$$

Since E_1, E_2, E_3 are pairwise disjoint.
And since

$$P(D|E_i) = \frac{P(E_i \cap D)}{P(E_i)}$$

then

$$P(E_i \cap D) = P(E_i)P(D|E_i)$$

Therefore

$$P(D) = P(E_1)P(D|E_1) + P(E_2)P(D|E_2) + P(E_3)P(D|E_3)$$

and

$$P(E_i|D) = \frac{P(E_i)P(D|E_i)}{P(D)}$$

$$= \frac{P(E_i)P(D|E_i)}{P(E_1)P(D|E_1) + P(E_2)P(D|E_2) + P(E_3)P(D|E_3)}$$

Note: Without loss of generality, Bayes' theorem can be proved for $E_1, E_2, \ldots, E_n$, provided $E_i \cap E_j = \emptyset$ if $i \neq j$ and $E_1 \cup E_2 \cup \cdots \cup E_n = S$.

Problem Set 5.7

1. If E and F are events in a sample space such that $p(E) = 0.5$, $p(F) = 0.2$, and $p(E \cap F) = 0.1$, find:
   (a) The probability of event E occurring, given event F has already occurred.
   (b) The probability of event F occurring, given event E has already occurred.
   (c) Are E and F independent events?

2. There are 35 applicants for supervisory positions in an oil corporation. Some of the applicants have previous supervisory experience and others do not. Some of the applicants are college graduates and some are not. All pertinent information is given as

	Previous supervisory experience	No previous supervisory experience
College graduate:	13	9
Non-college graduate:	5	8

Let

E = applicants with previous supervisory experience

F = applicants with no previous supervisory experience

G = college graduates

H = noncollege graduates

If an applicant is to be chosen at random and invited for an interview, find the following probabilities:

(a) $P(E \cap G)$ (b) $P(E \cap H)$ (c) $P(F \cap G)$ (d) $P(F \cap H)$

(e) $P(E|G)$ (f) $P(G|E)$ (g) $P(E|H)$ (h) $P(H|E)$

(i) $P(F|G)$ (j) $P(G|F)$ (k) $P(F|H)$ (l) $P(H|F)$

3. A committee of three is to be selected randomly from five possible candidates (A, B, C, D, or E). If K is the event that candidate B is on the committee chosen, and L is the event that candidate C is on the committee chosen, find

(a) $P(K|L)$.

(b) $P(L|K)$.

(c) Are K and L independent events?

4. Given events E and F are events in a sample space S, such that $P(E) = 0.50$, $P(F) = 0.30$, and $P(E \cap F) = 0.15$, show that E and F are independent events.

5. Five machines produce the total output of a certain product. Machines E_1, E_2, E_3, E_4, and E_5 produce 10%, 20%, 15%, 25%, and 30% of the product, respectively. Machines E_1, E_2, E_3, E_4, and E_5 produce 0.01, 0.01, 0.02, 0.001, and 0.02 defective items respectively of their individual outputs. If an item is chosen at random and found to be defective, what is the probability it was (a) produced by machine E_4? (b) produced by machine E_3?

6. In a certain community college, 20% of the first-year students, 15% of the second-year students, and 5% of the nonclassified students are enrolled in a mathematics course. It has been determined that of the school population, 60% are first-year students, 30% are second-year students, and 10% are nonclassified students. If a student is selected at random and found to be a second-year student, what is the probability that he is enrolled in a mathematics course?

7. Given E and F are events in a sample space S, $P(E|F) = 0.5$ and $P(F) = 0.2$. Find

(a) $P(E \cap F)$.

(b) If $P(F|E) = 0.4$, what must $P(E)$ equal? *Hint*: $P(E|F) = P(E \cap F)/P(F)$ and $P(F|E) = P(E \cap F)/P(E)$. Therefore,

$$P(E \cap F) = P(F)P(E|F) = P(E)P(F|E).$$

5.16

The Binomial Experiment

Many experiments result in exactly one of two possible outcomes each time we perform the experiment. For example: A fender is tested and classified as G (good) or D (defective); the recording of a voter's viewpoint as Y (Yes) or N (No) is made on an important issue; the position of a lever on a switch O (open) or 1 (closed) is noted; or P (passing) or F (failing) on an examination is recorded.

A binomial experiment must have the following properties:

1. There are n independent trials of the same experiment.

2. Each trial of the experiment must result in one of two possible outcomes (success or failure).

3. The probability of the two possible outcomes must remain the same in each independent trial of the experiment. (We will let p = the probability of success on any one trial and q = the probability of failure on any one trial. Note that $p + q = 1$.)

For a specific example of a binomial experiment, let us consider randomly selecting three fenders from a lot of fenders, and then testing each of the three fenders selected and classifying them G (good) or D (defective), where the probability of a good fender on any one trial is 0.9. Then

$$S = \{(G,G,G), (G,G,D), (G,D,G), (G,D,D), (D,G,G),$$

$$(D,G,D), (D,D,G), (D,D,D)\}$$

Now let A_i, where $i = 0,1,2$, or 3, be the event where we obtain exactly i good fenders. Then

$$P(A_0) = p(D,D,D)$$
$$= (0.1)(0.1)(0.1)$$
$$= 1(0.1)^3$$

$$P(A_1) = p(G,D,D) + p(D,G,D) + p(D,D,G)$$
$$= (0.9)(0.1)(0.1) + (0.1)(0.9)(0.1) + (0.1)(0.1)(0.9)$$
$$= 3(0.9)(0.1)^2$$

$$P(A_2) = p(G,G,D) + p(G,D,G) + p(D,G,G)$$
$$= (0.9)(0.9)(0.1) + (0.9)(0.1)(0.9) + (0.1)(0.9)(0.9)$$
$$= 3(0.9)^2(0.1)$$

$$P(A_3) = p(G,G,G)$$
$$= (0.9)(0.9)(0.9)$$
$$= 1(0.9)^3$$

Note:

$$(0.9 + 0.1)^3 = {}_3C_3(0.9)^3 + {}_3C_2(0.9)^2(0.1) + {}_3C_1(0.9)(0.1)^2 + {}_3C_0(0.1)^3$$

$$= 1(0.9)^3 + 3(0.9)^2(0.1) + 3(0.9)(0.1)^2 + 1(0.1)^3$$

In general, in three trials of a binomial experiment, where p = the probability of success on any one trial and q = the probability of failure on any one trial,

$$P(A_0) = 1q^3$$
$$P(A_1) = 3pq^2$$
$$P(A_2) = 3p^2q$$
$$P(A_3) = 1p^3$$

where A_i = exactly i successes, *and*

$$(p + q)^3 = {}_3C_3p^3 + {}_3C_2p^2q + {}_3C_1pq^2 + {}_3C_0q^3$$
$$= 1p^3 + 3p^2q + 3pq^2 + 1q^3$$

By illustrating a number of binomial experiments with n trials of the binomial experiment, we can develop the following theorem.

THEOREM 4

The probability of r successes in n trials of a binomial experiment, where p = the probability of success on any one trial and q = the probability of failure on any one trial is ${}_nC_rp^rq^{n-r}$.

$$p + q = 1, \qquad q = 1 - p$$

EXAMPLES

1. Five fenders are selected from a lot of fenders and tested for defects. If the probability of a good (G) fender on any one trial is 0.9, find the probability of obtaining

(a) Exactly four good fenders. Since we know $n = 5$, $p = 0.9$, $q = 1 - 0.9 = 0.1$, $r = 4$, then

$${}_5C_4(0.9)^4(0.1)^1 = 5(0.6561)(0.1)$$
$$= 0.32805 \approx 0.33$$

(b) At least four good fenders. Since we know $n = 5$, $p = 0.9$, $q = 1 - 0.9 = 0.1$, $r = 4,5$, then

$$P(\text{at least 4 good}) = P(4 \text{ good}) + P(5 \text{ good})$$
$$= {}_5C_4(0.9)^4(0.1)^1 + {}_5C_5(0.9)^5(0.1)^0$$
$$= 5(0.6561)(0.1) + (1)(0.59049)(1)$$
$$= 0.32805 + 0.59049$$
$$= 0.91854$$
$$\approx 0.92$$

(c) At most two defective (D) fenders. Since we know $n = 5$, $p = 0.1$, $q = 0.9$, $r = 0,1,2$, then

$$P(\text{at most 2 defective}) = P(0 \text{ defective}) + P(1 \text{ defective})$$
$$+ P(2 \text{ defective})$$
$$= {}_5C_0(0.1)^0(0.9)^5 + {}_5C_1(0.1)^1(0.9)^4$$
$$+ {}_5C_2(0.1)^2(0.9)^3$$
$$= 0.59049 + 0.32805 + 0.0729$$
$$= 0.99144 \approx 0.99$$

2. The probability that a student enrolling in a remedial mathematics course will pass the course is 0.7. The only two possible grades are P (pass), F (fail). If six students enroll in the course, what is the probability that

(a) At least five of the six students will pass the course? Since we know $n = 6$, $p = 0.7$, $q = 0.3$, $r = 5,6$, then

$$P(\text{at least 5 pass}) = P(5 \text{ pass}) + P(6 \text{ pass})$$
$$= {}_6C_5(0.7)^5(0.3)^1 + {}_6C_6(0.7)^6(0.3)^0$$
$$= 6(0.16807)(0.3) + (1)(0.117649)(1)$$
$$= 0.302526 + 0.117649$$
$$= 0.420175 \approx 0.42$$

(b) At least one of the six students will pass? Let event E be the event such that at least one of the six students will pass; event E' is the event such that none of the six students will pass. *Remember*: $P(E) = 1 - P(E')$. Then $p(\text{at least 1 passes}) = 1 - P(0 \text{ pass})$. Since we know $n = 6$, $p = 0.7$, $q = 0.3$, $r = 0$, then

$$P(\text{at least 1 passes}) = 1 - {}_6C_0(0.7)^0(0.3)^6$$
$$= 1 - (1)(1)(0.000729)$$
$$= 1 - 0.000729$$
$$= 0.999271 \approx 0.999$$

Problem Set 5.8

1. The probability that a flu vaccine will be effective on any one person is 0.8. If four people are selected at random and injected with the vaccine, what is the probability that none of the four people will contract the flu?

2. A certain professional basketball player shoots his foul shots with a 0.6 accuracy. What is the probability that he will miss five of the next ten foul shots he attempts?

3. The probability that any one battery produced by the Live Wire Company will be rejected is 0.01. If three batteries are selected at random, then tested and classified *A* (accepted) or *R* (rejected), what is the probability that at least two of the three randomly selected batteries tested will be accepted?

4. A woman professional golfer qualifies for 0.7 of the tournaments in which she desires to participate. What is the probability that she will *not* qualify for two of five randomly selected tournaments she wishes to enter?

5. The Snapshot Company advertises that its flashbulbs work with 0.999 accuracy. If the company's claim is true, what is the probability that all of three randomly selected flashbulbs will be defective?

5.17

A Prepackaged Program for the Binomial Experiment

Name: STAT2

Description: This program computes the probability of *r* successes in *n* independent trials of a binomial experiment.

Instructions: Enter the data beginning in line 150 as follows:

150   DATA N,R,P,D

where:

N = number of independent trials of the binomial experiment.

R = number of desired successes.

P = probability of success on any one trial of the experiment.

$D = 0$ $\left\{\begin{array}{l}\text{if we want to print the desired } \textit{total} \text{ binomial} \\ \quad\text{probability, or} \\ 1 \text{ if we want to compute and print a } \textit{partial} \\ \quad \textit{sum} \text{ for a binomial probability.}\end{array}\right.$

Note: (1) Line 200 is the END statement. (2) If you want the probability of at least R successes, or at most R successes, you must enter more than one set of DATA. (3) $R \neq 0$.

SAMPLE PROBLEMS

1. Find the probability of obtaining exactly five successes in seven trials of a binomial experiment where the probability of success on any one trial is 0.83.

User's Input

```
GET-STAT2
150 DATA 7,5,.83,0
RUN
```

Computer Output

#TRIALS	#SUCCESSES	PR. OF SUCC.	BINOMIAL PROB.
7	5	.83	.23906

#TRIALS	#SUCCESSES	PR. OF SUCC.	BINOMIAL PROB.

LINE   35:   END OF DATA

TIME 0.0 SE CS.

2. Find the probability of obtaining at least five successes in seven trials of a binomial experiment where the probability of success on any one trial is 0.83.

User's Input

```
GET-STAT2
150 DATA 7,5,.83,1
151 DATA 7,6,.83,1
152 DATA 7,7,.83,0
RUN
```

See computer output on page 246.

Figure 5.10

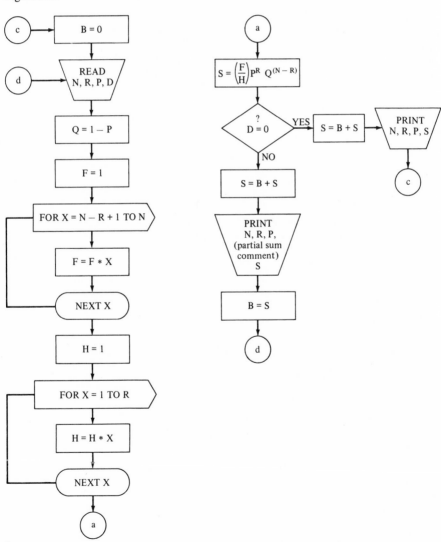

Computer Output

#TRIALS	#SUCCESSES	PR. OF SUCC.	BINOMIAL PROB.
7	5	.83	PARTIAL SUM =
.23906			
7	6	.83	PARTIAL SUM =
.628119			
7	7	.83	.899479

#TRIALS	#SUCCESSES	PR. OF SUCC.	BINOMIAL PROB.

LINE   35:   END OF DATA

TIME 0.0 SECS.

Let us look at the flowchart of STAT2 (Figure 5.10) which is followed by its coding.

The coding of STAT2 is as follows:

```
5 LET B = 0
10 PRINT
15 PRINT
20 PRINT
25 PRINT "#TRIALS", "#SUCCESSES", "PR. OF SUCC.", " BINOMIAL PROB."
30 PRINT
35 READ N, R, P, D
40 LET Q = 1 - P
45 LET F = 1
50 FOR X = N - R + 1 TO N
55    LET F= F*X
60 NEXT X
65 LET H= 1
70 FOR X = 1 TO R
75    LET H=H*X
80 NEXT X
85 LET S = F/H*P↑R*Q↑(N-R)
90 IF D = 0 THEN 115
95 LET S= B+S
100 PRINT N, R, P, "PARTIAL SUM = "S
105 LET B= S
110 GOTO 35
115 LET S= B+S
120 PRINT N, R, P, S
125 GO TO 5
200 END
```

Problem Set 5.9

Check your manual solutions to each of the five exercises in Problem Set 5.8 by using STAT2 to solve them.

6

Descriptive Statistics and Related Computer Programs

6.1

Introduction

Descriptive statistics is that area of mathematics which deals with the collection and analysis of numerical or nominal data. The data are sometimes called *measurements* or *observations*. For example, if we were given the daily prices of one share of Southern Oil Corporation stock during a certain week ($31.85, $31.00, $31.00, $30.15, $30.50), we might want to describe a central price and the deviation from this central price during the week. Or we might be told the number of days during an entire year for which one share of Southern Oil Corporation stock sold for a price ranging from $20 to $24, $25 to $29, $30 to $34, $35 to $39, and $40 to $44. In the first example the data are ungrouped because daily prices are listed "as is" and not put into certain class intervals. You can clearly see that the data in the second example are grouped and placed into class intervals.

Inferential statistics allows us to make predictions or decisions about a population based on information contained in a sample. For example, if we wanted to make a prediction about the outcome of a national election, it would be impractical to question every person of voting age in the United States (the population). However, we could randomly select as our sample, using some arbitrary method and not some set pattern, 1000 voters from the eastern states, 1000 voters from the western states, 1000 voters from the northern states, and 1000 voters from the southern states. We could question the voters in these groups on their choice of candidate. Then we could use the information obtained from our sample to make our prediction.

If we wanted to decide whether one method of teaching statistics yielded better results than another, it might be impossible to use the total population of all students enrolled in statistics courses. Therefore, we might randomly select as a sample 200 students enrolled in a statistics course, then randomly place 100 of them in sections teaching statistics by method 1, and place the remaining 100 students in sections teaching statistics by method 2. Then, by administering a test to each student at the beginning and end of the course, we might be able to decide whether one method yields better results than the other method.

It is important to note that the basic tools of inferential statistics are descriptive statistics and elementary probability. This chapter deals primarily with descriptive statistics.

6.2

Descriptive Statistics—Ungrouped Data

If the data under investigation are not arranged into different classes or groups, but left "as is," we call this information *ungrouped data*. The ungrouped data are sometimes called measurements, observations, or raw scores. Variables, such as X, are often used to represent raw scores. For example, suppose the price range of one share of Southern Oil Corporation stock on the American Stock Exchange for the week of March 15, 1976, was as follows:

Mon.: X_1 = \$31.85   Thurs.: X_4 = \$30.15

Tues.: X_2 = \$31.00   Fri.: X_5 = \$30.50

Wed.: X_3 = \$31.00

There are several ways to describe the central price for the week of March 15, 1976. Let us consider the following definitions.

6.3

Three Measures of Central Tendency—Ungrouped Data

The Mean

Given the measurements $X_1, X_2, \ldots, X_n$, their *arithmetic mean* $(\bar{X})$ is denoted by

$$\bar{X} = \frac{X_1 + X_2 + X_3 + \cdots + X_n}{n}$$

where n is the total number of measurements in our sample.

SIGMA NOTATION

Another way to represent the sum of n raw scores $(X_1 + X_2 + X_3 \cdots + X_n)$ is by using the *summation*, or *Sigma*, notation:

$$\sum_{i=1}^{n} X_i$$

It is read as: the sum of X_i as i goes from 1 to n by increments of 1. Therefore, we could write the formula for the arithmetic mean as follows:

$$\bar{X} = \frac{\sum\limits_{i=1}^{n} X_i}{n}$$

In the sample problem concerning the mean price of one share of stock for the week of March 15 (Article 6.1),

$$\bar{X} = \frac{\sum\limits_{i=1}^{5} X_i}{5} = \frac{X_1 + X_2 + X_3 + X_4 + X_5}{5}$$

$$= \frac{\$31.85 + \$31.00 + \$31.00 + \$30.15 + \$30.50}{5}$$

$$= \frac{\$154.50}{5}$$

$$= \$30.90$$

This mean price of one share of stock for the week of March 15 does not tell us much about the mean price of one share of stock for the entire year of 1976 because our sample of one week, or five daily prices, is too small. You can see that the mean or average is a measure of central tendency, which depends directly on the size of the measurements in the sample. If the sum of our five daily stock prices were larger, then the mean would be greater; and if the sum of our five daily stock prices were smaller, then the mean would be less.

The Median

Given the set of measurements $X_1, X_2, X_3, \ldots, X_n$ arranged in numerical order, from smallest to largest or largest to smallest, their *median*, which is denoted by the symbol Md, is the middle score if n is odd, or is the average of the two middle scores if n is even. In our sampling of the five daily stock prices ($31.85, $31.00, $31.00, $30.15, $30.50), n is odd. If we arrange them from smallest to largest amount as $30.15, $30.50, $31.00, $31.00, $31.85, the third score is the median score, or Md = $31.00.

If we were given the measurements 97, 55, 32, 21, 95, 34, 87, 52, 65, 91, we could arrange them from smallest to largest: 21, 32, 34, 52, 55, 65, 87, 91, 95, 97. There is an even number of scores ($n = 10$); therefore, the fifth and the sixth scores would be the middle scores, and their average would be the median score. Thus,

$$\text{Md} = \frac{55 + 65}{2} = \frac{120}{2} = 60$$

In writing a computer program, we can make use of the following formula, which utilizes *subscripted variables*, to direct the computer to evaluate the median of n measurements. Given the set of n measurements $X_1, X_2, X_3, \ldots, X_n$ arranged in numerical order, their *median* is denoted by

$$Md = \begin{cases} X_{(n+1)/2} & \text{if } n \text{ is odd} \\ \dfrac{X_{n/2} + X_{(n+2)/2}}{2} & \text{if } n \text{ is even} \end{cases}$$

For example, we could use subscripted variables when arranging the five daily stock prices in numerical order from smallest to largest:

$$X_1 = \$30.15 \qquad X_4 = \$31.00$$
$$X_2 = \$30.50 \qquad X_5 = \$31.85$$
$$X_3 = \$31.00$$

Since n is odd ($n = 5$),

$$Md = X_{(n+1)/2} = X_{(5+1)/2} = X_3 = \$31.00$$

If we use subscripted variables while arranging the measurements of 97, 55, 32, 21, 95, 34, 87, 52, 65, 91 in numerical order from smallest to largest, we write

$$X_1 = 21 \qquad X_6 = 65$$
$$X_2 = 32 \qquad X_7 = 87$$
$$X_3 = 34 \qquad X_8 = 91$$
$$X_4 = 52 \qquad X_9 = 95$$
$$X_5 = 55 \qquad X_{10} = 97$$

Since n is even ($n = 10$), then

$$Md = \frac{X_{n/2} + X_{(n+2)/2}}{2}$$

$$= \frac{X_{10/2} + X_{(10+2)/2}}{2}$$

$$= \frac{X_5 + X_6}{2} = \frac{55 + 65}{2}$$

$$= \frac{120}{2} = 60$$

Thus, the median (Md) is a score for a given distribution such that there are the same number of measurements less than or equal to Md as there are measurements greater than or equal to Md.

The Mode

Given the measurements $X_1, X_2, X_3, \ldots, X_n$, their *mode*, denoted by the symbol Mo, is the measurement or measurements that occur most frequently in the sample. In our example of the five daily stock prices of $31.85, $31.00, $31.00, $30.15, $30.50, Mo = $31.00.

Now consider the following three sets of data:

(a)   70, 80, 70, 80, 95, 80; then Mo = 80.
(b)   70, 80, 70, 80, 95, 96; then Mo = 70 and 80.
(c)   70, 51, 32, 80, 95, 97; then Mo does not exist.

DEVIATION FROM THE MEAN

Suppose five students in each of two sections of statistics obtained the following scores on their final exam:

$$\text{Section I:}\quad 70, 72, 68, 73, 67; \text{ then } \bar{X} = 70$$

$$\text{Section II:}\quad 70, 50, 90, 100, 40; \text{ then } \bar{X} = 70$$

It is obvious that each section scored a mean grade of 70 on the final exam, but it would be incorrect to say that the performances of the sections were similar. Why? As you can see, all scores in the first section were close to the mean score, where $\bar{X} = 70$; while the scores in the second section were not close to the mean score, where $\bar{X} = 70$. What we want to be able to do is to describe in some way the *average deviation* from the mean. If we subtracted the mean from each score and added the deviations from the mean for each section, we would obtain the results in Table 6.1.

Now, if we divided each zero sum by the number of measurements in each section (that is, $n = 5$), we would find the average deviation from the mean to be zero. But certainly this is not useful because measurements in each section *do deviate* an actual amount from the mean. Therefore, we square

Table 6.1

Section I		Section II	
X	$X - \bar{X}$	X	$X - \bar{X}$
70	0	70	0
72	2	50	−20
68	−2	90	20
73	3	100	30
67	−3	40	−30
	SUM = 0		SUM = 0

each deviation from the mean before summing and before dividing by n. Statisticians have developed appropriate formulas called *measures of deviation*, which are known as variance, standard deviation, and range.

6.4

Measures of Deviation—Ungrouped Data

Variance

Given the measurements $X_1, X_2, X_3, \ldots, X_n$, their *variance* (s^2) is denoted by

$$s^2 = \frac{(X_1 - \bar{X})^2 + (X_2 - \bar{X})^2 + \cdots + (X_n - \bar{X})^2}{n}$$

or

$$s^2 = \frac{\sum_{i=1}^{n} (X_i - \bar{X})^2}{n}$$

where n is the total number of measurements in the sample and $\bar{X}$ is their mean. Applying this formula to the scores for the two sections of statistics given previously in Table 6.1, we can derive Table 6.2 and compute the following variances. With

$$\bar{X}_1 = \frac{350}{5} = 70 \qquad \bar{X}_2 = \frac{350}{5} = 70$$

Table 6.2

	Section I			Section II		
X	$X - \bar{X}$	$(X - \bar{X})^2$		X	$X - \bar{X}$	$(X - \bar{X})^2$
70	0	0		70	0	0
72	2	4		50	−20	400
68	−2	4		90	20	400
73	3	9		100	30	900
67	−3	9		40	−30	900
$\Sigma X = 350$		$\Sigma(X - \bar{X})^2 = 26$		$\Sigma X = 350$		$\Sigma(X - \bar{X})^2 = 2600$

we obtain variances

$$s_1^2 = \frac{26}{5} = 5.2 \text{ and}$$

$$s_2^2 = \frac{2600}{5} = 520$$

The variance gives us the average of the squares of the deviations from the mean. Squaring the deviations from the mean eliminates the problem of summing the deviations from the mean and obtaining zero. In order to obtain the average deviation from the mean we define standard deviation.

Standard Deviation

Given the measurements $X_1, X_2, X_3, \ldots, X_n$, their *standard deviation* is denoted by

$$s = \sqrt{\frac{(X_1 - \bar{X})^2 + (X_2 - \bar{X})^2 + \cdots + (X_n - \bar{X})^2}{n}}$$

$$= \sqrt{\text{variance}}$$

or

$$s = \sqrt{\frac{\sum\limits_{i=1}^{n} (X_i - \bar{X})^2}{n}}$$

where n is the total number of measurements in the sample and $\bar{X}$ is their mean. (See Table 1 of Squares and Square Roots, Appendix H.)

Again referring to Sections I and II, we can compute for *Section I*:

$$\text{variance} = s^2 = 5.2$$

$$\text{standard deviation} = s = \sqrt{5.2} = 2.28$$

and for *Section II*:

$$\text{variance} = s^2 = 520$$

$$\text{standard deviation} = s = \sqrt{520} = 22.8$$

Now we can see that although both sections had a mean score of 70 on the final examination, the standard deviation of 2.28 for Section I was much smaller than the standard deviation of 22.8 for Section II. Therefore, the two sections did not perform similarly on the final exam.

Now let us consider the prices for one share of Southern Oil Corporation stock for the week of March 15, 1976, as shown in Table 6.3.

Table 6.3

X	$X - \bar{X}$	$(X - \bar{X})^2$
$31.85	+0.95	0.9025
$31.00	+0.10	0.01
$31.00	+0.10	0.01
$30.15	−0.75	0.5625
$30.50	−0.40	0.1600
ΣX		$\Sigma(X - \bar{X})^2$
$= \$154.50$		$= \$1.645$

With $\bar{X} = 154.50/5 = \$30.90$, we obtain

$$\text{variance} = s^2 = \frac{\$1.645}{5} = \$0.329 \approx \$0.33$$

Note: The symbol $\approx$ is read "approximately equal to." Therefore,

$$\text{standard deviation} = s = \sqrt{\text{variance}}$$
$$= \sqrt{0.329}$$
$$\approx \$0.5733 \approx \$0.57 \qquad \text{(or 57¢)}$$

Alternate Formula for Computing Variance

The previously stated formula for computing the variance,

$$s^2 = \frac{\sum\limits_{i=1}^{n} (X_i - \bar{X})^2}{n}$$

can be shown to be equivalent to

$$s^2 = \frac{\sum\limits_{i=1}^{n} (X_i{}^2) - \left[\left(\sum\limits_{i=1}^{n} X_i\right)^2 \Big/ n\right]}{n}$$

For example, (see Table 6.4) consider the final examination grades for each of the two sections of statistics we have mentioned previously. We now use the alternative formula (see Table 6.5).

Notice that the results are equal to those obtained by using the first formula given for the variance.

Table 6.4

	Section I		Section II	
X	X^2		X	X^2
70	4900		70	4900
72	5184		50	2500
68	4624		90	8100
73	5329		100	10000
67	4489		40	1600
$\Sigma X = 350$	ΣX^2		$\Sigma X = 350$	ΣX^2
	$= 24526$			$= 27100$

Table 6.5

Section I	Section II
$s^2 = \dfrac{24526 - (350)^2/5}{5}$	$s^2 = \dfrac{27100 - (350)^2/5}{5}$
$= \dfrac{24526 - 24500}{5}$	$= \dfrac{27100 - 24500}{5}$
$= \dfrac{26}{5} = 5.2$ and	$= \dfrac{2600}{5} = 520$ and
$s = \sqrt{5.2} = 2.28$	$s = \sqrt{520} = 22.8$

X	X^2
$31.85	$1014.4225
31.00	961.0000
31.00	961.0000
30.15	909.0225
30.50	930.2500
$\Sigma X = \$154.50$	$\Sigma X^2 = \$4775.6950$

Using the first formula, we also determined the variance for the Southern Oil Corporation stock price as $s^2 = \$0.329 \approx \$0.33$. Let us use the alternate formula to compute the variance for this stock price.

Using the data in Table 6.6,

$$s^2 = \frac{(4775.6950) - (154.50)^2/5}{5}$$

$$= \frac{(4775.6950) - (23870.2500)/5}{5}$$

$$= \frac{4775.6950 - 4774.05}{5} = \frac{1.6450}{5}$$

$$= \$0.3290 \approx \$0.33$$

Range

Given the measurements $X_1, X_2, X_3, \ldots, X_n$ their *range* = (largest measure) − (smallest measure).

Consider the three previously discussed sample problems:

1. Five daily prices of one share of Southern Oil Stock: $31.85, $31.00, $31.00, $30.15, $30.50.

$$\text{Range} = \$31.85 - \$30.15 = \$1.70$$

2. Section I: 70, 72, 68, 73, 67.

$$\text{Range} = 73 - 67 = 6$$

3. Section II: 70, 50, 90, 100, 40.

$$\text{Range} = 100 - 40 = 60$$

The range tells us only how much the measurements vary from highest to lowest, and is therefore unstable because it depends on only two measurements in the entire sample.

Problem Set 6.1

1. Ten students scored the following number of correct responses on a 12-item true-false test: 4, 7, 6, 9, 6, 7, 7, 10, 9, 11. *Compute* the following information for the given distribution: (a) mean ($\bar{X}$), (b) median (Md), (c) mode (Mo), (d) range, (e) variance (s^2), and (f) standard deviation (s).

2. From a lot of 1000 radio tubes, 100 tubes were selected and tested for defects. This procedure was repeated for five consecutive days. The number of defectives found in the 100 tubes that were tested for the five consecutive days were as follows: 5, 3, 4, 2, 7. *Compute* the following information for the number of defective tubes: (a) mean ($\bar{X}$), (b) median (Md), (c) mode (Mo), (d) standard deviation (s).

3. The following table lists the final exam grades for two sections of an elementary statistics course.

Section 1	Section 2
75	75
70	55
82	95
81	80
68	81
70	82
70	70
75	91
81	67
82	52

(a) Compute the measures of central tendency ($\bar{X}$, Md, Mo) for each section.

(b) Compute the measures of deviation (s^2, s, range) for each section.

4. (a) Without performing any calculations, determine which one of these two samples has the larger standard deviation:

Sample 1	Sample 2
5	3
5	5
5	8
6	14
6	29
6	53

(b) Explain the reason for your choice.

5. Find the mean ($\bar{X}$), standard deviation (s), and range for *each* of the following distributions:

Distribution A	Distribution B
26	36
25	36
24	35
21	32
20	30
18	29
17	28
14	25
14	25
12	22
11	18
10	15
8	
4	
1	

6. Compute the mean, median, and mode for *each* of the following three sets of data:
   (a) 26, 25, 24, 21, 20, 18, 17, 17, 14, 12, 11, 10
   (b) 18, 25, 29, 30, 33, 35, 37, 37, 39, 42, 46
   (c) 35, 30, 28, 28, 28, 25, 23, 23, 23, 18

7. Find the mean, median, mode, range, and standard deviation for *each* of the following score distributions:
   (a) 26, 24, 23, 19, 15, 13, 12, 9, 9, 8, 6.
   (b) 23, 21, 18, 17, 15, 14, 14, 12, 9, 7, 5.
   (c) 18, 22, 26, 30, 32, 33, 35, 35, 35, 37, 38, 40, 43, 46, 46, 47, 49, 51, 53.

6.5

A Prepackaged Program for Ungrouped Data

Name: STAT3

Description: This program computes the arithmetic mean, variance, and standard deviation of N numbers.

Instructions: Enter the data beginning in line 150 as follows:

$$150 \quad \text{DATA } N, X_1, X_2, X_3, \ldots, X_n$$

where:

N = number of raw scores.

$X_1, X_2, \ldots, X_n$ = raw scores

Note: Line 200 is the END statement.

EXAMPLE

User's Input
```
GET-STAT3
150 DATA 5,73,90,100,40,50
151 DATA 5,73,68,72,67,73
RUN
```

Computer Output
```
MEAN= 70     VARIANCE= 520   ST. DEV.= 22.8035
MEAN= 70     VARIANCE= 5.2   ST. DEV.= 2.28035

LINE      5:   END OF DATA

TIME 0.0 SECS.
```

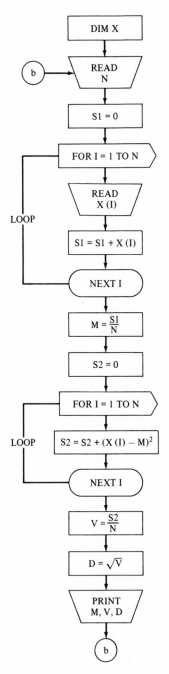

Figure 6.1

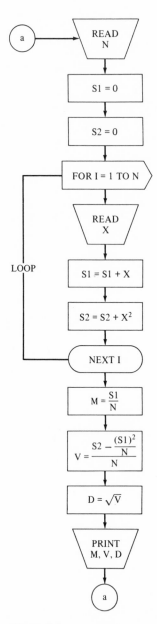

Figure 6.2

Let us look at a development of this prepackaged program.

   Given: $N, X_1, X_2, \ldots, X_n$.

   Wanted: A BASIC program to compute and print out the arithmetic mean, variance, and standard deviation of the N measurements.

Desired Output: MEAN = ? VARIANCE = ? ST.DEV. = ?

The program could be constructed using either of the two formulas for the variance. Using

(2)
$$s^2 = \frac{\sum\limits_{i=1}^{n} (X - \bar{X})^2}{n}$$

we can construct the flowchart of Figure 6.1. Using

(2)
$$s^2 = \frac{\sum\limits_{i=1}^{n} (X_i^2) - \left[\left(\sum\limits_{i=1}^{n} X_i\right)^2 \middle/ n\right]}{n}$$

we can formulate the flowchart for Figure 6.2, for which the coding is as follows:

```
 5 READ N
10 LET S1=0
15 LETS2=0
20 FOR I=1 TO  N
25    READ X
30    LET S1=S1+X
35    LET S2=S2+X↑2
40 NEXT I
45 LET M=S1/N
50 LET V=(S2-(S1)↑2/N)/N
55 LET D=SQR(V)
60 PRINT "M EAN= 'M; "VARI ANCE= "V; "ST.  DEV.="D
65 GO TO 5
200 END
```

Notice that the actual coding was done using the second formula for computing the variance. This formula is easier to use when coding because it eliminates the use of subscripted variables.

Problem Set 6.2

1. The following final examination scores for two different sections of statistics were listed in Problem Set 6.1, Problem 3.

Section 1	Section 2
75	75
70	55
82	95
81	80
68	81
70	82
70	70
75	91
81	67
82	52

Use STAT3 to compute $\bar{X}$, s^2, and s for each section.

2. Use STAT3 to compute $\bar{X}$, s^2, s for the five daily stock prices ($31.85, $31, $31, $30.15, $30.50).

3. Use STAT3 to compute $\bar{X}$, s^2, and s for the following sampling of 20 senior grade-point averages at Orange University: 3.2, 2.5, 3.1, 2.1, 3.3, 3.7, 1.9, 2.2, 2.2, 2.6, 2.1, 2.9, 2.8, 3.6, 3.0, 2.0, 3.5, 2.2, 2.6, 3.1.

4. Use STAT3 to compute $\bar{X}$, s^2, and s for the following amounts, which represent a truck driver's weekly gross earnings for the past nine weeks: $257, $315, $291, $301, $315, $288, $313, $352, $299.

6.6

Normal Distributions

The most widely used probability distribution in statistics is the *normal probability distribution*, which is generated by the formula

$$p(X) = \frac{1}{\sigma\sqrt{2\pi}}\, e^{-(1/2)(X-\mu)^2/\sigma^2}$$

where $-\infty < X < \infty$ (that is, X is any real number), and

$\pi \approx 3.14159$

$e \approx 2.71828$

μ = the mean of a population

σ = the standard deviation of a population

The graphs of normal probability distributions are bell-shaped, but their widths and heights can vary with different population means and standard deviations, as illustrated in Figure 6.3.

Figure 6.3

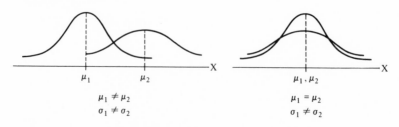

$\mu_1 \neq \mu_2$
$\sigma_1 \neq \sigma_2$

$\mu_1 = \mu_2$
$\sigma_1 \neq \sigma_2$

However, all normal probability distributions have the following properties (as shown in Figure 6.4):

1. The total area (probability) under $p(X) = 1$.

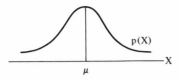

Figure 6.4

2. The area (probability) is symmetric about μ (the mean).

3. $p(X)$ is greatest when $X = \mu$ and $p(X)$ increases as X gets closer to μ.

4. $p(X)$ approaches 0 as X approaches $+\infty$ or $-\infty$.

6.7

The Standard Normal Distribution

Any sufficiently large sampling of an experiment with a random variable X defined for it will produce a normal probability distribution. The integral calculus enables us to compute areas (probabilities) under normal curves. A table is constructed and listed in statistics textbooks for use in calculating specific areas under normal curves. Such a table is discussed in Article 6.8.

We saw previously that normal curves can take on many different shapes. In order to use *only* one area table, we convert our normal distribution (X distribution) to a *standard normal distribution* or Z-distribution, which has $\mu = 0$ and $\sigma = 1$. We do this by means of the following conversion formula:

$$Z = \frac{X - \mu}{\sigma}$$

where $X =$ value assumed by a random variable

$\mu =$ population mean

$\sigma =$ population standard deviation

See Figure 6.5 for graphical presentation.

Figure 6.5

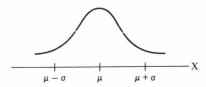

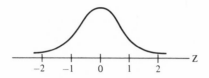

Figure 6.6

If $Z = (X - \mu)/\sigma$, then

$$Z_\mu = \frac{\mu - \mu}{\sigma} = 0$$

$$Z_{\mu + \sigma} = \frac{\mu + \sigma - \mu}{\sigma} = 1$$

$$Z_{\mu - \sigma} = \frac{\mu - \sigma - \mu}{\sigma} = -1$$

$$Z_{\mu + 2\sigma} = \frac{\mu + 2\sigma - \mu}{\sigma} = 2$$

$$Z_{\mu - 2\sigma} = \frac{\mu - 2\sigma - \mu}{\sigma} = -2$$

and so on

This is shown graphically in Figure 6.6.

6.8

Using a Table for Computing Areas (Probabilities) Under the Standard Normal (Z) Curve

Figure 6.7 depicts the standard normal (Z) curve. From Table 4 in Appendix H, we can locate a value for a Z_i score from 0 to 3.99. In the extreme left column of that table we read a value of Z_i from 0.0 to 3.9 with increments of 0.1. The columns to the right of the Z column allow us to increment Z_i by one-hundredths. When we locate the desired value of Z_i by moving vertically to the tenths' place of Z_i, and horizontally to the hundredths' place of Z_i, this value is the approximate area (probability) under the curve from 0 to Z_i, denoted by $P(0 < Z < Z_i)$. This value also is the approximate area (probability) under the curve from $-Z_i$ to 0, denoted by $p(-Z_i < Z < 0)$.

Let us consider the following exercises in order to become more familiar with the use of Table 4 (Appendix H).

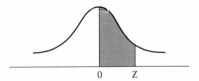

Figure 6.7

EXERCISES

1. What percent of the population in a normal distribution have Z scores that lie within one standard deviation of the mean? (That is, find $p(-1 < Z < 1)$.)
   If we locate $Z = 1.00$, we find $p(0 < Z < 1) = 0.3413$; also,

$$p(-1 < Z < 0) = 0.3413.$$

Therefore, approximately 68.26% of the population have a Z score within one standard deviation of the mean.

2. What percent of the population in a normal distribution have Z scores that lie within two standard deviations of the mean? (That is, find $p(-2 < Z < 2)$.)
   If we locate $Z = 2.00$, we find $p(0 < Z < 2) = 0.4772$; also,

$$p(-2 < Z < 0) = 0.4772.$$

Therefore, 95.44% of the population have a Z score within two standard deviations of the mean.

3. What percent of the population in a normal distribution have Z scores that lie within three standard deviations of the mean?
   If we locate $Z = 3.00$, we find $p(0 < Z < 3) = 0.4987$. Therefore, 99.74% of the population have a Z score within three standard deviations of the mean.

Figure 6.8

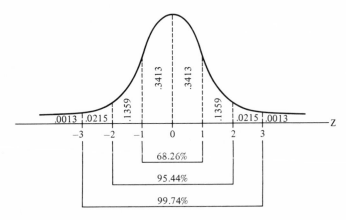

Note: Exercises 1 through 3 allow us to look more closely at the standard normal curve; see Figure 6.8. Only .26% of the population in a normal distribution will have a Z score that lies beyond three standard deviations of the mean.

4. Find $p(Z > 2.51)$. Refer to Figure 6.9. Locate $Z = 2.51$ in Table 4, Appendix H, and we have $p(0 < Z < 2.51) = 0.4940$. Therefore,

$$p(Z > 2.51) = p(Z > 0) - p(0 < Z < 2.51)$$
$$= 0.5000 - 0.4940$$
$$= 0.006$$

Figure 6.9

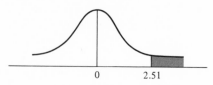

Note: 0.5000 of the area is to the left of $Z = 0$, and 0.5000 of the area is to the right of $Z = 0$.

5. Find $p(Z < -1.07)$. Refer to Figure 6.10.

$$p(Z < -1.07) = p(Z < 0) - p(-1.07 < Z < 0)$$
$$= 0.5000 - 0.3577$$
$$= 0.1423$$

Figure 6.10

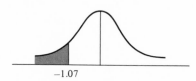

6. Find $p(Z > -1.07)$. Refer to Figure 6.11.

$$p(Z > -1.07) = p(-1.07 < Z < 0) + p(Z > 0)$$
$$= 0.3577 + 0.5000$$
$$= 0.8577$$

Figure 6.11

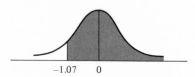

7. If a national IQ test is normally distributed with $\mu = 100$ and $\sigma = 16$, find the probability that a student's raw (X) score will lie between 92 and 112 (that is, find $p(92 < X < 112)$. Refer to Figure 6.12.

First we must convert our X scores to Z scores:

$$Z = \frac{X - \mu}{\sigma}$$

$$Z_{92} = \frac{92 - 100}{16} = \frac{-8}{16} = -\frac{1}{2} = -0.5$$

$$Z_{112} = \frac{112 - 100}{16} = \frac{12}{15} = \frac{3}{4} = 0.75$$

For $p(92 < X < 112)$,

$$p(-0.5 < Z < 0.75) = p(-0.5 < Z < 0) + p(0 < Z < 0.75)$$
$$= 0.1915 + 0.2734$$
$$= 0.4649$$

that is, 46.49% of the population will have an IQ score between 92 and 112.

Figure 6.12

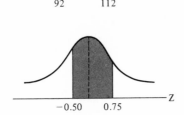

8. If scores on a national college entrance exam are approximately normally distributed with $\mu = 500$ and $\sigma = 100$, find the probability that a student's raw (X) score is
   (a) Equal to 650 (that is, $p(X = 650)$).
   (b) Less than or equal to 577 (that is, $p(X \leq 577)$).

Solution:
(a) By computing Z_{650} and using Table 4, Appendix H, we could find $p(X > 650)$ or $p(X < 650)$, but we could not find $p(X = 650)$. In order to approximate $p(X) = 650$, we compute Z scores immediately to the left of Z_{650} and immediately to the right of Z_{650}, and then find the area *between*

these two Z scores. Refer to Figure 6.13. Thus, we have $Z = (X - \mu)/\sigma$, or

$$Z_{649.5} = \frac{649.5 - 500}{100} = \frac{149.5}{100} = 1.495 \approx 1.50$$

$$Z_{650.5} = \frac{650.5 - 500}{100} = \frac{150.5}{100} = 1.505 \approx 1.51$$

and

$$p(X = 650) \approx p(0 < Z < 1.51) - p(0 < Z < 1.50)$$
$$= 0.4345 - 0.4332$$
$$= 0.0013$$

that is, approximately 0.13% of the population will obtain a college entrance score of 650.

Figure 6.13

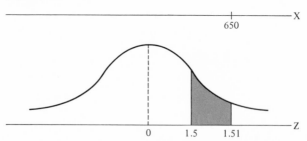

(b) $p(X \leq 577) = ?$
In order to include $p(X) = 577$ in our approximation, we compute

$$Z_{577.5} = \frac{577.5 - 500}{100} = \frac{77.5}{100} = 0.775 \approx 0.78$$

Refer to Figure 6.14. Then

$$p(X \leq 577) = p(Z < 0.78)$$
$$= p(Z < 0) + p(0 < Z < 0.78)$$
$$= 0.5000 + 0.2823$$
$$= 0.7823$$

Figure 6.14

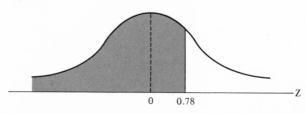

that is, approximately 78.23% of the population will have a college entrance score less than or equal to 577.

9. Consider Exercise 8, where we were given that a national college entrance exam has $\mu = 500$ and $\sigma = 100$. Suppose we were asked to find a raw score X such that only 10% of the population obtains a score greater than X (that is, find an X such that $p(X_i > X) = 0.1000$).

Solution: We are looking for a raw score X, but we must use our *standard normal curve* (Z scores) to find it.

Note: $Z \doteq (X - \mu)/\sigma$, which implies that $Z\sigma = X - \mu$, $\mu + Z\sigma = X$, or $X = \mu + Z\sigma$. We know $\mu = 500$ and $\sigma = 100$; now we must find a Z such that $p(Z_i > Z) = 0.1000$. Refer to Figure 6.15.

If $p(Z_i > Z) = 0.1000$, then $p(0 < Z_i < Z) = 0.4000$. In Table 4, Appendix H, we find $Z = 1.28$ such that $p(0 < Z_i < 1.28) = 0.3997$, which we will use as our approximation for the value of Z we are looking for. Refer to Figure 6.16.

Therefore, if $X = \mu + Z\sigma$,

$$X = 500 + (1.28)(100)$$

$$= 500 + 128$$

$$= 628$$

that is, approximately 10% of the population will have a college entrance score greater than 628.

Figure 6.15

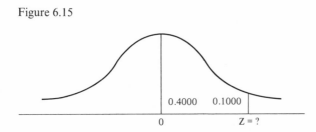

Figure 6.16

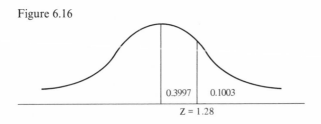

Problem Set 6.3

1. Using Table 4 (Appendix H) of standard normal Z scores, find
   (a) $p(Z > 1.25)$ (f) $p(1 < Z < 1.5)$
   (b) $p(Z < -2.1)$ (g) $p(-1.3 < Z < -0.55)$
   (c) $p(Z < 1.25)$ (h) $p(Z < 0)$
   (d) $p(Z > -2.1)$ (i) $p(-3 < Z < 3)$
   (e) $p(-0.51 < Z < 0.79)$ (j) $p(Z > 3)$

2. The entrance examination at State University is normally distributed with $\mu = 300$ and $\sigma = 60$. Let X be the continuous random variable that represents a student's raw score on the State University's entrance examination. Find
   (a) $p(X > 350)$ (b) $p(X \leq 360)$ (c) $p(180 < X < 420)$
   (d) $p(X \geq 200)$ (e) $p(200 \leq X \leq 420)$ (f) $p(X \leq 300)$

3. In Problem 2, where $\mu = 300$ and $\sigma = 60$ for the State University's entrance examination, find a student's raw score X such that
   (a) 25% of the population obtains a score greater than X.
   (b) 69.5% of the population obtains a score less than X.
   Note: If $Z = (X - \mu)/\sigma$, then $X = \mu + Z\sigma$.

4. The On Time Bus Company reports that its daily trip from Home Town, Arkansas, to Small Town, Arkansas, is normally distributed with a mean time of 45 minutes and a standard deviation of 3 minutes. What is the probability that a randomly selected trip from Home Town to Small Town will
   (a) Take more than 45 minutes?
   (b) Take more than 50 minutes?
   (c) Take less than 40 minutes?
   (d) Find the length of time X such that 30% of the trips will exceed the time X.

5. The Mini Car Company reports that its mid-priced car's life span is normally distributed with a mean of 6 years and a standard deviation of 1.5 years. What is the probability that a randomly selected mid-priced Mini Car will have a life span
   (a) Greater than or equal to 7.5 years?
   (b) Between 4 and 7.5 years?

6. The State Track Association reports that the time for the 100-yard dash at its annual track meet is normally distributed with a mean of 11.25 seconds and a standard deviation of 1.05 seconds. What is the probability that a randomly selected participant in the annual State-sponsored 100-yard dash will register a time of
   (a) Less than 10 seconds?
   (b) More than 12 seconds?
   (c) Between 10 seconds and 12 seconds?
   (d) At least 9.8 seconds?
   (e) Less than 9.5 seconds?

6.9

Using the Standard Normal Curve to Approximate Binomial Probabilities

Discrete Random Variables

A discrete random variable is a function from the sample space of an experiment that assigns each sample point in a sample space S to exactly one real number. The discrete random variable X also generates a set of ordered pairs $\{(X_i, p(X_i))\}$, called the *probability function* or distribution of X, where $\{X_i\}$ contains all possible real numbers assigned to sample points in S, and $p(X_i)$ represents their associated probabilities. If $\{X_i\}$ contains separate points on a number line, then X is a discrete random variable.

If the experiment is binomial, then we are dealing with a *binomial random variable*.

In Chapter 5 we saw that the probability of r successes in n independent trials of a binomial experiment, where p = the probability of success on any one trial and q = the probability of failure on any one trial, can be computed as follows: $_nC_r p^r q^{n-r}$, where $q = 1 - p$. For example, if ten fenders are selected at random from a lot of fenders and tested for defects, and the probability of a good fender on any one trial is 0.9, find the probability of obtaining exactly six good fenders.

Exact Probability

If X is the random variable that represents the number of good fenders selected, then

$$P(X = 6) = {}_{10}C_6(0.9)^6(0.1)^4$$

$$= (210)(0.531441)(0.0001)$$

$$\approx 0.0112$$

Normal Curve Approximation

Let X be the random variable that represents the number of good fenders selected. We can show that the mean and standard deviation of a binomial random variable are

$$\mu = np \quad \text{and} \quad \sigma = \sqrt{npq}$$

where n = number of trials of binomial experiment

p = probability of success on any one trial

q = probability of failure on any one trial

In the previous example,

$$\mu = 10(0.9) = 9 \quad \text{and} \quad \sigma = \sqrt{10(0.9)(0.1)} \approx 0.95$$

To approximate $p(X = 6)$, using the standard normal curve areas in Table 4 (Appendix H), we compute $Z = (X - \mu)/\sigma$. Then

$$Z_{5.5} = \frac{5.5 - 9}{0.95} = \frac{-3.5}{0.95} \approx -3.68$$

and

$$Z_{6.5} = \frac{6.5 - 9}{0.95} = \frac{-2.5}{0.95} \approx -2.63$$

Refer to Figure 6.17.

Therefore,

$$p(X = 6) = p(-3.68 < Z < 0) - p(-2.63 < Z < 0)$$

$$= 0.4999 - 0.4957 = 0.0042$$

Although the normal approximation is close to the exact area, one might question the use of the normal approximation if the exact probability is readily available. However, in a very large sampling of a binomial random variable, the computation of the exact probability may be very tedious. Consider the following variation of the problem of randomly selecting and testing fenders.

Figure 6.17

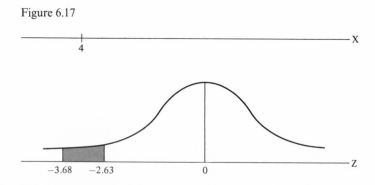

SAMPLE PROBLEM

Suppose we were to select at random 40 fenders from a lot of fenders and test them for defects, where $p = 0.9$. If we let X be the random variable that represents the number of good fenders selected, we can find the probability of obtaining exactly 30 good fenders ($p(X = 30)$). Then

1. The exact probability would be extremely tedious to compute:

$$p(X = 30) = {}_{40}C_{30}(0.9)^{30}(0.1)^{10}$$

2. The normal approximation of $p(X = 30)$ would be computed as follows:

$$\mu = np \qquad\qquad \sigma = \sqrt{npq}$$
$$= (40)(0.9) \qquad\quad = \sqrt{40(0.9)(0.1)}$$
$$= 36 \qquad\qquad\quad \approx 1.9$$

Then

$$Z_{29.5} = \frac{29.5 - 36}{1.9} \qquad \text{and} \qquad Z_{30.5} = \frac{30.5 - 36}{1.9}$$

$$= \frac{-6.5}{1.9} \qquad\qquad\qquad\qquad = \frac{-5.5}{1.9}$$

$$\approx -3.42 \qquad\qquad\qquad\qquad \approx -2.89$$

Refer to Figure 6.18.
Therefore,

$$p(X = 30) \approx p(-3.42 < Z < 0) - p(-2.9 < Z < 0)$$
$$= 0.4997 - 0.4981 = 0.0016$$

Now let us consider some more sample problems of large binomial random sampling for which we will use the normal curve to compute an approximation for the desired binomial probabilities.

Figure 6.18

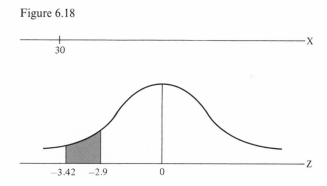

SAMPLE PROBLEMS

1. In the preceding experiment we randomly selected 40 fenders from a lot of fenders and tested them for defects, where $p = 0.9$. If we let X be the random variable which represents the number of good fenders selected, we can find the normal curve approximation for the probability of

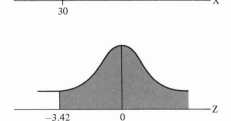

Figure 6.19

(a) Obtaining at least 30 good fenders; that is,

$$p(X \geq 30) = p(X = 30) + p(X = 31) + \cdots + p(X = 40)$$

$$\mu = np = 40(0.9) = 36$$

$$\sigma = \sqrt{npq} = \sqrt{40(0.9)(0.1)} \approx 1.9$$

Then

$$Z_{29.5} = \frac{29.5 - 36}{1.9} \approx -3.42$$

Refer to Figure 6.19.
    Therefore,

$$p(X \geq 30) \approx p(-3.42 < Z < 0) + p(Z > 0)$$

$$= 0.4997 + 0.5000$$

$$= 0.9997$$

(b) Obtaining at most 30 good fenders; that is, $p(X \leq 30) = p(X = 30) + p(X = 29) + \cdots + p(X = 1) + p(X = 0)$

$$\mu = np = 40(0.9) = 36$$

$$\sigma = \sqrt{npq} = \sqrt{40(0.9)(0.1)} \approx 1.9$$

Then

$$Z_{30.5} = \frac{30.5 - 36}{1.9} \approx -2.89$$

Refer to Figure 6.20.
    Therefore

$$p(X \leq 30) \approx p(Z < 0) - p(-2.89 < Z < 0)$$

$$= 0.5000 - 0.4981$$

$$= 0.0019$$

2. The probability that a student enrolling in a remedial mathematics course will pass the course is 0.7 (the only two possible grades are P (pass) and F (fail)).

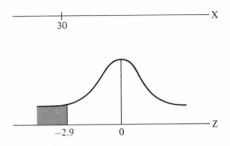

Figure 6.20

If 700 students enroll in the remedial course, and we let X be the random variable that represents the number of students who pass, find the normal curve approximation to the probability that

(a) Between 200 and 225 students will fail the course (that is, if we let $p =$ the probability of failing $= 0.3$, and $q =$ the probability of passing $= 0.7$). Find $p(200 < X < 225)$.

$$\mu = np = 700(0.3) = 210$$

$$\sigma = \sqrt{npq} = \sqrt{700(0.3)(0.7)}$$

$$= \sqrt{147} \approx 12.124$$

Since the binomial distribution represents a discrete random variable, we must use a *continuity correction* when approximating binomial probabilities via the standard normal distribution.

$$Z_{199.5} = \frac{199.5 - 210}{12.124} = \frac{-10.5}{12.124} \approx -0.87$$

$$Z_{225.5} = \frac{225.5 - 210}{12.124} = \frac{15.5}{12.124} \approx 1.29$$

Refer to Figure 6.21.

Figure 6.21

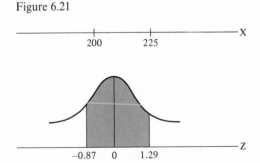

Therefore,

$$p(200 < X < 225) \approx p(-0.87 < Z < 0) + p(0 < Z < 1.29)$$
$$= 0.3078 + 0.4015$$
$$= 0.7093$$

Figure 6.22

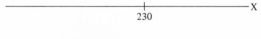

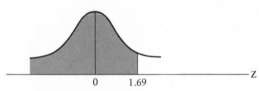

(b) Less than 230 students will fail the course; that is, find $p(X < 230)$, where $p = 0.3$ and $q = 0.7$.

$$\mu = (700)(0.3) = 210 \qquad \sigma = \sqrt{700(0.3)(0.7)} \approx 12.124$$

Using the continuity correction, we obtain

$$Z_{230.5} = \frac{230.5 - 210}{12.124} = \frac{20.5}{12.124} \approx 1.69$$

Refer to Figure 6.22.
Therefore,

$$p(X < 230) \approx p(0 < Z < 1.69) + p(Z < 0)$$
$$= 0.4545 + 0.5000 = 0.9545$$

Problem Set 6.4

Use the *standard normal curve* to approximate the desired binomial probabilities in each of the following exercises.

1. The probability that a flu vaccine will be effective on any one person is 0.8. If 200 people are selected at random, and injected with the vaccine, what is the probability that less than 20 people will contract the flu?

2. A certain professional basketball player shoots his foul shots with a 0.9 accuracy. What is the probability that he will make at least 35 of 40 randomly selected foul shots he attempts?

3. The probability that any one battery produced by the Live Wire Company is rejected is 0.01. If 100 batteries are selected at random, then tested and classified *A*

(accepted) or R (rejected), what is the probability that at least two batteries are rejected, but at most four batteries are rejected (that is, $p(2 \leq X \leq 4) = p(X = 2) + p(X = 3) + p(X = 4)$)?

4. A certain woman professional golfer qualifies for five of ten tournaments in which she desires to participate. What is the probability that she will qualify for exactly 35 of 50 randomly selected tournaments she wishes to enter?

5. The Snap Shot Company advertises that its flash bulbs work with 0.999 accuracy. If its claim is true, what is the probability that at most 4 of 1000 randomly selected flashbulbs are defective?

6. A marksman claims he hits the bull's-eye on six of every ten shots he fires. If his claim is true, what is the probability that he will not hit the bull's-eye on 6 of his next 15 shots?

6.10

A Prepackaged Program for Computing the Z Score/Scores When Using the Normal Curve to Approximate Binomial Probabilities

Name: STAT4

Description: This program computes the Z score/scores and tells which area to compute when using the normal curve to approximate binomial probabilities.

Instructions: Enter the data beginning in line 150 as follows:

$$150 \quad \text{DATA } N,P,R_1,R_2,X$$

where:

$N =$ number of independent trials in the binomial experiment

$P =$ probability of success on any one trial

R_1 and $R_2 =$ desired number of successes if we have a lower limit and upper limit; otherwise, $R_1 = R_2$

$$X = \begin{cases} 0 & \text{if we want exactly } R_1 = R_2 \text{ successes} \\ 1 & \text{if we want less than } R_1 = R_2 \text{ successes} \\ 2 & \text{if we want more than } R_1 = R_2 \text{ successes} \\ 3 & \text{if we want at most } R_1 = R_2 \text{ successes} \\ 4 & \text{if we want at least } R_1 = R_2 \text{ successes} \\ 5 & \text{if we want between } R_1 \text{ and } R_2 \text{ successes} \\ 6 & \text{if we want between } R_1 \text{ and } R_2 \text{ inclusive successes} \end{cases}$$

Note: Line 200 is the END statement.

SAMPLE PROBLEM

If we randomly select and test ten fenders from a lot of fenders, where the probability of selecting a good fender on any one try is 0.7, we use the normal curve approximation to find the probability of obtaining the following outcomes.

1. Exactly five good fenders: $(P(x = 5))$.

User's Input

    GET-STAT4

    150   DATA 10,.7,5,5,0

    RUN

Computer Output

    FIND AREA BETWEEN $Z = -1.72516$ AND $Z = -1.0351$

User's Calculations

    $p(-1.73 < Z < -1.04) = 0.4582 - 0.3508 = 0.1074$

2. Less then five good fenders: $(P(X < 5))$.

User's Input

    GET-STAT4

    150   DATA 10,.7,5,5,1

    RUN

Computer Output

    FIND THE AREA TO THE LEFT OF $Z = -1.38013$

User's Calculations

    $p(Z < -1.38) = 0.5000 - 0.4162 = 0.0838$

3. More than five good fenders: $(P(X > 5))$.

User's Input

    GET-STAT4

    150   DATA 10,.7,5,5,2

    RUN

Computer Output

    FIND THE AREA TO THE RIGHT OF $Z = -1.38013$

User's Calculations

$$p(Z > -1.38) = 0.5000 + 0.4162 = 0.9162$$

4. At most five good fenders: $(p(X \leq 5))$.

User's Input

GET-STAT4

150   DATA 10,.7,5,5,3

RUN

Computer Output

FIND THE AREA TO THE LEFT OF $Z = -1.0351$

User's Calculations

$$p(Z < -1.04) = 0.5000 - 0.3508 = 0.1492$$

5. At least five good fenders: $(P(X \geq 5))$.

User's Input

GET-STAT4

150   DATA 10,.7,5,5,4

RUN

Computer Output

FIND THE AREA TO THE RIGHT OF $Z = -1.72516$

User's Calculations

$$p(Z > -1.73) = 0.5000 + 0.4582 = 0.9582$$

6. Between four and nine fenders: $(P(4 < X < 9))$.

User's Input

GET-STAT4

150   DATA 10,.7,4,9,5

RUN

Computer Output

FIND AREA BETWEEN $Z = -2.0702$ AND $Z = 1.38013$

User's Calculations

$$p(-2.07 < Z < 1.38) = 0.4808 + 0.4162 = 0.8970$$

7. Between four and nine inclusive good fenders: $(P(4 \leq X \leq 9))$.

User's Input

> GET-STAT4
>
> 150   DATA 10,.7,4,9,6
>
> RUN

Computer Output

> FIND AREA BETWEEN $Z = -2.41623$ AND $Z = 1.72516$

User's Calculations

$$p(-2.42 < Z < 1.73) = 0.4922 + 0.4582 = 0.9504$$

Let us look at Figure 6.23, the flowcharting of STAT4. The coding of STAT4 is as follows:

```
5 READ N, P, R1, R2, X
10 LET M=N*P
15 LET D= SQR(N*P*(1-P))
20 IF X=0 THEN 70
25 IF X=1 THEN 85
30 IF X=2 THEN 100
35 IF X=3 THEN115
40 IF X=4 THEN125
45 IF X=5 THEN 135
50 LET Z1=((R1-.5)-M)/D
55 LET Z2=((R2+.5)-M)/D
60 PRINT "FIND AREA BETWEEN Z="Z1;"AND Z="Z2
65 GO TO 5
70 LET Z1=((R1-.5)-M)/D
75 LET Z2=((R1+.5)-M)/D
80 GO TO 60
85 LET Z=(R1-M)/D
90 PRINT "FIND THE AREA TO THE LEFT OF Z="Z
95 GO TO 5
100 LET Z=(R1-M)/D
105 PRINT "FIND THE AREA TO THE RIGHT OF Z="Z
110 GO TO 5
115 LET Z=((R1+.5)-M)/D
120 GO TO 90
125 LET Z=((R1-.5)-M)/D
130 GO TO 105
135 LET Z1=(R1-M)/D
140 LET Z2=(R2-M)/D
145 GO TO 60
200 END
```

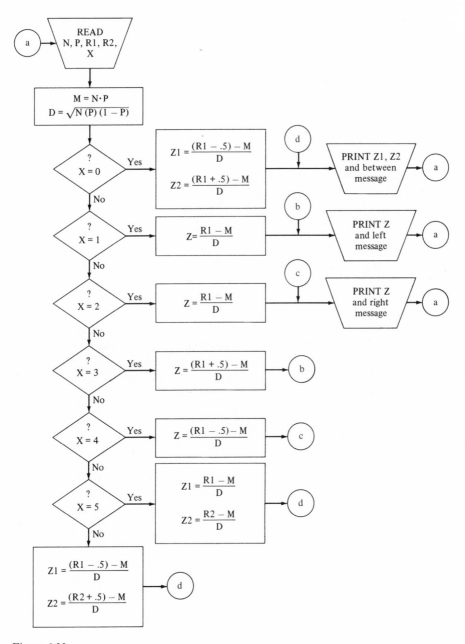

Figure 6.23

Problem Set 6.5

Test your solutions to each of the six exercises in Problem Set 6.4 by using STAT4 to solve them.

6.11

Normalizing Raw Test Scores via a Prepackaged Computer Program

How many times in the past have you or a fellow classmate asked a teacher to "curve" the results of a test? The proper terminology is *normalizing test results*. To normalize a raw test score X, one must compute a normal score $N = \mu + Z\sigma$, where $Z = (X - \bar{X})/s$, and $\mu = $ the population mean (or an estimate of the population mean), $\sigma = $ the population standard deviation (or an estimate of the population standard deviation).

For example, suppose the final examination grades in Statistics I at New College have yielded a mean $\mu = 75$ and a standard deviation $\sigma = 15$ during the past 20 semesters. Suppose two sections of Statistics I at New College achieve the following results on their final examination during the past semester (see Table 6.7).

Using the data in Table 6.7,

$$\bar{X}_1 = \frac{307}{5} = 61.4 \qquad\qquad \bar{X}_2 = \frac{380}{5} = 76$$

$$s_1 = \sqrt{\frac{\Sigma X^2 - (\Sigma X)^2/n}{n}} \qquad\qquad s_2 = \sqrt{\frac{29850 - (380)^2/5}{5}}$$

$$= \sqrt{\frac{20049 - (307)^2/5}{5}} \qquad\qquad = \sqrt{\frac{29850 - 28880}{5}}$$

$$= \sqrt{\frac{20049 - 18849.8}{5}} \qquad\qquad = \sqrt{194}$$

$$= \sqrt{239.84} \qquad\qquad\qquad \approx 13.93$$

$$\approx 15.49$$

Note: $Z_i = (X_i - \bar{X})/s$, $N_i = \mu + Z_i\sigma$. Now, using the population of 20 semesters of Statistics I, we obtain $N_i = 75 + Z_i(15)$.

For Section I (in Table 6.7), each normal score is higher than its corresponding raw score, while for Section II only one normal score is higher than its corresponding raw score.

Table 6.7

	Section I				Section II		
X_i	X_i^2	Z_i	N_i	X_i	X_i^2	Z_i	N_i
50	2500	−0.74	63.9	60	3600	−1.15	57.75
40	1600	−1.38	54.3	95	9025	1.36	95.4
75	5625	0.88	88.2	85	7225	0.65	84.75
82	6724	1.32	94.8	80	6400	0.28	79.2
60	3600	−0.09	73.65	60	3600	−1.14	57.9
$\Sigma X = 307$	$\Sigma X^2 = 20049$			$\Sigma X = 380$	$\Sigma X^2 = 29850$		

Name: STAT5

Description: This program normalizes a set of n raw scores, where $n \leq 30$.

Instructions: Enter the data beginning in line 150 as follows:

$$150 \quad \text{DATA } N, X_1, X_2, \ldots, X_n, U, D$$

where:

N = number of raw scores

$X_1, X_2, \ldots, X_n$ = actual raw scores

U = mean or approximated mean of the population

D = standard deviation or approximated standard deviation of the population

Note: Line 200 is the END statement.

SAMPLE PROBLEM

User's Input

```
GET-STAT5
150 DATA 5,60,95,85,80,60,75,15
RUN
```

Computer Output

```
X         Z              N
60      -1.14873       57.769
95       1.36412       95.4618
85       .646162       84.6924
80       .287183       79.3077
60      -1.14873       57.769
X         Z              N

LINE    10:    END OF DATA

TIME 0.0 SECS.
```

User's Input

```
GET-STAT5
15Ø DATA 5,5Ø,4Ø,75,32,6Ø,75,15
RUN
```

Computer Output

```
X          Z              N
 50     -.736111        63.9583
 40     -1.38132        54.2727
 75      .378163        88.1725
 82      1.33017        94.9525
 60     -9.03992E-02      73.644
X          Z              N

LINE    1Ø:   END OF DATA

TIME Ø.Ø SECS.
```

Let us look at Figure 6.24, the flowcharting of STAT5. The coding for STAT5 is as follows:

```
2 DIM X(3Ø), Z(3Ø), N(3Ø)
5 PRINT "X           Z              N"
10 READ N
15 LET S1=Ø
2Ø LET S2=Ø
25 FOR I=1 TO N
30    READ X(I)
35    LET S1=S1+X(I)
4Ø    LET S2=S2+(X(I))↑2
45 NEXT I
5Ø LET M=S1/N
55 LET S= SQR((S2-S1↑2/N)/N)
6Ø READ U,D
65 FOR I=1 TO  N
7Ø    LET Z(I)=(X(I)-M)/S
75    LET N(I)=U+Z(I)*D
8Ø    PRINT X(I);Z(I);N(I)
85 NEXT I
87 GO TO 5
15Ø END
2ØØ END
```

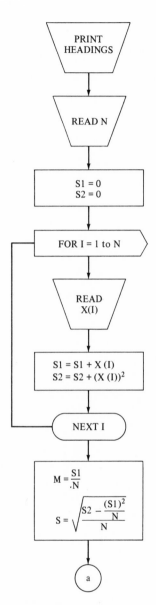

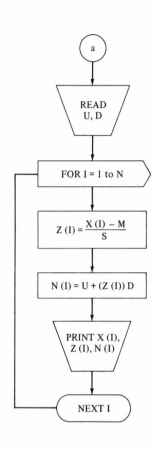

Figure 6.24

Problem Set 6.6

Use STAT5 to normalize the raw-score test results for each of the following two sections of statistics, given the population mean = 70 and the population standard deviation = 10.

Section I X_i		Section II X_i	
64	80	90	61
76	84	67	78
62	73	85	95
60	46	67	70
65	58	65	66
65	37	75	100
74	48	82	70
70	91	78	
55	70	84	
61	70	70	
78	33	98	
87	65	74	
51		48	
30		90	
64			

Appendix A: Programming Projects

Instructions

Construct a flowchart for each of the following programming projects, code your flowchart in the BASIC programming language, and run the program. Each project requires a considerable amount of thought and effort. Any one of the problems can be done by an individual, but it is suggested that all be done by groups of two or more people. It is very unlikely that your first attempt to run the program will be perfect.

An account should be kept of each run, the encountered errors, and your corrections.

1. *Given*: DATA R(1), R(2), R(3), R(4), R(5), R(6) (rates of pay) and DATA I,N,G,H,C,D,S for *each employee* in a certain factory, where

> I = identification number
>
> N = employee's name
>
> G = gross yearly pay previous to this week
>
> H = number of hours worked this week
>
> C = 1,2,3,4,5,6 to indicate employee's rate of pay
>
> D = employee's number of dependents
>
> S = 0,1, where 1 implies a savings bond deduction of $18.75 and 0 implies no savings bond deduction.

Wanted: A BASIC program to read and process this information. The following will apply to *each* employee:

(a) A 5% Social Security deduction (based on gross weekly pay) is made for each employee until his gross yearly pay totals $7,600; beyond this figure there is no deduction.

(b) Income tax deduction:
   (1) 35% if 0 dependents
   (2) 27% if 1 dependent
   (3) 21% if 2 dependents
   (4) 13% if 3 dependents
   (5) 10% if 4 dependents
   (6) 0% if 5 or more dependents

(c) Regular time is 35 hours and each overtime hour is paid at regular time time and one-half.

Form of Output

ID   NAME   WEEKS GROSS PAY   WEEKS NET PAY

YEARLY GROSS PAY

Sample Data

2.75, 3.50, 3.75, 4.25, 4.75, 5.35

891, F. KELSO, 4701.91, 42, 5, 2, 0

902, J. JONES, 6800.05, 35, 4, 3, 1

811, T. TONKY, 7801.93, 51, 6, 1, 1

2. *Given*: The Taylor series for approximating sine(X) and cosine(X).

$$\sin(X) = X - \frac{X^3}{3!} + \frac{X^5}{5!} - \frac{X^7}{7!} + \cdots$$

$$\cos(X) = 1 - \frac{X^2}{2!} + \frac{X^4}{4!} - \frac{X^6}{6!} + \cdots$$

where X is in radian measure.

Wanted: A BASIC program that will approximate sine(X) and cosine(X) in the following manner: Have the computer approximate the sine(X) and the cosine(X) by adding or subtracting terms until |term| < 0.000001.

Degrees	Radians	sine(X)	cosine(X)
0			
1			
2			
⋮			
45			

Job completed by _____.

(Name)

3. *Given*: N real numbers as follows:

DATA N,A_1,A_2,A_3, . . . ,A_n.

Wanted: A BASIC program to sort and arrange N numbers from smallest to largest.

SAMPLE DATA

$$5,7,8,2,10,2$$

$$12,2,7,1,99,72,84,6,-8,16,-9,10,101$$

4. In Chapter 7 we used Sigma notation to represent the sum of n raw scores:

$$\sum_{i=1}^{n} X_i = X_1 + X_2 + \cdots + X_n$$

Similarly,

$$\sum_{i=1}^{5} X^2 = 1^2 + 2^2 + 3^2 + 4^2 + 5^2 = 55$$

$$\sum_{x=1}^{3} (X^3 + 1) = (1^3 + 1) + (2^3 + 1) + (3^3 + 1) = 39$$

$$\sum_{i=1}^{5} 2 = 2 + 2 + 2 + 2 + 2 = 10$$

$$\sum_{y=3}^{5} (2y^3) = 2 \cdot 3^3 + 2 \cdot 4^3 + 2 \cdot 5^3 = 432$$

Given: (a) The rule for a function of f, which will be defined in some set statement such as

15　LET F=F+(rule for function in terms of K)

For example, if $f(K) = K^2$, we would enter

15　LET F=F+K↑2

(b) I $=$ initial value of f, and M $=$ maximum value of f.

Wanted: A BASIC program that computes the sum of a function of f from some initial value of $f(K)$ to some maximum value of $f(M)$ by increments of 1.

SAMPLE DATA

(a)　　　$f(K) = K^2$,　　$I = 7$,　　$M = 21$

$$\left(\text{We want: } \sum_{k=7}^{21} K^2. \right)$$

(b)　　　$f(K) = 3K^3 - 2K + 7$,　　$I = 1$,　　$M = 11$

$$\left(\text{We want: } \sum_{k=1}^{11} (3K^3 - 2K + 7). \right)$$

5. Medical laboratory technicians conduct many different urine tests. One common test is to find the total urinary sulfates in a 24-hour period. The normal values for total urinary sulfates in a 24-hour period are 0.6 to 1.2 grams. Values greater than 1.2 grams indicate acute fevers, while values less than 0.6 gram indicate decreased metabolic activity. To find the amount of sulfur in a 24-hour specimen of urine, technicians use the following formula: $T = A(B/C)$, where

A = weight of sulfur in sample

B = ml of 24-hour sample

C = ml used in Folin Method test.

Given: $N, A_1, B_1, C_1, A_2, B_2, C_2, \ldots, A_n, B_n, C_n$.

Wanted: A BASIC program to compute and print out the following information:

Urine Test X	A	B	C	Total Weight of Sulfur in 24-Hour Specimen T
1				
2				
3				
⋮				
N				

6. Revise Problem 5 to print out the following information:

Urine Test X_i	A	B	C	Total Weight of Sulfur in 24-Hour Specimen T_i
X_1				
X_2				
X_3				
⋮				
X_n				

Mean total weight of specimens:

$$\bar{T} = \frac{\sum_{i=1}^{n} T_i}{n}$$

Variance for total weight of specimens:

$$s^2 = \frac{\sum_{i=1}^{n} (T_i^2) - \left(\sum_{i=1}^{n} T_i\right)^2 / n}{n}$$

Standard deviation for total weight of specimens:

$$s = \sqrt{s^2}$$

7. *Given*: The following information for *each* student in a certain two-year college for a given semester: N,A,B,C,D,F,W,I, where

$$N = \begin{cases} 1, & \text{if the student is in his first year} \\ 2, & \text{if the student is in his second year} \\ 3, & \text{if the student is nonmatriculated} \\ 4, & \text{signifies that there are no more data to be processed.} \end{cases}$$

A = number of A's obtained by the student this semester

B = number of B's obtained by the student this semester

C = number of C's for this semester

D = number of D's for this semester

F = number of F's for this semester

W = number of withdrawals this semester

I = number of incompletes this semester

Wanted: A BASIC program to compute and print out:

TOTAL FIRST YEAR STUDENTS =

TOTAL SECOND YEAR STUDENTS =

TOTAL NONMATRICULATED STUDENTS =

Average Number of:	A	B	C	D	F	W	I
(a) For first year students							
(b) For second year students							
(c) For nonmatriculated students							

SAMPLE DATA

2,2,3,1,1,0,0,1

1,0,0,1,3,1,1,1

2,1,2,1,0,1,1,0

3,0,2,2,0,0,0,1

3,3,2,1,0,0,0,0

1,0,0,2,2,0,1,0

4,0,0,0,0,0,0,0

8. *Given*: The following rules for the game of "craps" (dice):
   (a) If a 7 or 11 is rolled on the first roll, the shooter wins.
   (b) If a 2, 3, or 12 is rolled on the first roll, the shooter loses.
   (c) If any other number is rolled on the first roll, that number becomes the shooter's point and he/she keeps rolling until his/her point turns up and the shooter wins, or a 7 is rolled and the shooter loses.
   (d) Assume the house limit on any one bet is $5,000.
   (e) Assume if you bet $50 and win, you win $50; if you bet $50 and lose, you lose $50, and so on, regardless of what point you are trying to make (of course this is not true in the real game of "craps").
   Wanted: A BASIC program to simulate the game of "craps."

Sample Output

    YOUR BET IS?

    ? 100

    YOU ROLL: 10

    YOU ROLL: 5

    YOU ROLL: 7

    YOU LOSE!!

    YOUR WINNINGS ARE: $ − 100

    DO YOU WANT TO PLAY AGAIN?

    ? YES

    YOUR BET IS?

    ? 150

    YOU ROLL: 8

    YOU ROLL: 3

    YOU ROLL: 5

    YOU ROLL: 8

    YOU WIN!!!

    YOUR WINNINGS ARE: $ + 50

    DO YOU WANT TO PLAY AGAIN?

    ? NO

    DOES ANYONE ELSE WANT TO PLAY?

    ? NO

9. In Chapter 5 we saw that

$$0! = 1$$

$$1! = 1$$

$$2! = 2 \cdot 1 = 2$$

$$3! = 3 \cdot 2 \cdot 1 = 6$$

$$\vdots$$

$$n! = n(n - 1)(n - 2) \cdots (1)$$

where $n \, \varepsilon \{1,2,3, \ldots\}$ and $n! = n(n - 1)!$.

Given: A, B, where A and B are counting numbers and $A < B$.

Wanted: A BASIC program to print out the following table of values:

N	N-Factorial
A	$A!$
$(A + 1)$	$(A + 1)!$
$(A + 2)$	$(A + 2)!$
$\vdots$	$\vdots$
B	$B!$

SAMPLE DATA

5,11

7,13

13,20

10. *Given:* The following information is given for each of 500 blood donors at Sweet Charity Hospital:

$N\$, A, X$

where $N\$$ = name of donor (DIM $N\$(15)$) (see Appendix G)

A = age of donor

$$X = \begin{cases} 1, & \text{if donor has blood type A} \\ 2, & \text{if donor has blood type B} \\ 3, & \text{if donor has blood type AB} \\ 4, & \text{if donor has blood type O} \end{cases}$$

Wanted: A BASIC Program that can be used in an emergency situation to print out a list of names for any one of the four blood types. That is, if we INPUT

$X = 1$, we get a list of names of blood donors with type A

$X = 2$, we get a list of names of blood donors with type B

$X = 3,$ we get a list of names of blood donors with type AB

$X = 4,$ we get a list of names of blood donors with type O

11. Home mortgages are usually computed in such a way that the borrower pays for the same amount each month. For the beginning payments on the mortgage, most of each monthly payment is for interest due and a small amount is for the principal due. In later monthly payments, the interest due decreases while the principal due increases.

Given: A, R, N

where A = total amount of loan

R = *monthly* interest rate written in decimal form

N = total number of monthly payments

Wanted: The following mortgage table, where

P = amount of monthly payment

$= R \cdot A[(1 + R)^N/(1 + R)^N - 1]$

I = monthly interest payment

$= R \cdot B$, where B = outstanding balance

M = monthly principal payment $= P - I$

SAMPLE DATA

$A = \$20,000$ $R = 0.0075$ (9% annual rate) $N = 240$

Payment	Monthly Amount of Payment (P)	Interest (I)	Principal (M)
1			
2			
3			
⋮			
N			

Appendix B: Common BASIC Programming Statements

Type of Statement		Sample	Reference
READ	5	READ X,Y	
	13	READ T(1),A,Z(4)	Article 1.5
INPUT	11	INPUT X,T,R	
	29	INPUT T(5),S(9)	Article 1.5
DATA	112	DATA 2,3.2,97.533,8	Article 1.5
LET	27	LET X = 2 + 3↑2	
	94	LET T = A + 3*B(4) − 7	Article 1.5
PRINT	35	PRINT 2 + 3↑5 − 27	
	40	PRINT T(3),X	
	143	PRINT "SUM1 =",S	Article 1.5
GO TO	22	GO TO 5	Article 1.5
IF-THEN	25	IF N > 27 THEN 9	
	37	IF A − B = C + 7 THEN 10	Article 1.5
FOR	12	FOR X = 1 TO 23	
	33	FOR Y = 5 TO 7 STEP 1	
	94	FOR T = R TO S STEP 2	Article 1.5
NEXT	55	NEXT Y	
	66	NEXT S2	Article 1.5
END	200	END	Article 1.5
DIM	2	DIM A(5),B(34),T(2,3)	Article 1.7
STOP	123	STOP	Article 1.5
REM	5	REM THIS IS QUADRATIC PROGRAM	Article 1.5

Type of Statement		Sample	Reference
DEF	57	DEF FNA(T) = T↑2 − 3*T + 2	Article 2.10
GO SUB	10	GO SUB 222	Article 2.3
RETURN	226	RETURN	Article 2.3
TAB	80	PRINT X,TAB(X + 20);Y	Article 1.5

The RESTORE Statement

General Form: n RESTORE, where n is any statement number.

For example: 220 RESTORE

The RESTORE statement commands the computer to restore the data pointer to the beginning of the DATA list. That is, after a set of DATA has been used, it can be used again in the same BASIC program.

Appendix C: Common BASIC System Commands

Command	Reference
LIST	Article 1.6
RUN	Article 1.6
TAPE	Article 1.6
SCR(SCRATCH), NEW	Article 1.6
GET, ENTER, LOAD	Article 1.8
SAV(SAVE)	Article 1.8

Additional Common BASIC Commands

1. The BYE command: The user is logged off the BASIC system, and the total computer time used is printed out.

2. The CATALOG command: The computer prints out the names of all the user programs stored in memory.

3. The KILL-program name (UNSAVE-program name) command: The computer erases the program from the user's catalog.

4. The LIBRARY command: The computer prints the names of the specific BASIC system's library programs.

5. The NAME-program name command: The computer gives a specific name to a program. The NAME command is usually used in conjunction with the SAVE command.

6. The PUNCH command: The computer will punch the current program on paper tape, provided the tape unit is turned on.

7. The RENUMBER command: The computer will renumber the statements of the current program. Some BASIC compilers will number the statements 10, 20, 30, . . . ; others will number the statements 100, 200, 300, . . . (consult your BASIC system user's manual).

Appendix D: Common BASIC User Predefined Functions

Function	Reference
SIN(R)	Article 1.5
COS(R)	Article 1.5
TAN(R)	Article 1.5
ABS(R)	Article 1.5
ATN(R)	Article 1.5
SQR(R)	Article 1.5
INT(R)	Article 1.5; Appendix G
LOG(R)	Article 1.5
EXP(R)	Article 1.5
SGN(R)	Article 1.5
RND(R)	Appendix G

Appendix E: Common BASIC Matrix Commands

Command	Reference
MAT READ	Article 3.4
MAT PRINT	Article 3.4
MAT addition	Article 3.4
MAT subtraction	Article 3.4
MAT multiplication	Article 3.4
MAT multiplication by a scalar	Article 3.4
MAT inverse	Article 3.4
DET of a matrix	Article 3.4
MAT transposition	Article 3.4
MAT identity	Article 3.4
MAT zero	Article 3.4

Appendix F: Common BASIC
Compiler Error Messages

ALMOST A SINGULAR MATRIX

BAD DATA

BAD FORMAT

BAD INPUT

DIMENSIONS DO NOT ALLOW MULTIPLICATION

EXPONENTIAL OVERFLOW-WARNING

FOR WITHOUT MATCHING NEXT

FUNCTION DEFINED MORE THAN ONCE

GO SUB WITHOUT MATCHING RETURN

ILLEGAL OR MISSING BINARY OPERATOR

ILLEGAL OR MISSING FUNCTION NAME

ILLEGAL OR MISSING RELATIONAL OPERATOR

ILLEGAL OR MISSING STEP

ILLEGAL OR MISSING STRING DIMENSION

ILLEGAL OR MISSING THEN

LAST STATEMENT NOT END

LOG OF A NEGATIVE ARGUMENT

MATRIX HAS A ZERO DIMENSION

MATRIX ON BOTH SIDES

MATRIX NOT SQUARE

MISSING OR ILLEGAL TO

MISSING LEFT (RIGHT) PARENTHESIS

MISSING LEFT (RIGHT) QUOTE MARKS

NEXT WITHOUT MATCHING FOR

NO MORE DATA

NO MORE STORAGE

OVERFLOW-WARNING

UNDERFLOW-WARNING

RETURN WITHOUT MATCHING GO SUB

SIN OR TAN ARGUMENT IS TOO LARGE

SQUARE ROOT OF A NEGATIVE ARGUMENT

SUBSCRIPTED VARIABLE EXCEEDS ITS DIMENSION

SUBSCRIPTED VARIABLE NOT DIMENSIONED

SUBSCRIPTED VARIABLE TOO LARGE

SYNTAX ERROR

UNACCEPTABLE OR MISSING SUBSCRIPT

UNACCEPTABLE VARIABLE NAME

UNDEFINED STATEMENT REFERRED TO

UNDEFINED VARIABLE

UNDERFLOW-WARNING

Appendix G: Additional BASIC Functions and Statements

G. 1

The Random Number Function

In selecting one number from a set of numbers or one object from a set of objects, the selection is called a *random selection* if each number or each object in the given set has an *equal chance* of being selected.

GENERAL FORM

RND(X), where X is any real number (X is a meaningless but necessary part of the internal function), commands the computer to select a random number between 0 and 1.

Sample BASIC Program

```
5 FOR I=1 TO 4
10    PRINT RND(8);RND(27)
15 NEXT I
20 END
RUN
  •21132   •14464
  •852625  •927054
  •162866  •433095
  •563933  •20965

*READY
```

Many problems associated with probability and statistics require random number selections, but not necessarily random numbers between 0 and 1. The previous program illustrates that the command RND(X) gives us numbers of the form:

.0xxxxx
.1xxxxx
.2xxxxx
⋮
.9xxxxx

where $x = 0,1,2,\ldots,9$.

If we combine INT(X) and RND(X) in the following two ways:

(1)   INT(10∗RND(X))

where X is any real number, the computer will select a random number between 0 and 9, inclusive.

(2)   INT(10∗RND(X)+1)

where X is any real number, the computer will select a random number between 1 and 10, inclusive.

Suppose we wanted the computer to select a six-digit weekly lottery number.

The flowchart solution is given in Figure G.1.

Figure G.1

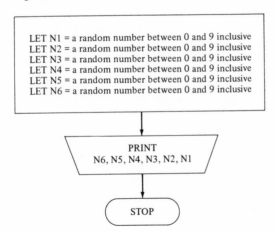

```
LET N1 = a random number between 0 and 9 inclusive
LET N2 = a random number between 0 and 9 inclusive
LET N3 = a random number between 0 and 9 inclusive
LET N4 = a random number between 0 and 9 inclusive
LET N5 = a random number between 0 and 9 inclusive
LET N6 = a random number between 0 and 9 inclusive
```

PRINT
N6, N5, N4, N3, N2, N1

STOP

Problem Set G.1

1. Write a BASIC program to print out the greatest integer in each of the following numbers: $-2.7, 3.891, -2/9$.

2. Write a BASIC program to print out three random numbers between 1 and 10, inclusive.

3. Code the flowchart in Figure G.1 for selecting a six-digit weekly lottery number in the BASIC language.

4. Run Problems 1 through 3 above.

5. Article G.1 illustrates how to direct the computer to select a random number between 0 and 1, 0 and 9, inclusive, and 1 and 10, inclusive. In general, if we want a random number between B and $A+B-1$, inclusive, we can use the formula $INT(A*RND(X)+B)$, where X is any real number. For example, if we want the computer to select a random number between 27 and 54, inclusive, we compute A and B as follows:

$$B=27 \qquad A+B-1=54$$
$$A+27-1=54$$
$$A+26=54$$
$$A=28$$

and use $INT(28*RND(X)+27)$, where X is any real number in the program.
Now write and run a BASIC program that will print out
(a) A random number between 27 and 54, inclusive.
(b) A random number between 1 and 500, inclusive.
(c) A random number between 60 and 90, inclusive.

G.2

Alphanumeric (String) Variables

An alphanumeric (string) variable is a sequence of characters (numbers, letters, or special symbols) used to represent expressions such as names, addresses, and yes-no answers to computer-directed questions, or other information.

GENERAL FORM

Simple alphanumeric (string) variables are represented by using a single letter followed by the $ sign. For example, A$,B$, . . . ,Z$. A DIM (dimension) statement is used to reserve the maximum length of a string variable. For example, 10 DIM A$(13),B$(10), says that A$ is a string variable of at most 13 characters and B$ has at most 10 characters. The maximum number of characters that can be used in a string variable varies from one BASIC compiler to another. One must consult the BASIC system user's manual for this maximum length.
    Alphanumeric variables can be used with BASIC input and output (READ, INPUT, PRINT) statements. The following BASIC program illustrates the use of a string variable with the READ and PRINT statements.

```
10 DIM N$(10)
20 READ N$,A
30 PRINT N$,A
40 GO TO 20
50 REM     NOW LIST THE NAMES AND AGES AS FOLLOWS:
60 REM        70 DATA "NAME", AGE, "NAME", AGE, ...
70 DATA "JOHN", 4, "JENNIFER", 2
80 END


RUN

              15:32     06/24/75

JOHN                    4
JENNIFER                2

LINE    20:    END OF DATA

TIME 0.0 SECS.
```

Note in the printout the use of the quotes around the string in the DATA statement and the mixing of alphanumeric variables with simple BASIC variables in the READ and PRINT statements. One should also note that when a string variable is followed by a semicolon in the PRINT statement, the next output is printed in the very next column.

We can revise this sample program to make use of the INPUT statement instead of the READ statement.

```
10 DIM N$(10)
20 PRINT "ENTER YOUR NAME AND AGE"
30 INPUT N$,A
40 PRINT N$,A
50 GO TO 20
60 END



RUN

              15:40     06/24/75

ENTER YOUR NAME AND AGE
? "JANE", 24
JANE                    24
ENTER YOUR NAME AND AGE
? "FRANK", 34
FRANK                   34
ENTER YOUR NAME AND AGE
? "ROWLAND", 76
ROWLAND                 76
ENTER YOUR NAME AND AGE
?
```

Alphanumeric variables can be used with the IF-THEN statement. For example, when we program a computer to play the dice game, we might have a section of the program which allows the user to decide whether he or she wants to play the game a second time. This procedure might take the following form:

```
10 DIM A$(3)
   •
   •
   •
90 PRINT
100 PRINT "ENTER YES TO START THE GAME OR NO TO RECEIVE "
110 PRINT "YOUR TOTAL WINNINGS OR LOSSES"
120 INPUT A$
130 IF A$="YES" THEN 200
140 IF A$="NO" THEN 250
150 PRINT "TYPE IN YES OR NO"
160 GO TO 120
    •
    •
    •
200 GO SUB 500
    •
    •
    •
250 GO SUB 600
    •
    •
    •
499 REM     SUBROUTINE 500 STARTS THE DICE GAME
500
    •
    •
    •
599 REM     SUBROUTINE 600 ENDS THE DICE GAME
600
    •
    •
    •
990 END
```

Note: Line 90 PRINT in the preceding program illustrates how we can have the computer skip a line. This technique will be useful in the spacing of computer output for future programs.

String variables can also be used with the LET statement. For example,

90   LET F$ = "POLYNOMIAL"

200   LET T$ = R$

One important thing to note is that you *cannot* perform the operations of addition (+), subtraction (−), multiplication (∗), division (/), and raising to a power (↑) with alphanumeric (string) variables.

G.3

Nested For-Next Statements (Loops)

In Chapter 1 we saw how to use a pair of matching FOR and NEXT statements to direct the computer to execute and repeat a certain sequence of statements a finite number of times in a BASIC program. Many future BASIC programs may require the use of *nested loops*—that is, one or more loops completely within another loop.

Multiple loops are acceptable in the BASIC language as long as no two loops overlap; that is, the inner loops are completely contained within the outer loops.

The following examples illustrate one acceptable and one unacceptable nested loop.

Acceptable	Unacceptable
10 FOR X = 1 TO 3 STEP 1	10 FOR X = 1 TO 3 STEP 1
20 FOR Y = 2 TO 6 STEP 2	20 FOR Y = 2 TO 6 STEP 2
30 · · ·	30 · · ·
40 · · ·	40 · · ·
50 · · ·	50 · · ·
60 NEXT Y	60 NEXT X
70 NEXT X	70 NEXT Y

In the acceptable nested loop the computer will execute the statements in the loop nine times in precisely the following order:

Run 1:   X = 1   Y = 2   Run 6:   X = 2   Y = 6

Run 2:   X = 1   Y = 4   Run 7:   X = 3   Y = 2

Run 3:   X = 1   Y = 6   Run 8:   X = 3   Y = 4

Run 4:   X = 2   Y = 2   Run 9:   X = 3   Y = 6

Run 5:   X = 2   Y = 4

Notice the inner (FOR Y) loop is satisfied for the given Y values first. As shown above, the first three executions occur with X = 1 and Y = 2, then Y = 4, then Y = 6. The next three executions occur with X = 2 and Y = 2, then Y = 4, then Y = 6. The final three executions occur with X = 3 and Y = 2, then Y = 4, then Y = 6.

Many programs necessitate the use of such nested loops.

SAMPLE BASIC PROGRAM

```
10 PRINT " A      B      A↑2    B↑2    A*B"
20 FOR A= 1 TO 4
30 FOR B= 2 TO 10 STEP 2
```

```
40      PRINT A; B; A↑2; B↑2; A*B
50 NEXT B
60 NEXT A
70 END


RUN

                      8:00    06/30/75

        A         B       A↑2     B↑2     A*B
        1         2       1       4       2
        1         4       1       16      4
        1         6       1       36      6
        1         8       1       64      8
        1         10      1       100     10
        2         2       4       4       4
        2         4       4       16      8
        2         6       4       36      12
        2         8       4       64      16
        2         10      4       100     20
        3         2       9       4       6
        3         4       9       16      12
        3         6       9       36      18
        3         8       9       64      24
        3         10      9       100     30
        4         2       16      4       8
        4         4       16      16      16
        4         6       16      36      24
        4         8       16      64      32
        4         10      16      100     40

TIME 0.0 SECS.
```

Problem Set G.2

1. Code the flowchart in Figure G.2 in the BASIC language.

2. Explain what task the flowchart in Figure G.2 can accomplish.

3. Type the coding of the flowchart in Problem 1 (Figure G.2) and run the program with the following data: LOU, 27, JAMES, 15, MARY, 19, SUE, 29, CLARA, 51, BOB, 62, ANNIE, 97.

4. Revise the program in Problem 1 so that it will print out lists of names and ages for people whose $29 < \text{age} < 65$.

5. Run the following BASIC program:

```
10   DIM A$(10),B$(3)
20   LET B$ = "ABC"
30   READ A$
```

```
40   IF A$ < > "ENOUGH" THEN 60
50   STOP
60   IF A$ = B$ THEN 100
70   PRINT "A$ DOES NOT EQUAL B$"
80   PRINT
90   GO TO 30
100  PRINT "A$ = B$",B$
110  PRINT
120  PRINT
130  GO TO 30
140  DATA "ABCD", "ABC D", "ABC", "ABCDEFGHIJ", "ENOUGH",
     "ABC"
150  END
```

Which of the following diagrams illustrates an unacceptable use of nested FOR and NEXT statements?

(a) FOR T = _____   (b) FOR T = _____
    FOR R = _____   FOR R = _____
    FOR S = _____   FOR S = _____

    _____   _____
    _____   _____
    _____   _____
    _____   _____

    NEXT S   NEXT S
    NEXT T   NEXT R
    NEXT R   NEXT T

Figure G.2

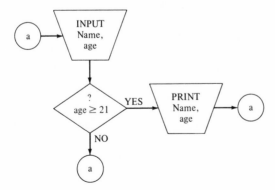

Appendix H: Mathematical Tables

Table 1. Squares and Square Roots for Numbers 1 Through 1,000

n	n^2	$\sqrt{n}$	$\sqrt{10n}$	n	n^2	$\sqrt{n}$	$\sqrt{10n}$
1	1	1.000 000	3.162 278	50	2 500	7.071 068	22.36068
2	4	1.414 214	4.472 136	51	2 601	7.141 428	22.58318
3	9	1.732 051	5.477 226	52	2 704	7.211 103	22.80351
4	16	2.000 000	6.324 555	53	2 809	7.280 110	23.02173
				54	2 916	7.348 469	23.23790
5	25	2.236 068	7.071 068	55	3 025	7.416 198	23.45208
6	36	2.449 490	7.745 967	56	3 136	7.483 315	23.66432
7	49	2.645 751	8.366 600	57	3 249	7.549 834	23.87467
8	64	2.828 427	8.944 272	58	3 364	7.615 773	24.08319
9	81	3.000 000	9.486 833	59	3 481	7.681 146	24.28992
10	100	3.162 278	10.00000	60	3 600	7.745 967	24.49490
11	121	3.316 625	10.48809	61	3 721	7.810 250	24.69818
12	144	3.464 102	10.95445	62	3 844	7.874 008	24.89980
13	169	3.605 551	11.40175	63	3 969	7.937 254	25.09980
14	196	3.741 657	11.83216	64	4 096	8.000 000	25.29822
15	225	3.872 983	12.24745	65	4 225	8.062 258	25.49510
16	256	4.000 000	12.64911	66	4 356	8.124 038	25.69047
17	289	4.123 106	13.03840	67	4 489	8.185 353	25.88436
18	324	4.242 641	13.41641	68	4 624	8.246 211	26.07681
19	361	4.358 899	13.78405	69	4 761	8.306 624	26.26785
20	400	4.472 136	14.14214	70	4 900	8.366 600	26.45751
21	441	4.582 576	14.49138	71	5 041	8.426 150	26.64583
22	484	4.690 416	14.83240	72	5 184	8.485 281	26.83282
23	529	4.795 832	15.16575	73	5 329	8.544 004	27.01851
24	576	4.898 979	15.49193	74	5 476	8.602 325	27.20294
25	625	5.000 000	15.81139	75	5 625	8.660 254	27.38613
26	676	5.099 020	16.12452	76	5 776	8.717 798	27.56810
27	729	5.196 152	16.43168	77	5 929	8.774 964	27.74887
28	784	5.291 503	16.73320	78	6 084	8.831 761	27.92848
29	841	5.385 165	17.02939	79	6 241	8.888 194	28.10694
30	900	5.477 226	17.32051	80	6 400	8.944 272	28.28427
31	961	5.567 764	17.60682	81	6 561	9.000 000	28.46050
32	1 024	5.656 854	17.88854	82	6 724	9.055 385	28.63564
33	1 089	5.744 563	18.16590	83	6 889	9.110 434	28.80972
34	1 156	5.830 952	18.43909	84	7 056	9.165 151	28.98275
35	1 225	5.916 080	18.70829	85	7 225	9.219 544	29.15476
36	1 296	6.000 000	18.97367	86	7 396	9.273 618	29.32576
37	1 369	6.082 763	19.23538	87	7 569	9.327 379	29.49576
38	1 444	6.164 414	19.49359	88	7 744	9.380 832	29.66479
39	1 521	6.244 998	19.74842	89	7 921	9.433 981	29.83287
40	1 600	6.324 555	20.00000	90	8 100	9.486 833	30.00000
41	1 681	6.403 124	20.24846	91	8 281	9.539 392	30.16621
42	1 764	6.480 741	20.49390	92	8 464	9.591 663	30.33150
43	1 849	6.557 439	20.73644	93	8 649	9.643 651	30.49590
44	1 936	6.633 250	20.97618	94	8 836	9.695 360	30.65942
45	2 025	6.708 204	21.21320	95	9 025	9.746 794	30.82207
46	2 116	6.782 330	21.44761	96	9 216	9.797 959	30.98387
47	2 209	6.855 655	21.67948	97	9 409	9.848 858	31.14482
48	2 304	6.928 203	21.90890	98	9 604	9.899 495	31.30495
49	2 401	7.000 000	22.13594	99	9 801	9.949 874	31.46427
				100	10 000	10.00000	31.62278
				101	10 201	10.04988	31.78050
				102	10 404	10.09950	31.93744
				103	10 609	10.14889	32.09361
				104	10 816	10.19804	32.24903
				105	11 025	10.24695	32.40370
				106	11 236	10.29563	32.55764
				107	11 449	10.34408	32.71085
				108	11 664	10.39230	32.86335
				109	11 881	10.44031	33.01515

Squares and Square Roots (Continued)

n	n²	√n	√10n	n	n²	√n	√10n
110	12 100	10.48809	33.16625	**170**	28 900	13.03840	41.23106
111	12 321	10.53565	33.31666	171	29 241	13.07670	41.35215
112	12 544	10.58301	33.46640	172	29 584	13.11488	41.47288
113	12 769	10.63015	33.61547	173	29 929	13.15295	41.59327
114	12 996	10.67708	33.76389	174	30 276	13.19091	41.71331
115	13 225	10.72381	33.91165	175	30 625	13.22876	41.83300
116	13 456	10.77033	34.05877	176	30 976	13.26650	41.95235
117	13 689	10.81665	34.20526	177	31 329	13.30413	42.07137
118	13 924	10.86278	34.35113	178	31 684	13.34166	42.19005
119	14 161	10.90871	34.49638	179	32 041	13.37909	42.30839
120	14 400	10.95445	34.64102	**180**	32 400	13.41641	42.42641
121	14 641	11.00000	34.78505	181	32 761	13.45362	42.54409
122	14 884	11.04536	34.92850	182	33 124	13.49074	42.66146
123	15 129	11.09054	35.07136	183	33 489	13.52775	42.77850
124	15 376	11.13553	35.21363	184	33 856	13.56466	42.89522
125	15 625	11.18034	35.35534	185	34 225	13.60147	43.01163
126	15 876	11.22497	35.49648	186	34 596	13.63818	43.12772
127	16 129	11.26943	35.63706	187	34 969	13.67479	43.24350
128	16 384	11.31371	35.77709	188	35 344	13.71131	43.35897
129	16 641	11.35782	35.91657	189	35 721	13.74773	43.47413
130	16 900	11.40175	36.05551	**190**	36 100	13.78405	43.58899
131	17 161	11.44552	36.19392	191	36 481	13.82027	43.70355
132	17 424	11.48913	36.33180	192	36 864	13.85641	43.81780
133	17 689	11.53256	36.46917	193	37 249	13.89244	43.93177
134	17 956	11.57584	36.60601	194	37 636	13.92839	44.04543
135	18 225	11.61895	36.74235	195	38 025	13.96424	44.15880
136	18 496	11.66190	36.87818	196	38 416	14.00000	44.27189
137	18 769	11.70470	37.01351	197	38 809	14.03567	44.38468
138	19 044	11.74734	37.14835	198	39 204	14.07125	44.49719
139	19 321	11.78983	37.28270	199	39 601	14.10674	44.60942
140	19 600	11.83216	37.41657	**200**	40 000	14.14214	44.72136
141	19 881	11.87434	37.54997	201	40 401	14.17745	44.83302
142	20 164	11.91638	37.68289	202	40 804	14.21267	44.94441
143	20 449	11.95826	37.81534	203	41 209	14.24781	45.05552
144	20 736	12.00000	37.94733	204	41 616	14.28286	45.16636
145	21 025	12.04159	38.07887	205	42 025	14.31782	45.27693
146	21 316	12.08305	38.20995	206	42 436	14.35270	45.38722
147	21 609	12.12436	38.34058	207	42 849	14.38749	45.49725
148	21 904	12.16553	38.47077	208	43 264	14.42221	45.60702
149	22 201	12.20656	38.60052	209	43 681	14.45683	45.71652
150	22 500	12.24745	38.72983	**210**	44 100	14.49138	45.82576
151	22 801	12.28821	38.85872	211	44 521	14.52584	45.93474
152	23 104	12.32883	38.98718	212	44 944	14.56022	46.04346
153	23 409	12.36932	39.11521	213	45 369	14.59452	46.15192
154	23 716	12.40967	39.24283	214	45 796	14.62874	46.26013
155	24 025	12.44990	39.37004	215	46 225	14.66288	46.36809
156	24 336	12.49000	39.49684	216	46 656	14.69694	46.47580
157	24 649	12.52996	39.62323	217	47 089	14.73092	46.58326
158	24 964	12.56981	39.74921	218	47 524	14.76482	46.69047
159	25 281	12.60952	39.87480	219	47 961	14.79865	46.79744
160	25 600	12.64911	40.00000	**220**	48 400	14.83240	46.90416
161	25 921	12.68858	40.12481	221	48 841	14.86607	47.01064
162	26 244	12.72792	40.24922	222	49 284	14.89966	47.11688
163	26 569	12.76715	40.37326	223	49 729	14.93318	47.22288
164	26 896	12.80625	40.49691	224	50 176	14.96663	47.32864
165	27 225	12.84523	40.62019	225	50 625	15.00000	47.43416
166	27 556	12.88410	40.74310	226	51 076	15.03330	47.53946
167	27 889	12.92285	40.86563	227	51 529	15.06652	47.64452
168	28 224	12.96148	40.98780	228	51 984	15.09967	47.74935
169	28 561	13.00000	41.10961	229	52 441	15.13275	47.85394

Squares and Square Roots (Continued)

n	n^2	$\sqrt{n}$	$\sqrt{10n}$	n	n^2	$\sqrt{n}$	$\sqrt{10n}$
230	52 900	15.16575	47.95832	**290**	84 100	17.02939	53.85165
231	53 361	15.19868	48.06246	291	84 681	17.05872	53.94442
232	53 824	15.23155	48.16638	292	85 264	17.08801	54.03702
233	54 289	15.26434	48.27007	293	85 849	17.11724	54.12947
234	54 756	15.29706	48.37355	294	86 436	17.14643	54.22177
235	55 225	15.32971	48.47680	295	87 025	17.17556	54.31390
236	55 696	15.36229	48.57983	296	87 616	17.20465	54.40588
237	56 169	15.39480	48.68265	297	88 209	17.23369	54.49771
238	56 644	15.42725	48.78524	298	88 804	17.26268	54.58938
239	57 121	15.45962	48.88763	299	89 401	17.29162	54.68089
240	57 600	15.49193	48.98979	**300**	90 000	17.32051	54.77226
241	58 081	15.52417	49.09175	301	90 601	17.34935	54.86347
242	58 564	15.55635	49.19350	302	91 204	17.37815	54.95453
243	59 049	15.58846	49.29503	303	91 809	17.40690	55.04544
244	59 536	15.62050	49.39636	304	92 416	17.43560	55.13620
245	60 025	15.65248	49.49747	305	93 025	17.46425	55.22681
246	60 516	15.68439	49.59839	306	93 636	17.49286	55.31727
247	61 009	15.71623	49.69909	307	94 249	17.52142	55.40758
248	61 504	15.74802	49.79960	308	94 864	17.54993	55.49775
249	62 001	15.77973	49.89990	309	95 481	17.57840	55.58777
250	62 500	15.81139	50.00000	**310**	96 100	17.60682	55.67764
251	63 001	15.84298	50.09990	311	96 721	17.63519	55.76737
252	63 504	15.87451	50.19960	312	97 344	17.66352	55.85696
253	64 009	15.90597	50.29911	313	97 969	17.69181	55.94640
254	64 516	15.93738	50.39841	314	98 596	17.72005	56.03570
255	65 025	15.96872	50.49752	315	99 225	17.74824	56.12486
256	65 536	16.00000	50.59644	316	99 856	17.77639	56.21388
257	66 049	16.03122	50.69517	317	100 489	17.80449	56.30275
258	66 564	16.06238	50.79370	318	101 124	17.83255	56.39149
259	67 081	16.09348	50.89204	319	101 761	17.86057	56.48008
260	67 600	16.12452	50.99020	**320**	102 400	17.88854	56.56854
261	68 121	16.15549	51.08816	321	103 041	17.91647	56.65686
262	68 644	16.18641	51.18594	322	103 684	17.94436	56.74504
263	69 169	16.21727	51.28353	323	104 329	17.97220	56.83309
264	69 696	16.24808	51.38093	324	104 976	18.00000	56.92100
265	70 225	16.27882	51.47815	325	105 625	18.02776	57.00877
266	70 756	16.30951	51.57519	326	106 276	18.05547	57.09641
267	71 289	16.34013	51.67204	327	106 929	18.08314	57.18391
268	71 824	16.37071	51.76872	328	107 584	18.11077	57.27128
269	72 361	16.40122	51.86521	329	108 241	18.13836	57.35852
270	72 900	16.43168	51.96152	**330**	108 900	18.16590	57.44563
271	73 441	16.46208	52.05766	331	109 561	18.19341	57.53260
272	73 984	16.49242	52.15362	332	110 224	18.22087	57.61944
273	74 529	16.52271	52.24940	333	110 889	18.24829	57.70615
274	75 076	16.55295	52.34501	334	111 556	18.27567	57.79273
275	75 625	16.58312	52.44044	335	112 225	18.30301	57.87918
276	76 176	16.61325	52.53570	336	112 896	18.33030	57.96551
277	76 729	16.64332	52.63079	337	113 569	18.35756	58.05170
278	77 284	16.67333	52.72571	338	114 244	18.38478	58.13777
279	77 841	16.70329	52.82045	339	114 921	18.41195	58.22371
280	78 400	16.73320	52.91503	**340**	115 600	18.43909	58.30952
281	78 961	16.76305	53.00943	341	116 281	18.46619	58.39521
282	79 524	16.79286	53.10367	342	116 964	18.49324	58.48077
283	80 089	16.82260	53.19774	343	117 649	18.52026	58.56620
284	80 656	16.85230	53.29165	344	118 336	18.54724	58.65151
285	81 225	16.88194	53.38539	345	119 025	18.57418	58.73670
286	81 796	16.91153	53.47897	346	119 716	18.60108	58.82176
287	82 369	16.94107	53.57238	347	120 409	18.62794	58.90671
288	82 944	16.97056	53.66563	348	121 104	18.65476	58.99152
289	83 521	17.00000	53.75872	349	121 801	18.68154	59.07622

Squares and Square Roots (Continued)

n	n^2	$\sqrt{n}$	$\sqrt{10n}$	n	n^2	$\sqrt{n}$	$\sqrt{10n}$
350	122 500	18.70829	59.16080	**410**	168 100	20.24846	64.03124
351	123 201	18.73499	59.24525	411	168 921	20.27313	64.10928
352	123 904	18.76166	59.32959	412	169 744	20.29778	64.18723
353	124 609	18.78829	59.41380	413	170 569	20.32240	64.26508
354	125 316	18.81489	59.49790	414	171 396	20.34699	64.34283
355	126 025	18.84144	59.58188	415	172 225	20.37155	64.42049
356	126 736	18.86796	59.66574	416	173 056	20.39608	64.49806
357	127 449	18.89444	59.74948	417	173 889	20.42058	64.57554
358	128 164	18.92089	59.83310	418	174 724	20.44505	64.65292
359	128 881	18.94730	59.91661	419	175 561	20.46949	64.73021
360	129 600	18.97367	60.00000	**420**	176 400	20.49390	64.80741
361	130 321	19.00000	60.08328	421	177 241	20.51828	64.88451
362	131 044	19.02630	60.16644	422	178 084	20.54264	64.96153
363	131 769	19.05256	60.24948	423	178 929	20.56696	65.03845
364	132 496	19.07878	60.33241	424	179 776	20.59126	65.11528
365	133 225	19.10497	60.41523	425	180 625	20.61553	65.19202
366	133 956	19.13113	60.49793	426	181 476	20.63977	65.26868
367	134 689	19.15724	60.58052	427	182 329	20.66398	65.34524
368	135 424	19.18333	60.66300	428	183 184	20.68816	65.42171
369	136 161	19.20937	60.74537	429	184 041	20.71232	65.49809
370	136 900	19.23538	60.82763	**430**	184 900	20.73644	65.57439
371	137 641	19.26136	60.90977	431	185 761	20.76054	65.65059
372	138 384	19.28730	60.99180	432	186 624	20.78461	65.72671
373	139 129	19.31321	61.07373	433	187 489	20.80865	65.80274
374	139 876	19.33908	61.15554	434	188 356	20.83267	65.87868
375	140 625	19.36492	61.23724	435	189 225	20.85665	65.95453
376	141 376	19.39072	61.31884	436	190 096	20.88061	66.03030
377	142 129	19.41649	61.40033	437	190 969	20.90454	66.10598
378	142 884	19.44222	61.48170	438	191 844	20.92845	66.18157
379	143 641	19.46792	61.56298	439	192 721	20.95233	66.25708
380	144 400	19.49359	61.64414	**440**	193 600	20.97618	66.33250
381	145 161	19.51922	61.72520	441	194 481	21.00000	66.40783
382	145 924	19.54482	61.80615	442	195 364	21.02380	66.48308
383	146 689	19.57039	61.88699	443	196 249	21.04757	66.55825
384	147 456	19.59592	61.96773	444	197 136	21.07131	66.63332
385	148 225	19.62142	62.04837	445	198 025	21.09502	66.70832
386	148 996	19.64688	62.12890	446	198 916	21.11871	66.78323
387	149 769	19.67232	62.20932	447	199 809	21.14237	66.85806
388	150 544	19.69772	62.28965	448	200 704	21.16601	66.93280
389	151 321	19.72308	62.36986	449	201 601	21.18962	67.00746
390	152 100	19.74842	62.44998	**450**	202 500	21.21320	67.08204
391	152 881	19.77372	62.52999	451	203 401	21.23676	67.15653
392	153 664	19.79899	62.60990	452	204 304	21.26029	67.23095
393	154 449	19.82423	62.68971	453	205 209	21.28380	67.30527
394	155 236	19.84943	62.76942	454	206 116	21.30728	67.37952
395	156 025	19.87461	62.84903	455	207 025	21.33073	67.45369
396	156 816	19.89975	62.92853	456	207 936	21.35416	67.52777
397	157 609	19.92486	63.00794	457	208 849	21.37756	67.60178
398	158 404	19.94994	63.08724	458	209 764	21.40093	67.67570
399	159 201	19.97498	63.16645	459	210 681	21.42429	67.74954
400	160 000	20.00000	63.24555	**460**	211 600	21.44761	67.82330
401	160 801	20.02498	63.32456	461	212 521	21.47091	67.89698
402	161 604	20.04994	63.40347	462	213 444	21.49419	67.97058
403	162 409	20.07486	63.48228	463	214 369	21.51743	68.04410
404	163 216	20.09975	63.56099	464	215 296	21.54066	68.11755
405	164 025	20.12461	63.63961	465	216 225	21.56386	68.19091
406	164 836	20.14944	63.71813	466	217 156	21.58703	68.26419
407	165 649	20.17424	63.79655	467	218 089	21.61018	68.33740
408	166 464	20.19901	63.87488	468	219 024	21.63331	68.41053
409	167 281	20.22375	63.95311	469	219 961	21.65641	68.48357

Squares and Square Roots (Continued)

n	n²	√n	√10n	n	n²	√n	√10n
470	220 900	21.67948	68.55655	530	280 900	23.02173	72.80110
471	221 841	21.70253	68.62944	531	281 961	23.04344	72.86975
472	222 784	21.72556	68.70226	532	283 024	23.06513	72.93833
473	223 729	21.74856	68.77500	533	284 089	23.08679	73.00685
474	224 676	21.77154	68.84766	534	285 156	23.10844	73.07530
475	225 625	21.79449	68.92024	535	286 225	23.13007	73.14369
476	226 576	21.81742	68.99275	536	287 296	23.15167	73.21202
477	227 529	21.84033	69.06519	537	288 369	23.17326	73.28028
478	228 484	21.86321	69.13754	538	289 444	23.19483	73.34848
479	229 441	21.88607	69.20983	539	290 521	23.21637	73.41662
480	230 400	21.90890	69.28203	540	291 600	23.23790	73.48469
481	231 361	21.93171	69.35416	541	292 681	23.25941	73.55270
482	232 324	21.95450	69.42622	542	293 764	23.28089	73.62065
483	233 289	21.97726	69.49820	543	294 849	23.30236	73.68853
484	234 256	22.00000	69.57011	544	295 936	23.32381	73.75636
485	235 225	22.02272	69.64194	545	297 025	23.34524	73.82412
486	236 196	22.04541	69.71370	546	298 116	23.36664	73.89181
487	237 169	22.06808	69.78539	547	299 209	23.38803	73.95945
488	238 144	22.09072	69.85700	548	300 304	23.40940	74.02702
489	239 121	22.11334	69.92853	549	301 401	23.43075	74.09453
490	240 100	22.13594	70.00000	550	302 500	23.45208	74.16198
491	241 081	22.15852	70.07139	551	303 601	23.47339	74.22937
492	242 064	22.18107	70.14271	552	304 704	23.49468	74.29670
493	243 049	22.20360	70.21396	553	305 809	23.51595	74.36397
494	244 036	22.22611	70.28513	554	306 916	23.53720	74.43118
495	245 025	22.24860	70.35624	555	308 025	23.55844	74.49832
496	246 016	22.27106	70.42727	556	309 136	23.57965	74.56541
497	247 009	22.29350	70.49823	557	310 249	23.60085	74.63243
498	248 004	22.31591	70.56912	558	311 364	23.62202	74.69940
499	249 001	22.33831	70.63993	559	312 481	23.64318	74.76630
500	250 000	22.36068	70.71068	560	313 600	23.66432	74.83315
501	251 001	22.38303	70.78135	561	314 721	23.68544	74.89993
502	252 004	22.40536	70.85196	562	315 844	23.70654	74.96666
503	253 009	22.42766	70.92249	563	316 969	23.72762	75.03333
504	254 016	22.44994	70.99296	564	318 096	23.74868	75.09993
505	255 025	22.47221	71.06335	565	319 225	23.76973	75.16648
506	256 036	22.49444	71.13368	566	320 356	23.79075	75.23297
507	257 049	22.51666	71.20393	567	321 489	23.81176	75.29940
508	258 064	22.53886	71.27412	568	322 624	23.83275	75.36577
509	259 081	22.56103	71.34424	569	323 761	23.85372	75.43209
510	260 100	22.58318	71.41428	570	324 900	23.87467	75.49834
511	261 121	22.60531	71.48426	571	326 041	23.89561	75.56454
512	262 144	22.62742	71.55418	572	327 184	23.91652	75.63068
513	263 169	22.64950	71.62402	573	328 329	23.93742	75.69676
514	264 196	22.67157	71.69379	574	329 476	23.95830	75.76279
515	265 225	22.69361	71.76350	575	330 625	23.97916	75.82875
516	266 256	22.71563	71.83314	576	331 776	24.00000	75.89466
517	267 289	22.73763	71.90271	577	332 929	24.02082	75.96052
518	268 324	22.75961	71.97222	578	334 084	24.04163	76.02631
519	269 361	22.78157	72.04165	579	335 241	24.06242	76.09205
520	270 400	22.80351	72.11103	580	336 400	24.08319	76.15773
521	271 441	22.82542	72.18033	581	337 561	24.10394	76.22336
522	272 484	22.84732	72.24957	582	338 724	24.12468	76.28892
523	273 529	22.86919	72.31874	583	339 889	24.14539	76.35444
524	274 576	22.89105	72.38784	584	341 056	24.16609	76.41989
525	275 625	22.91288	72.45688	585	342 225	24.18677	76.48529
526	276 676	22.93469	72.52586	586	343 396	24.20744	76.55064
527	277 729	22.95648	72.59477	587	344 569	24.22808	76.61593
528	278 784	22.97825	72.66361	588	345 744	24.24871	76.68116
529	279 841	23.00000	72.73239	589	346 921	24.26932	76.74634

Squares and Square Roots (Continued)

n	n²	√n	√10n	n	n²	√n	√10n
590	348 100	24.28992	76.81146	**650**	422 500	25.49510	80.62258
591	349 281	24.31049	76.87652	651	423 801	25.51470	80.68457
592	350 464	24.33105	76.94154	652	425 104	25.53429	80.74652
593	351 649	24.35159	77.00649	653	426 409	25.55386	80.80842
594	352 836	24.37212	77.07140	654	427 716	25.57342	80.87027
595	354 025	24.39262	77.13624	655	429 025	25.59297	80.93207
596	355 216	24.41311	77.20104	656	430 336	25.61250	80.99383
597	356 409	24.43358	77.26578	657	431 649	25.63201	81.05554
598	357 604	24.45404	77.33046	658	432 964	25.65151	81.11720
599	358 801	24.47448	77.39509	659	434 281	25.67100	81.17881
600	360 000	24.49490	77.45967	**660**	435 600	25.69047	81.24038
601	361 201	24.51530	77.52419	661	436 921	25.70992	81.30191
602	362 404	24.53569	77.58866	662	438 244	25.72936	81.36338
603	363 609	24.55606	77.65307	663	439 569	25.74879	81.42481
604	364 816	24.57641	77.71744	664	440 896	25.76820	81.48620
605	366 025	24.59675	77.78175	665	442 225	25.78759	81.54753
606	367 236	24.61707	77.84600	666	443 556	25.80698	81.60882
607	368 449	24.63737	77.91020	667	444 889	25.82634	81.67007
608	369 664	24.65766	77.97435	668	446 224	25.84570	81.73127
609	370 881	24.67793	78.03845	669	447 561	25.86503	81.79242
610	372 100	24.69818	78.10250	**670**	448 900	25.88436	81.85353
611	373 321	24.71841	78.16649	671	450 241	25.90367	81.91459
612	374 544	24.73863	78.23043	672	451 584	25.92296	81.97561
613	375 769	24.75884	78.29432	673	452 929	25.94224	82.03658
614	376 996	24.77902	78.35815	674	454 276	25.96151	82.09750
615	378 225	24.79919	78.42194	675	455 625	25.98076	82.15838
616	379 456	24.81935	78.48567	676	456 976	26.00000	82.21922
617	380 689	24.83948	78.54935	677	458 329	26.01922	82.28001
618	381 924	24.85961	78.61298	678	459 684	26.03843	82.34076
619	383 161	24.87971	78.67655	679	461 041	26.05763	82.40146
620	384 400	24.89980	78.74008	**680**	462 400	26.07681	82.46211
621	385 641	24.91987	78.80355	681	463 761	26.09598	82.52272
622	386 884	24.93993	78.86698	682	465 124	26.11513	82.58329
623	388 129	24.95997	78.93035	683	466 489	26.13427	82.64381
624	389 376	24.97999	78.99367	684	467 856	26.15339	82.70429
625	390 625	25.00000	79.05694	685	469 225	26.17250	82.76473
626	391 876	25.01999	79.12016	686	470 596	26.19160	82.82512
627	393 129	25.03997	79.18333	687	471 969	26.21068	82.88546
628	394 384	25.05993	79.24645	688	473 344	26.22975	82.94577
629	395 641	25.07987	79.30952	689	474 721	26.24881	83.00602
630	396 900	25.09980	79.37254	**690**	476 100	26.26785	83.06624
631	398 161	25.11971	79.43551	691	477 481	26.28688	83.12641
632	399 424	25.13961	79.49843	692	478 864	26.30589	83.18654
633	400 689	25.15949	79.56130	693	480 249	26.32489	83.24662
634	401 956	25.17936	79.62412	694	481 636	26.34388	83.30666
635	403 225	25.19921	79.68689	695	483 025	26.36285	83.36666
636	404 496	25.21904	79.74961	696	484 416	26.38181	83.42661
637	405 769	25.23886	79.81228	697	485 809	26.40076	83.48653
638	407 044	25.25866	79.87490	698	487 204	26.41969	83.54639
639	408 321	25.27845	79.93748	699	488 601	26.43861	83.60622
640	409 600	25.29822	80.00000	**700**	490 000	26.45751	83.66600
641	410 881	25.31798	80.06248	701	491 401	26.47640	83.72574
642	412 164	25.33772	80.12490	702	492 804	26.49528	83.78544
643	413 449	25.35744	80.18728	703	494 209	26.51415	83.84510
644	414 736	25.37716	80.24961	704	495 616	26.53300	83.90471
645	416 025	25.39685	80.31189	705	497 025	26.55184	83.96428
646	417 316	25.41653	80.37413	706	498 436	26.57066	84.02381
647	418 609	25.43619	80.43631	707	499 849	26.58947	84.08329
648	419 904	25.45584	80.49845	708	501 264	26.60827	84.14274
649	421 201	25.47548	80.56054	709	502 681	26.62705	84.20214

Squares and Square Roots (Continued)

n	n^2	$\sqrt{n}$	$\sqrt{10n}$	n	n^2	$\sqrt{n}$	$\sqrt{10n}$
710	504 100	26.64583	84.26150	770	592 900	27.74887	87.74964
711	505 521	26.66458	84.32082	771	594 441	27.76689	87.80661
712	506 944	26.68333	84.38009	772	595 984	27.78489	87.86353
713	508 369	26.70206	84.43933	773	597 529	27.80288	87.92042
714	509 796	26.72078	84.49852	774	599 076	27.82086	87.97727
715	511 225	26.73948	84.55767	775	600 625	27.83882	88.03408
716	512 656	26.75818	84.61678	776	602 176	27.85678	88.09086
717	514 089	26.77686	84.67585	777	603 729	27.87472	88.14760
718	515 524	26.79552	84.73488	778	605 284	27.89265	88.20431
719	516 961	26.81418	84.79387	779	606 841	27.91057	88.26098
720	518 400	26.83282	84.85281	780	608 400	27.92848	88.31761
721	519 841	26.85144	84.91172	781	609 961	27.94638	88.37420
722	521 284	26.87006	84.97058	782	611 524	27.96426	88.43076
723	522 729	26.88866	85.02941	783	613 089	27.98214	88.48729
724	524 176	26.90725	85.08819	784	614 656	28.00000	88.54377
725	525 625	26.92582	85.14693	785	616 225	28.01785	88.60023
726	527 076	26.94439	85.20563	786	617 796	28.03569	88.65664
727	528 529	26.96294	85.26429	787	619 369	28.05352	88.71302
728	529 984	26.98148	85.32292	788	620 944	28.07134	88.76936
729	531 441	27.00000	85.38150	789	622 521	28.08914	88.82567
730	532 900	27.01851	85.44004	790	624 100	28.10694	88.88194
731	534 361	27.03701	85.49854	791	625 681	28.12472	88.93818
732	535 824	27.05550	85.55700	792	627 264	28.14249	88.99438
733	537 289	27.07397	85.61542	793	628 849	28.16026	89.05055
734	538 756	27.09243	85.67380	794	630 436	28.17801	89.10668
735	540 225	27.11088	85.73214	795	632 025	28.19574	89.16277
736	541 696	27.12932	85.79044	796	633 616	28.21347	89.21883
737	543 169	27.14774	85.84870	797	635 209	28.23119	89.27486
738	544 644	27.16616	85.90693	798	636 804	28.24889	89.33085
739	546 121	27.18455	85.96511	799	638 401	28.26659	89.38680
740	547 600	27.20294	86.02325	800	640 000	28.28427	89.44272
741	549 081	27.22132	86.08136	801	641 601	28.30194	89.49860
742	550 564	27.23968	86.13942	802	643 204	28.31960	89.55445
743	552 049	27.25803	86.19745	803	644 809	28.33725	89.61027
744	553 536	27.27636	86.25543	804	646 416	28.35489	89.66605
745	555 025	27.29469	86.31338	805	648 025	28.37252	89.72179
746	556 516	27.31300	86.37129	806	649 636	28.39014	89.77750
747	558 009	27.33130	86.42916	807	651 249	28.40775	89.83318
748	559 504	27.34959	86.48699	808	652 864	28.42534	89.88882
749	561 001	27.36786	86.54479	809	654 481	28.44293	89.94443
750	562 500	27.38613	86.60254	810	656 100	28.46050	90.00000
751	564 001	27.40438	86.66026	811	657 721	28.47806	90.05554
752	565 504	27.42262	86.71793	812	659 344	28.49561	90.11104
753	567 009	27.44085	86.77557	813	660 969	28.51315	90.16651
754	568 516	27.45906	86.83317	814	662 596	28.53069	90.22195
755	570 025	27.47726	86.89074	815	664 225	28.54820	90.27735
756	571 536	27.49545	86.94826	816	665 856	28.56571	90.33272
757	573 049	27.51363	87.00575	817	667 489	28.58321	90.38805
758	574 564	27.53180	87.06320	818	669 124	28.60070	90.44335
759	576 081	27.54995	87.12061	819	670 761	28.61818	90.49862
760	577 600	27.56810	87.17798	820	672 400	28.63564	90.55385
761	579 121	27.58623	87.23531	821	674 041	28.65310	90.60905
762	580 644	27.60435	87.20261	822	675 684	28.67054	90.66422
763	582 169	27.62245	87.34987	823	677 329	28.68798	90.71935
764	583 696	27.64055	87.40709	824	678 976	28.70540	90.77445
765	585 225	27.65863	87.46428	825	680 625	28.72281	90.82951
766	586 756	27.67671	87.52143	826	682 276	28.74022	90.88454
767	588 289	27.69476	87.57854	827	683 929	28.75761	90.93954
768	589 824	27.71281	87.63561	828	685 584	28.77499	90.99451
769	591 361	27.73085	87.69265	829	687 241	28.79236	91.04944

Squares and Square Roots (Continued)

n	n^2	$\sqrt{n}$	$\sqrt{10n}$	n	n^2	$\sqrt{n}$	$\sqrt{10n}$
830	688 900	28.80972	91.10434	**890**	792 100	29.83287	94.33981
831	690 561	28.82707	91.15920	891	793 881	29.84962	94.39280
832	692 224	28.84441	91.21403	892	795 664	29.86637	94.44575
833	693 889	28.86174	91.26883	893	797 449	29.88311	94.49868
834	695 556	28.87906	91.32360	894	799 236	29.89983	94.55157
835	697 225	28.89637	91.37833	895	801 025	29.91655	94.60444
836	698 896	28.91366	91.43304	896	802 816	29.93326	94.65728
837	700 569	28.93095	91.48770	897	804 609	29.94996	94.71008
838	702 244	28.94823	91.54234	898	806 404	29.96665	94.76286
839	703 921	28.96550	91.59694	899	808 201	29.98333	94.81561
840	705 600	28.98275	91.65151	**900**	810 000	30.00000	94.86833
841	707 281	29.00000	91.70605	901	811 801	30.01666	94.92102
842	708 964	29.01724	91.76056	902	813 604	30.03331	94.97368
843	710 649	29.03446	91.81503	903	815 409	30.04996	95.02631
844	712 336	29.05168	91.86947	904	817 216	30.06659	95.07891
845	714 025	29.06888	91.92388	905	819 025	30.08322	95.13149
846	715 716	29.08608	91.97826	906	820 836	30.09983	95.18403
847	717 409	29.10326	92.03260	907	822 649	30.11644	95.23655
848	719 104	29.12044	92.08692	908	824 464	30.13304	95.28903
849	720 801	29.13760	92.14120	909	826 281	30.14963	95.34149
850	722 500	29.15476	92.19544	**910**	828 100	30.16621	95.39392
851	724 201	29.17190	92.24966	911	829 921	30.18278	95.44632
852	725 904	29.18904	92.30385	912	831 744	30.19934	95.49869
853	727 609	29.20616	92.35800	913	833 569	30.21589	95.55103
854	729 316	29.22328	92.41212	914	835 396	30.23243	95.60335
855	731 025	29.24038	92.46621	915	837 225	30.24897	95.65563
856	732 736	29.25748	92.52027	916	839 056	30.26549	95.70789
857	734 449	29.27456	92.57429	917	840 889	30.28201	95.76012
858	736 164	29.29164	92.62829	918	842 724	30.29851	95.81232
859	737 881	29.30870	92.68225	919	844 561	30.31501	95.86449
860	739 600	29.32576	92.73618	**920**	846 400	30.33150	95.91663
861	741 321	29.34280	92.79009	921	848 241	30.34798	95.96874
862	743 044	29.35984	92.84396	922	850 084	30.36445	96.02083
863	744 769	29.37686	92.89779	923	851 929	30.38092	96.07289
864	746 496	29.39388	92.95160	924	853 776	30.39737	96.12492
865	748 225	29.41088	93.00538	925	855 625	30.41381	96.17692
866	749 956	29.42788	93.05912	926	857 476	30.43025	96.22889
867	751 689	29.44486	93.11283	927	859 329	30.44667	96.28084
868	753 424	29.46184	93.16652	928	861 184	30.46309	96.33276
869	755 161	29.47881	93.22017	929	863 041	30.47950	96.38465
870	756 900	29.49576	93.27379	**930**	864 900	30.49590	96.43651
871	758 641	29.51271	93.32738	931	866 761	30.51229	96.48834
872	760 384	29.52965	93.38094	932	868 624	30.52868	96.54015
873	762 129	29.54657	93.43447	933	870 489	30.54505	96.59193
874	763 876	29.56349	93.48797	934	872 356	30.56141	96.64368
875	765 625	29.58040	93.54143	935	874 225	30.57777	96.69540
876	767 376	29.59730	93.59487	936	876 096	30.59412	96.74709
877	769 129	29.61419	93.64828	937	877 969	30.61046	96.79876
878	770 884	29.63106	93.70165	938	879 844	30.62679	96.85040
879	772 641	29.64793	93.75500	939	881 721	30.64311	96.90201
880	774 400	29.66479	93.80832	**940**	883 600	30.65942	96.95360
881	776 161	29.68164	93.86160	941	885 481	30.67572	97.00515
882	777 924	29.69848	93.91486	942	887 364	30.69202	97.05668
883	779 689	29.71532	93.96808	943	889 249	30.70831	97.10819
884	781 456	29.73214	94.02127	944	891 136	30.72458	97.15966
885	783 225	29.74895	94.07444	945	893 025	30.74085	97.21111
886	784 996	29.76575	94.12757	946	894 916	30.75711	97.26253
887	786 769	29.78255	94.18068	947	896 809	30.77337	97.31393
888	788 544	29.79933	94.23375	948	898 704	30.78961	97.36529
889	790 321	29.81610	94.28680	949	900 601	30.80584	97.41663

Squares and Square Roots (Continued)

n	n^2	$\sqrt{n}$	$\sqrt{10n}$
950	902 500	30.82207	97.46794
951	904 401	30.83829	97.51923
952	906 304	30.85450	97.57049
953	908 209	30.87070	97.62172
954	910 116	30.88689	97.67292
955	912 025	30.90307	97.72410
956	913 936	30.91925	97.77525
957	915 849	30.93542	97.82638
958	917 764	30.95158	97.87747
959	919 681	30.96773	97.92855
960	921 600	30.98387	97.97959
961	923 521	31.00000	98.03061
962	925 444	31.01612	98.08160
963	927 369	31.03224	98.13256
964	929 296	31.04835	98.18350
965	931 225	31.06445	98.23441
966	933 156	31.08054	98.28530
967	935 089	31.09662	98.33616
968	937 024	31.11270	98.38699
969	938 961	31.12876	98.43780
970	940 900	31.14482	98.48858
971	942 841	31.16087	98.53933
972	944 784	31.17691	98.59006
973	946 729	31.19295	98.64076
974	948 676	31.20897	98.69144
975	950 625	31.22499	98.74209
976	952 576	31.24100	98.79271
977	954 529	31.25700	98.84331
978	956 484	31.27299	98.89388
979	958 441	31.28898	98.94443
980	960 400	31.30495	98.99495
981	962 361	31.32092	99.04544
982	964 324	31.33688	99.09591
983	966 289	31.35283	99.14636
984	968 256	31.36877	99.19677
985	970 225	31.38471	99.24717
986	972 196	31.40064	99.29753
987	974 169	31.41656	99.34787
988	976 144	31.43247	99.39819
989	978 121	31.44837	99.44848
990	980 100	31.46427	99.49874
991	982 081	31.48015	99.54898
992	984 064	31.49603	99.59920
993	986 049	31.51190	99.64939
994	988 036	31.52777	99.69955
995	990 025	31.54362	99.74969
996	992 016	31.55947	99.79980
997	994 009	31.57531	99.84989
998	996 004	31.59114	99.89995
999	998 001	31.60696	99.94999
1000	1 000 000	31.62278	100.00000

Table 2. Factorials

n	$n!$
0	1
1	1
2	2
3	6
4	24
5	120
6	720
7	5,040
8	40,320
9	362,880
10	3,628,800
11	39,916,800
12	479,001,600
13	6,227,020,800
14	87,178,291,200
15	1,307,674,368,000

Table 3.   Binomial Coefficients

							r				
n	0	1	2	3	4	5	6	7	8	9	10
0	1										
1	1	1									
2	1	2	1								
3	1	3	3	1							
4	1	4	6	4	1						
5	1	5	10	10	5	1					
6	1	6	15	20	15	6	1				
7	1	7	21	35	35	21	7	1			
8	1	8	28	56	70	56	28	8	1		
9	1	9	36	84	126	126	84	36	9	1	
10	1	10	45	120	210	252	210	120	45	10	1
11	1	11	55	165	330	462	462	330	165	55	11
12	1	12	66	220	495	792	924	792	495	220	66
13	1	13	78	286	715	1287	1716	1716	1287	715	286
14	1	14	91	364	1001	2002	3003	3432	3003	2002	1001
15	1	15	105	455	1365	3003	5005	6435	6435	5005	3003

Table 4. Areas Under the Standard Normal (Z) Curve

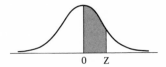

Z	.00	.01	.02	.03	.04	.05	.06	.07	.08	.09
0.0	.0000	.0040	.0080	.0120	.0160	.0199	.0239	.0279	.0319	.0359
0.1	.0398	.0438	.0478	.0517	.0557	.0596	.0636	.0675	.0714	.0753
0.2	.0793	.0832	.0871	.0910	.0948	.0987	.1026	.1064	.1103	.1141
0.3	.1179	.1217	.1255	.1293	.1331	.1368	.1406	.1443	.1480	.1517
0.4	.1554	.1591	.1628	.1664	.1700	.1736	.1772	.1808	.1844	.1879
0.5	.1915	.1950	.1985	.2019	.2054	.2088	.2123	.2157	.2190	.2224
0.6	.2257	.2291	.2324	.2357	.2389	.2422	.2454	.2486	.2518	.2549
0.7	.2580	.2612	.2642	.2673	.2704	.2734	.2764	.2794	.2823	.2852
0.8	.2881	.2910	.2939	.2967	.2995	.3023	.3051	.3078	.3106	.3133
0.9	.3159	.3186	.3212	.3238	.3264	.3289	.3315	.3340	.3365	.3389
1.0	.3413	.3438	.3461	.3485	.3508	.3531	.3554	.3577	.3599	.3621
1.1	.3643	.3665	.3686	.3708	.3729	.3749	.3770	.3790	.3810	.3830
1.2	.3849	.3869	.3888	.3907	.3925	.3944	.3962	.3980	.3997	.4015
1.3	.4032	.4049	.4066	.4082	.4099	.4115	.4131	.4147	.4162	.4177
1.4	.4192	.4207	.4222	.4236	.4251	.4265	.4279	.4292	.4306	.4319
1.5	.4332	.4345	.4357	.4370	.4382	.4394	.4406	.4418	.4429	.4441
1.6	.4452	.4463	.4474	.4484	.4495	.4505	.4515	.4525	.4535	.4545
1.7	.4554	.4564	.4573	.4582	.4591	.4599	.4608	.4616	.4625	.4633
1.8	.4641	.4649	.4656	.4664	.4671	.4678	.4686	.4693	.4699	.4706
1.9	.4713	.4719	.4726	.4732	.4738	.4744	.4750	.4756	.4761	.4767
2.0	.4772	.4778	.4783	.4788	.4793	.4798	.4803	.4808	.4812	.4817
2.1	.4821	.4826	.4830	.4834	.4838	.4842	.4846	.4850	.4854	.4857
2.2	.4861	.4864	.4868	.4871	.4875	.4878	.4881	.4884	.4887	.4890
2.3	.4893	.4896	.4898	.4901	.4904	.4906	.4909	.4911	.4913	.4916
2.4	.4918	.4920	.4922	.4925	.4927	.4929	.4931	.4932	.4934	.4936
2.5	.4938	.4940	.4941	.4943	.4945	.4946	.4948	.4949	.4951	.4952
2.6	.4953	.4955	.4956	.4957	.4959	.4960	.4961	.4962	.4963	.4964
2.7	.4965	.4966	.4967	.4968	.4969	.4970	.4971	.4972	.4973	.4974
2.8	.4974	.4975	.4976	.4977	.4977	.4978	.4979	.4979	.4980	.4981
2.9	.4981	.4982	.4982	.4983	.4984	.4984	.4985	.4985	.4986	.4986
3.0	.49865	.4987	.4987	.4988	.4988	.4989	.4989	.4989	.4990	.4990
3.1	.49903	.4991	.4991	.4991	.4992	.4992	.4992	.4992	.4993	.4993
3.2	.4993129	.4993	.4994	.4994	.4994	.4994	.4994	.4995	.4995	.4995
3.3	.4995166	.4995	.4995	.4996	.4996	.4996	.4996	.4996	.4996	.4997
3.4	.4996631	.4997	.4997	.4497	.4997	.4997	.4997	.4997	.4998	.4998
3.5	.4997674	.4998	.4998	.4998	.4998	.4998	.4998	.4998	.4998	.4998
3.6	.4998409	.4998	.4999	.4999	.4999	.4999	.4999	.4999	.4999	.4999
3.7	.4998922	.4999	.4999	.4999	.4999	.4999	.4999	.4999	.4999	.4999
3.8	.4999277	.4999	.4999	.4999	.4999	.4999	.4999	.5000	.5000	.5000
3.9	.4999519	.5000	.5000	.5000	.5000	.5000	.5000	.5000	.5000	.5000
4.0	.4999683									
4.5	.4999966									
5.0	.4999997133									

Answers to Selected Problems

Problem Set 1.1

1.

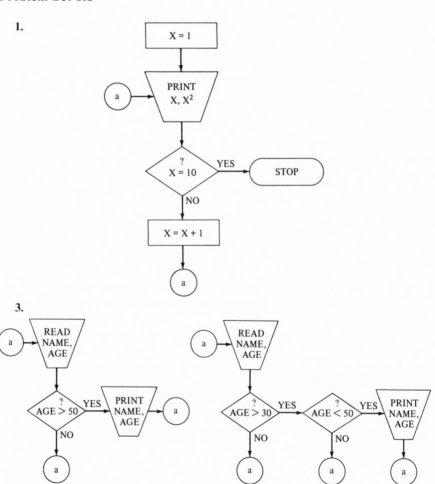

3.

5.

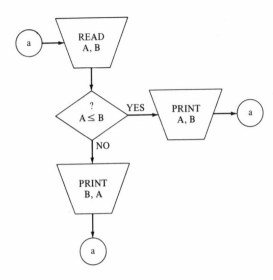

Problem Set 1.2

1.   5   PRINT "FRANK SCALZO—AUGUST 10, 1976"
          10   END

3.   2   PRINT "FRANK SCALZO"
            5   PRINT "JUNE 6, 1941"
            9   PRINT "35"
          12   END

Problem Set 1.3

1. (a)   2   LET $X = 5 - 2\uparrow 3$
   (b)   5   LET $Y = 2 - 17\uparrow 3 + 27/101$
   (c) 10   LET $T = (8 + 7\uparrow 2)/21$
   (d) 15   LET $S = A + B - 3*C\uparrow 2$
   (e) 27   LET $A = (T1 + T2 + T3 + T4)/4$
   (f) 90   LET $Y = SQR(57.321)$
   (g) 10   LET $C = SIN(X) + 3*COS(Y)$
   (h) 12   LET $F = 2*SQR(X\uparrow 2 - 1) + 2*X - 7$
   (i) 17   LET $S = 2 + 7 - 3\uparrow 3 + SQR(94)$
   (j) 27   LET $H = 1\uparrow 2 + 3\uparrow 2 + 5\uparrow 2 + 7\uparrow 2 + 9\uparrow 2$

Problem Set 1.4

1.
```
 5   READ A,B,C,D
10   IF D=1 THEN 30
15   LET M=(A+B+C)/3
20   PRINT M
25   GO TO 5
30   PRINT "FRANK SCALZO—AUGUST 10, 1976"
35   DATA 1,3,5,0,97,88,21,0,999,275,87,0,0,0,0,1
40   END
```

3. (a) 1   5   16   34
   (b) 9   1332   3   148
   (c) −1   2
   (d) −1   2
       2   7
   (e) 94   100   MEAN=97
   (f) X   X↑2   X↑3
       1   1   1
       2   4   8
       3   9   27
       4   16   64
       5   25   125
       6   36   216

5.
```
 2   LET T=0
 5   LET Y=10
 8   LET T=T+Y
11   IF Y=100 THEN 20
14   LET Y=Y+2
17   GO TO 8
20   PRINT "TOTAL="T
23   END
```

Problem Set 1.5

3.   COMPUTER OUTPUT
     2   4   6
     W=22   T=11
     12   0   1
     W=36   T=7
     18   −7   −3
     W=103   T=−1

5.   COMPUTER OUTPUT
     AVERAGE=5.666666
     AVERAGE=69.666666
     AVERAGE=62

6. *Hints*:
  (a) Use quotes in statement 10; omit initial comma in statement 40; SUM in statement 60 is neither a permissible nor a defined variable.
  (b) There is no output from this program.
  (c) Examine statement 30.

Problem Set 1.6

1.

1	10	99
2	−10	99
1	1	0
2	2	3
3	4	15
4	8	63
5	−9	80

2. Y is not dimensioned, so use 5 DIM X(5),Y(5); 25 should be 25 PRINT I,X(I),Y(I); 30 should be 30 NEXT I.

3.

N	X(N)	X(N)-MEAN
MEAN = 68.25		
1	55	−13.25
2	65	−3.25
3	72	3.75
4	81	12.75

N	X(N)	X(N)-MEAN
MEAN = 75.222222		
1	61	−14.222222
2	52	−23.222222
3	89	13.777778
4	94	18.777778
5	71	−4.222222
6	75	−0.222222
7	88	12.777778
8	97	21.777778
9	50	−25.222222

4. 5 DIM A(7),B(7),C(7). Note a number larger than 7 could also have been used, since we can overdimension.

5.
```
5 DIM A(7),B(7),C(7)
RUN
 −7    −10    −8    −100    −11    −26.5    −60
```

Problem Set 2.1

1.
```
 5  PRINT "ENTER A NATURAL NUMBER"
10  INPUT N
15  IF N<0 THEN 5
20  IF INT(N)=N THEN 35
25  PRINT N; "IS NOT A NATURAL NUMBER"
30  GO TO 5
35  IF INT(N/2)=N/2 THEN 50
40  PRINT N;"IS ODD"
45  GO TO 5
50  PRINT N;"IS EVEN"
55  GO TO 5
60  END
```

Note: Terminate above program using ESC or Break buttons.

3. Incorporate tests to see if N is both positive and an integer (see Problem 1 above, statements 15 and 20).

7.
```
 5  INPUT N
10  FOR I=1 TO 100
20  PRINT I*N;
30  NEXT I
40  END
```

This program gives the first 100 multiples of N. Adjust statement 10 for more or less multiples.

8.
```
 5  INPUT M,N
10  PRINT "SOME COMMON MULTIPLES OF";M;"AND";N;"ARE:"
15  LET X=M
20  IF INT (X/N)< >X/N THEN 30
25  PRINT X;
30  LET X=X+M
35  IF X< =M*N THEN 20
40  GO TO 5
45  END
```

Problem Set 2.2

1.
```
 5  PRINT "ENTER FAHRENHEIT DEGREES"
10  INPUT F
15  LET C=(5*F-160)/9
20  PRINT F; "DEGREES FAHRENHEIT EQUALS";C;"DEGREES
    CELSIUS"
25  GO TO 5
30  END
```

Note: Terminate above by ESC or Break keys.

3.   5   PRINT "TYPE 0 TO CONVERT FAHRENHEIT TO CELSIUS"
      10   PRINT "TYPE 1 TO CONVERT CELSIUS TO FAHRENHEIT"
      15   INPUT X
      20   IF X=0 THEN 50
      25   PRINT "ENTER CELSIUS DEGREES"
      30   INPUT C
      35   LET F=(9/5)*C+32
      40   PRINT C; "CELSIUS=";F;"FAHRENHEIT"
      45   GO TO 5
      50   PRINT "ENTER FAHRENHEIT DEGREES"
      55   INPUT F
      60   LET C=(5*F-160)/9
      65   PRINT F;"FAHRENHEIT=";C;"CELSIUS"
      70   GO TO 5
      75   END

Problem Set 2.3

1.   5   READ R
      10   LET A=3.14159*R↑2
      15   PRINT "R=",R,"AREA="A
      20   GO TO 5
      25   DATA 2,5.3,6.14,1.813
      30   END

3.   5   READ A,R,K,N
      10   LET R1=R/100
      15   LET P=A/(1+R1/K)↑(K*N)
      20   PRINT "A","R","K","N"
      25   PRINT A,R,K,N,"P="P
      30   DATA 2598,5,4,4
      35   END

Note: R is to be read as %; hence, we convert to the correct decimal, using the intermediate variable R1=R/100.

5. We assume Y ≤ N and note the first investment stays for N years, the second for N − 1 years, the third for N − 2 years, . . . , and the Yth investment for N−(Y−1)=N−Y+1 years.

      5   READ X,Y,R,K,N
      10   LET R1=R/100
      15   LET S=0
      20   FOR I=N−Y+1 TO N
      25   LET S=S+X*(1+R1/K)↑(I*K)
      30   NEXT I
      35   PRINT "ACCUMULATED SUM=$"S
      40   DATA 500,5,6,365,10
      45   END

7.   5 PRINT "ENTER FIRST TERM, # OF TERMS AND COMMON DIFFERENCE"
      10 INPUT A,N,D
      15 LET L=A+(N−1)∗D
      20 LET S=(N/2)∗(2∗A+(N−1)∗D)
      25 PRINT "LAST TERM="L,"SUM="S
      30 GO TO 5
      35 END

Problem Set 2.4

1. (a) AXB={(2,3),(2,7),(7,3),(7,7),(8,3),(8,7)}
 (b) BXA={(3,2),(3,7),(3,8),(7,2),(7,7),(7,8)}
 (c) AXA={(2,2),(2,7),(2,8),(7,2),(7,7),(7,8),(8,2),(8,7),(8,8)}
 (d) BXB={(3,3),(3,7),(7,3),(7,7)}

3. R1 and R5 are functions from B to A.

5. a, c, and e are functions.

7. (a) domain = $\mathcal{R}$, range = $\mathcal{R}$
 (b) domain = $[-a,a]$. See note below. Range = $[-b,b]$
 (c) domain = $\mathcal{R}$, range = {all real numbers $\geq a$}
 (d) domain = {all real numbers $\geq e$}, range = $\mathcal{R}$
 (e) domain = {d}, range = {f}
 (f) domain = {all real numbers $\geq a$ or $\leq(-a)$}, range = $\mathcal{R}$

Note: The symbol $[a,b]$ denotes the set of all numbers between a and b, inclusive. In other words, if $x \in [a,b]$, then $a \leq x \leq b$ or, equivalently, $[a,b] = \{x | a \leq x \leq b\}$.

Problem Set 2.5

1. (a) $f(x) = 5x - 3$.

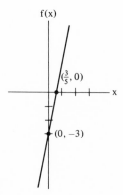

(b) $g(t) = 2t^2 - 8t + 5$. Roots are $(8 \pm \sqrt{24})/4 \approx 3.22, 0.77$.

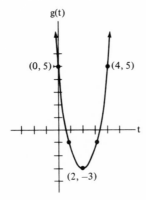

3.
```
 5  PRINT "ENTER A,B,C OF YOUR QUADRATIC"
10  INPUT A,B,C
15  IF A=0 THEN 55
20  LET D=B↑2−4*A*C
25  IF D<0 THEN 65
30  IF D=0 THEN 75
35  LET X1=(−B+SQR(D))/(2*A)
40  LET X2=(−B−SQR(D))/(2*A)
45  PRINT "ROOTS ARE", X1,X2
50  GO TO 5
55  PRINT "NOT A QUADRATIC"
60  GO TO 5
65  PRINT "NO REAL SOLUTIONS"
70  GO TO 5
75  LET X=−B/(2*A)
80  PRINT "X="X
85  GO TO 5
90  END
```

5.
```
 1  PRINT "X", "FUNCTION"
 5  DEF FNA(X)=5*X↑2−17*X+2
10  FOR I= −1 TO 1 STEP .1
20  PRINT I, FNA(I)
30  NEXT I
35  END
```

Problem Set 2.6

1. (a) 3;   (b) 4;   (c) 9;   (d) 1.

6.
```
 5  PRINT "N", "N FACTORIAL"
10  FOR J=1 TO 20
15  LET P=1
20  FOR L=1 TO J
25  LET P=P*L
30  NEXT L
35  PRINT J,P
40  NEXT J
45  END
```

Problem Set 3.1

1. (a)

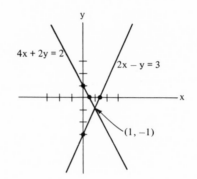

(b)

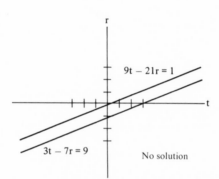

(c)

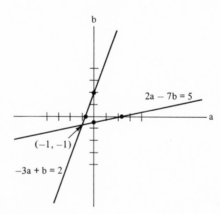

3. (a) $w = 26, z = 43$
(b) $a = 49/61, b = 18/61$
(c) $x = -28/3, y = -5/3$
(d) Inconsistent
(e) $a = 0, b = 11/3$
(f) $x = 11/3, y = (-1)/3$

5. We assume for simplicity that A_2, B_2, and C_2 are not zero.

```
 5  READ A1,B1,C1,A2,B2,C2
10  PRINT "A1="A1,"B1="B1,"C1="C1
15  PRINT "A2="A2,"B2="B2,"C2="C2
20  LET D=A1*B2-B1*A2
25  IF D=0 THEN 50
30  LET X=(C1*B2-B1*C2)/D
35  LET Y=(A1*C2-A2*C1)/D
40  PRINT "X="X,"Y="Y
45  GO TO 5
50  IF A1/A2=B1/B2 THEN 65
55  PRINT "INCONSISTENT"
60  GO TO 5
65  IF B1/B2=C1/C2 THEN 75
70  GO TO 55
75  PRINT "DEPENDENT"
80  GO TO 5
85  DATA 5,-3,1,2,-1,9,-5,17,1,3,2,3
86  DATA -1,5,1,2,-7,-7,5,-3,7,-15,9,1
87  DATA 2,3,11,-6,9,33,3,0,11,2,-5,9
90  END
```

Remark: We switched the two equations in 3*f* to insure that A_2, B_2, and C_2 are not zero. See last six DATA values and compare with 3*f*.

Problem Set 3.2

1. (a) $x = 2, y = -1, z = 3$
(b) $x = 3, y = -2, z = -1$
(c) $w = 26/7, t = 25/7, r = 12/7$
(d) System is dependent, and infinitely many solutions exist.

3. $t = -50/17$.

4. *Hint*: Use the expression that gives the value of a determinant in terms of its elements.

Problem Set 3.3

1. $A = (a_{23}), B = (b_{31}), C = (c_{33}), D = (d_{33})$

2. (a) $AB = \begin{bmatrix} -14 \\ -8 \end{bmatrix}$

(b) BA is not defined.

(e) $CD = \begin{bmatrix} 12 & 3 & -58 \\ 14 & -25 & 39 \\ 7 & 9 & -2 \end{bmatrix}$

Problem Set 3.4

1. (a) 11
  -0.333333

  (b) 11 -0.333333

  (c)   5   2
      -1 3

       0   1
       7   8

       0   -5
     -35 -40

      -5 -7
     -34 -43

       5   -6 -7
      47   -34 -35

3.   5 DIM A(2,2), B(2,3), C(2,4), F(2,2), G(2,2)
     10 DIM H(2,3), X(2,4), J(2,2), K(2,2), L(2,2)
     15 DIM M(2,2), N(2,2)
     20 MAT READ A,B,C,F
     25 MAT G=A−F
     30 MAT H=A∗B
     35 MAT X=A∗C
     40 MAT J=INV(A)
     45 MAT K=INV(F)
     50 MAT L=J∗K
     55 MAT M=A∗J
     60 MAT N=F∗K
     65 MAT PRINT G,H,X,J,K,L,M,N
     70 DATA 2,3,4,−1,1,7,8,9,−11,2
     75 DATA 3,4,5,16,−1,10,9,−11,8,0,−1,3
     80 END

5. Change the DIM statement.

7. (a) -36
  (b) cofactor of $f_{11} = -8$
      cofactor of $f_{12} = 1$
      cofactor of $f_{13} = 2$
      cofactor of $f_{21} = 4$
      cofactor of $f_{22} = 13$
      cofactor of $f_{23} = -10$
      cofactor of $f_{31} = 4$
      cofactor of $f_{32} = -5$
      cofactor of $f_{33} = -10$

$$(c) \ \bar{F} = \begin{bmatrix} \dfrac{8}{36} & \dfrac{-4}{36} & \dfrac{-4}{36} \\[2mm] \dfrac{-1}{36} & \dfrac{-13}{36} & \dfrac{5}{36} \\[2mm] \dfrac{-2}{36} & \dfrac{10}{36} & \dfrac{10}{36} \end{bmatrix}$$

Problem Set 3.5

1. $a = -56, b = 88, c = -7$
3. w arbitrary, $t = w, r = w, s = 0$
5. $x = 36/5, y = 28/5, z = -41/5, w = 34/5$

Problem Set 3.6

```
RUN

ECHELON       12:57      11/04/75

ENTER # OF ROWS AND COLUMNS INCLUDING RIGHT HAND SIDE
?3,4
ENTER MATRIX ROW WISE -CARRIAGE RETURN AFTER EACH ROW
?1,1,3,11

??3,2,1,1

??2,1,-5,11


1       1       3       11

3       2       1       1

2       1      -5       11


1       0       0      -56.

0       1       0       88.

0       0       1.      -7.


TIME 0.0 SE CS.
```

RUN

ECHELON   12:59   11/04/75

ENTER # OF ROWS AND COLUMNS INCLUDING RIGHT HAND SIDE
?3, 5
ENTER MATRIX ROW WISE - CARRIAGE RETURN AFTER EACH ROW
?1, -1, 2, 0, 0

??1, 2, 1, -3, 0

??1, 1, 0, -2, 0

1	-1	2	0	0
1	2	1	-3	0
1	1	0	-2	0

1	0	0	1.	0
0	1.	0	1.	0
0	0	1.	0	0

TIME 0.0 SE CS.

RUN

ECHELON   13:01   11/04/75

ENTER # OF RO WS AND COLUMNS INCLUDING RIGHT HAND SIDE
?4, 5
ENTER MATRIX ROWWISE - CARRIAGE RETURN AFTER EACH ROW
?1, 1, 1, 2, 7

??2, -3, 2, -1, 8

??3, 1, 1, -1, 1

??2, -3, 5, 1, -3

1	1	1	2	7
2	-3	2	-1	8
3	1	1	-1	1
2	-3	5	1	-3

1	0	0	0	7.2
0	1.	0	0	-5.59999
0	0	1	0	-8.19997
0	0	0	1.	6.79999

TIME 0.0 SE CS.

Problem Set 3.7

1.   Only *b* and *d* are true.

3. (a)

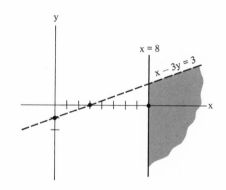

(b)

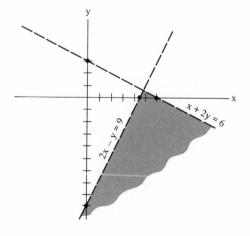

(c)

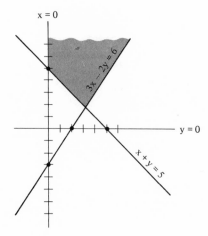

(d)

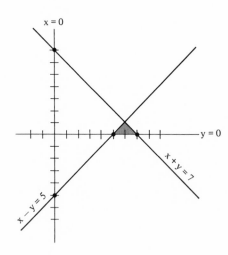

(e)

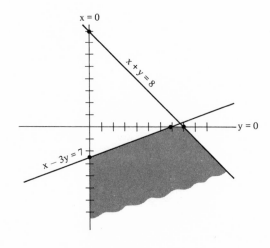

(f)

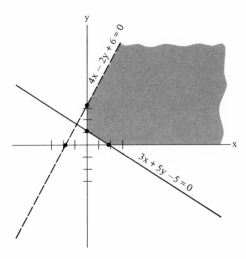

Problem Set 3.8

1. $f = 4x + y$
maximum $f = 60$
when $x = 15$ and $y = 0$.

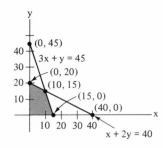

3. $f = 5x + 10y$
maximum $f = 200$
when $x = 0$ and $y = 20$.

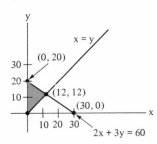

Problem Set 3.9

1.	Coordinates of Corner	In Common Solution Area?	Value of Objective Function $f = 2x + 5y + z$
	(0,0,0)	yes	—
	(0,0,26)	yes	26
	(0,0,42)	no	—
	(0,6.5,0)	no	—
	(0,6,0)	yes	30
	(13,0,0)	yes	26
	(21,0,0)	no	—
	(0,16/3,14/3)	yes	$31\frac{1}{3}$ (max f)
	(—,0,—)	—	—
	(7/3,16/3,0)	yes	$31\frac{1}{3}$ (max f)

Problem Set 3.10

2. (a)

```
RUN

SIMPLEX        11:03    06/16.76

ENTER NUMBER OF ROWS AND COLUMNS IN FIRST TABLEAU.
SEPARATE THE NUMBERS WITH A COMMA.   ?4,4
ENTER THE NUMBERS IN THE TABLEAU ONE ROW AT A TIME.
  SEPARATE THE NUMBERS BY COMMAS; DON'T FORGET THE MINUS
SIGNS.   PRESS 'RETURN' AFTER EACH ROW.
?0,1,5,3

??38,-1,-5,-3

??98,-2,-12,-5

??42,-1,-2,-3
```

		r	s	t
f	0	1	5	3
x	38	-1	-5*	-3
y	98	-2	-12	-5
z	42	-1	-2	-3

PIVOT ELEMENT IS -5   IN ROW 2   COLUMN 3

		r	x	t
f	38	0	-1	0
x	7.6	-.2	-.2	-.6
y	6.8	.4	2.4	2.2
z	26.8	-.6	.4	-1.8

maximum $f = 38$,
when $x = 0$, $y = 6.8$,
and $z = 26.8$

THE LAST TABLEAU ABOVE IS THE FINAL TABLEAU.
NOW YOU MUST GO BACK TO THE BEGINNING OF THE
PROBLEM AND PUT IN THE VARIABLES IN THE PROPER
POSITIONS, I.E. ALONG THE LEFT SIDE AND ACROSS
THE TOP, FOR EACH TABLEAU STARTING WITH THE
FIRST ONE.   WHEN YOU FINISH DOING THIS YOU WILL
BE ABLE TO READ YOUR ANSWER.

TIME 0.0 SECS.

(b)

RUN

SIMPLEX   11:06   06/16/76

ENTER NUMBER OF ROWS AND COLUMNS IN FIRST TABLEAU.
SEPARATE THE NUMBERS WITH A COMMA.   ?5,5
ENTER THE NUMBERS IN THE TABLEAU ONE ROW AT A TIME.
 SEPARATE THE NUMBERS BY COMMAS; DON'T FORGET THE MINUS
SIGNS.   PRESS 'RETURN' AFTER EACH ROW.
?0,15,30,40,10⁻

??60,-1,-2,-3,-4

??80,-2,-1,-1,-3

??100,-2,-2,-6,-1

??120,-5,-1,-4,-2

		r	s	t	u
f	0	15	30	40	10
x	60	-1	-2	-3·	-4
y	80	-2	-1	-1	-3
z	100	-2	-2	-6*	-1
w	120	-5	-1	-4	-2

PIVOT ELEMENT IS -6   IN ROW 4   COLUMN 4

		n	s	z	u
f	666.667	1.66667	16.6667	-6.66667	3.33333
x	10 0	-1*	.5	-3.5	
y	63.3333	-1.66667	-.666667	.166667	-2.83333
t	16.6667	-.333333	-.333333	-.166667	-.166667
w	53.3333	-3.66667	.333333	.666667	-1.33333

PIVOT ELEMENT IS -1   IN ROW 2   COLUMN 3

		n	x	z	u
f	833.333	1.66667	-16.6667	1.66666	-55.
s	10 0	-1	.5	-3.5	
y	56.6667	-1.66667	.666667	-.166667	-.5
t	13.3333	-.333333	.333333	-.333333	.999999
w	56.6667	-3.66667*	-.333333	.833333	-2.5

PIVOT ELEMENT IS -3.66667   IN ROW 5   COLUMN 2

		w	x	z	u
f	859.09	-.454545	-16.8182	2.04545	-56.1363
s	10. 0	-1	.5	-3.5	
y	30.9091	.454545	.818181	-.545454	.636363
t	8.18181	9.09091E-02	.363636	-.409091*	1.22727
n	15.4545	-.272727	-9.09091E-02	.227273	-.681818

PIVOT ELEMENT IS -.409091   IN ROW 4   COLUMN 4

		w	x	t	u
f	899.999	-8.74202E-07	-15.	-4.99999	-49.9999
s	20.	.111111	-.555556	-1.22222	-2
y	20	.333333	.333333	1.33333	-.999998
z	20.	.222222	.888889	-2.44445	3.
r	20.	-.222222	.111111	-.555556	-4.37101E-07

Therefore maximum $f = 900$ when $x = 0$, $y = 20$, $z = 20$, and $w = 0$.

THE LAST TABLEAU ABOVE IS THE FINAL TABLEAU.
NOW YOU MUST GO BACK TO THE BEGINNING OF THE
PROBLEM AND PUT IN THE VARIABLES IN THE PROPER
POSITIONS, I.E. ALONG THE LEFT SIDE AND ACROSS
THE TOP, FOR EACH TABLEAU STARTING WITH THE
FIRST ONE.   WHEN YOU FINISH DOING THIS YOU WILL
BE ABLE TO READ YOUR ANSWER.

TIME 0.1 SECS.

Problem Set 3.11

1.
RUN

(*t*)   SIMPLEX   12:08   06/16/76

ENTER NUMBER OF ROWS AND COLUMNS IN FIRST TABLEAU.
SEPARATE THE NUMBERS WITH A COMMA.   ?3,3
ENTER THE NUMBERS IN THE TABLEAU ONE ROW AT A TIME.
 SEPARATE THE NUMBERS BY COMMAS; DON'T FORGET THE MINUS
SIGNS. PRESS 'RETURN' AFTER EACH ROW.
?0,-2,-5

??-20,2,4

??-10,6,1

		r	s
$-f$	0	-2	-5
x	-20	2*	4
y	-10	6	1

```
PIVOT ELEMENT TO GET PROPER MATRIX IS 2     IN ROW 2
   COLUMN 2
```

		x	s
$-f$	-20	-1	-1
x	10	.5	-2
y	50	3	-11

If $-f = -20$, then $f = 20$.
Therefore minimum $f = 20$,
when $x = 0$ and $y = 50$.

```
THE LAST TABLEAU ABOVE IS THE FINAL TABLEAU.
NOW YOU MUST GO BACK TO THE BEGINNING OF THE
PROBLEM AND PUT IN THE VARIABLES IN THE PROPER
POSITIONS, I.E. ALONG THE LEFT SIDE AND ACROSS
THE TOP, FOR EACH TABLEAU STARTING WITH THE
FIRST ONE.  WHEN YOU FINISH DOING THIS YOU WILL
BE ABLE TO READ YOUR ANSWER.

TIME 0.1 SECS.
```

3.

```
RUN

SIMPLEX      11:13    06/16/76

ENTER NUMBER OF ROWS AND COLUMNS IN FIRST TABLEAU.
SEPARATE THE NUMBERS WITH A COMMA.   ?4,4
ENTER THE NUMBERS IN THE TABLEAU ONE ROW AT A TIME.
  SEPARATE THE NUMBERS BY COMMAS; DON'T FORGET THE MINUS
SIGNS. PRESS 'RETURN' AFTER EACH ROW.
?0,-1,-2,-1

??-4,2,2,1

??-6,2,0,1

??-10,4,2,4
```

		x	s	t
$-f$	0	-1	-2	-1
x	-4	2	2	1
y	-6	2*	0	1
z	-10	4	2	4

```
PIVOT ELEMENT TO GET PROPER MATRIX IS 2     IN ROW 3
   COLUMN 2
```

	y	s	t	
$-f$ -3	-.5	-2	-.5
x 2	1	2	0
r 3	.5	0	-.5
z 2	2	2	2

If $-f = -3$, then $f = 3$. Therefore minimum $f = 3$, when $x = 2$, $y = 0$, and $z = 2$.

```
THE LAST TABLEAU ABOVE IS THE FINAL TABLEAU.
NOW YOU MUST GO BACK TO THE BEGINNING OF THE
PROBLEM AND PUT IN THE VARIABLES IN THE PROPER
POSITIONS, I.E. ALONG THE LEFT SIDE AND ACROSS
THE TOP, FOR EACH TABLEAU STARTING WITH THE
FIRST ONE.   WHEN YOU FINISH DOING THIS YOU WILL
BE ABLE TO READ YOUR ANSWER.

TIME 0.0 SECS.
```

Problem Set 4.1

1. (a) T (g) F
(b) T (h) F
(c) T (i) T
(d) F (j) F
(e) F (k) F
(f) F (l) F

3. (a)

p	$\sim p$	$p \vee \sim p$	$\sim(p \vee \sim p)$
T	F	T	F
F	T	T	F

(b)

p	q	$\sim q$	$p \wedge \sim q$
T	T	F	F
T	F	T	T
F	T	F	F
F	F	T	F

(c)

p	q	$\sim q$	$\sim q \to p$
T	T	F	T
T	F	T	T
F	T	F	T
F	F	T	F

(d)

p	q	$\sim p$	$\sim p \leftrightarrow q$
T	T	F	F
T	F	F	T
F	T	T	T
F	F	T	F

(e)

p	q	$p \wedge q$	$\sim p$	$(p \wedge q) \to \sim p$
T	T	T	F	F
T	F	F	F	T
F	T	F	T	T
F	F	F	T	T

(f)

p	q	$p \wedge q$	$\sim q$	$(p \wedge q) \to \sim q$
T	T	T	F	F
T	F	F	T	T
F	T	F	F	T
F	F	F	T	T

(g)

p	q	$\sim q$	$p \wedge \sim q$	$\sim p$	$(p \wedge \sim q) \leftrightarrow \sim p$
T	T	F	F	F	T
T	F	T	T	F	F
F	T	F	F	T	F
F	F	T	T	T	F

(h)

p	q	$p \vee q$	$\sim p$	$(p \vee q) \to \sim p$
T	T	T	F	F
T	F	T	F	F
F	T	T	T	T
F	F	F	T	T

5. (a) Let S be the biconditional $p \wedge (q \wedge r) \leftrightarrow (p \wedge q) \wedge r$.

p	q	r	$q \wedge r$	$p \wedge q$	$p \wedge (q \wedge r)$	$(p \wedge q) \wedge r$	S
T	T	T	T	T	T	T	T
T	T	F	F	T	F	F	T
T	F	T	F	F	F	F	T
T	F	F	F	F	F	F	T
F	T	T	T	F	F	F	T
F	T	F	F	F	F	F	T
F	F	T	F	F	F	F	T
F	F	F	F	F	F	F	T

(b) Since part (b) is obtained by negating one side of the biconditional S, the new biconditional must have, in every instance, the opposite truth value of S; hence, it is always false.

Problem Set 4.2

1. (a) and (b)

p	q	$p \vee q$	$q \vee p$	$p \wedge q$	$q \wedge p$
T	T	T	T	T	T
T	F	T	T	F	F
F	T	T	T	F	F
F	F	F	F	F	F

Therefore

p	q	$(p \lor q) \leftrightarrow (q \lor p)$	$(p \land q) \leftrightarrow (q \land p)$
T	T	T	T
T	F	T	T
F	T	T	T
F	F	T	T

(c), (d), and (e)

Case	p	q	r	$p \lor q$	$q \lor r$	$p \lor r$	$p \land q$	$p \land r$	$q \land r$
1	T	T	T	T	T	T	T	T	T
2	T	T	F	T	T	T	T	F	F
3	T	F	T	T	T	T	F	T	F
4	T	F	F	T	F	T	F	F	F
5	F	T	T	T	T	T	F	F	T
6	F	T	F	T	T	F	F	F	F
7	F	F	T	F	T	T	F	F	F
8	F	F	F	F	F	F	F	F	F

Therefore

Case	$(p \lor q) \lor r$	$p \lor (q \lor r)$	$p \lor (q \land r)$	$(p \lor q) \land (p \lor r)$
1	T	T	T	T
2	T	T	T	T
3	T	T	T	T
4	T	T	T	T
5	T	T	T	T
6	T	T	F	F
7	T	T	F	F
8	F	F	F	F

And

Case	$p \land (q \lor r)$	$(p \land q) \lor (p \land r)$	$C_1 \leftrightarrow C_2$	$D_1 \leftrightarrow D_2$	$E_1 \leftrightarrow E_2$
1	T	T	T	T	T
2	T	T	T	T	T
3	T	T	T	T	T
4	F	F	T	T	T
5	F	F	T	T	T
6	F	F	T	T	T
7	F	F	T	T	T
8	F	F	T	T	T

where C_1 is the first compound statement in part c and C_2 is the second in part c; similarly for parts d and e.

3. (a) Let p: I go bowling
   q: I will play tennis

$$p \to \sim q$$
$$\underline{q}$$
$$\therefore \sim p \qquad (\textit{Note}: \text{This argument is valid.})$$

(b) Let p: I study for at least 5 hours
   q: I will pass the exam
   r: I can go bowling

$p \rightarrow q$

$\sim p \rightarrow \sim r$

$\therefore q \vee r$ (*Note*: Invalid argument.)

5.   Using the cases 1–8 as in Problem 1, part (c), we have:

Case	$p \rightarrow q$	$q \rightarrow r$	$p \rightarrow r$	$(p \rightarrow q) \wedge (q \rightarrow r)$
1	T	T	T	T
2	T	F	F	F
3	F	T	T	F
4	F	T	F	F
5	T	T	T	T
6	T	F	T	F
7	T	T	T	T
8	T	T	T	T

So we see that wherever the conjunction of the premises is true (see last column), the conclusion (column 3) is true. Therefore, we have a valid argument.

Problem Set 4.3

1. (a) $A = \{$Shari, Marian, Myself$\}$
   (b) $B = \{1,3,5,7,9\}$
   (c) $C = \{$Johnson, Nixon, Ford, Carter$\}$

3. (a) $B \cup C = \{2,3,4,5\}$
   (b) $B \cap C = \varnothing$
   (c) $E' = \{1,2,4\}$
   (d) $G' = \{2,3,4,5\}$
   (e) $U' = \varnothing$
   (f) $H' \cup B = \{2,4\}$
   (g) $(F \cup E)' = \{1\}$
   (h) $F' \cup E' = \{1,2,3,5\}$
   (i) $F' \cap E' = \{1\}$
   (j) $(E \cup H) \cup C = \{1,2,3,5\}$
   (k) $E \cup (H \cup C) = \{1,2,3,5\}$
   (l) $(F \cap H) \cap E = \varnothing$
   (m) $F \cap (H \cap E) = \varnothing$
   (n) $F \cup (H \cap E) = \{2,3,4,5\}$
   (o) $(F \cup H) \cap E = \{3,5\}$

5. (a) $A \cap B$
   (b) $A \cup B$
   (c) A'
   (d) $A \cap B'$
   (e) $A' \cap B$
   (f) $(A \cup B)'$
   (g) $(A \cap B') \cup (B \cap A')$

Problem Set 4.4

1.

p	$\sim p$
T	F
F	T

A	A'
$\in$	$\notin$
$\notin$	$\in$

3. We know two statements are logically equivalent if and only if they have the same truth values. Consider the consequence of knowing that the statements $x \in A$ and $x \in B$ are logically equivalent, and you will observe that $A = B$ for any element x of A (this means $x \in A$ is true) would make $x \in B$ true; hence, x is also in B, and conversely.

Problem Set 4.5

1. (a) ⟶o p o⟶⟶o q o⟶

(b) ⟶o p o⟶ [o q o / o r o] ⟶

(c) [o p o⟶o q o / o p o⟶o r o]

(d) [o p o / o q o] ⟶o r o⟶

3.

p	q	$\bar{p}$	$\bar{q}$	$p \oplus q$	$\overline{\bar{p} \odot \bar{q}}$	$\overline{p \oplus q}$
1	1	0	0	1	0	0
1	0	0	1	1	0	0
0	1	1	0	1	0	0
0	0	1	1	0	1	1

This table shows that the networks $\overline{\bar{p} \odot \bar{q}}$ and $\overline{p \oplus q}$ are open and closed under the same conditions; hence, they are equivalent.

5.

p	q	$\bar{p}$	$\bar{q}$	$p \odot q$	$\overline{p \odot q}$	$\bar{p} \oplus \bar{q}$
1	1	0	0	1	0	0
1	0	0	1	0	1	1
0	1	1	0	0	1	1
0	0	1	1	0	1	1

Since the networks $\overline{p \odot q}$ and $\bar{p} \oplus \bar{q}$ are open and closed under the same conditions, they are equivalent.

7. (a) $p \odot (p \oplus (\overline{p} \odot \overline{q})) \odot q$; call this S.

(b)

p	q	$\overline{p}$	$\overline{q}$	$\overline{p} \odot \overline{q}$	$p \oplus (\overline{p} \odot \overline{q})$	S
1	1	0	0	0	1	1
1	0	0	1	0	1	0
0	1	1	0	0	0	0
0	0	1	1	1	1	0

So, we see that current flows in the circuit corresponding to S if and only if switches p and q are closed.

Problem Set 4.6

1. (a) 75.875
   (b) 340
   (c) 2091.0625
   (d) 45.375
   (e) 8207
   (f) 120

3. (a) $E7_{\text{sixteen}}$
   (b) 191_{sixteen}
   (c) $5F4_{\text{sixteen}}$
   (d) $8FC_{\text{sixteen}}$

5. (a) 100111010_{two}
   (b) 11000001111_{two}
   (c) $101010110111_{\text{two}}$
   (d) $11000011001001_{\text{two}}$

Problem Set 4.7

Address	Contents	Comments
A1	$\cdots$	Enter value of A
A2	$\cdots$	Enter value of B
A3	$\cdots$	Enter value of C
A4	$\cdots$	Enter 4
A5	81A4	Clear and add 4 to accumulator
A6	84A1	Multiply accumulator by A
A7	84A3	Multiply accumulator by C
A8	E0F1	Store 4AC in F1
A9	81A2	Clear and add B to accumulator
AA	84A2	Multiply accumulator by B
AB	83F1	$B^2 - 4AC$ now in accumulator
AC	E0F2	Store $B^2 - 4AC$ in F2
AD	C1B3	Transfer to instruction at B3 if $B^2 - 4AC < 0$

Address	Contents	Comments
AE	91A1	PRINT A
AF	91A2	PRINT B
B0	91A3	PRINT C
B1	91F2	PRINT D
B2	C0B4	Transfer to instruction at B4
B3	91F2	PRINT D
B4	88	STOP

Problem Set 5.1

1. (a) 8
(b) {(A,A,A), (A,A,R), (A,R,A), (A,R,R), (R,A,A), (R,A,R), (R,R,A), (R,R,R)}

3. (a) 380
(b) 19

5. $9 \cdot 8 \cdot 7 \cdot 6 = 3024$

Problem Set 5.2

1. (a) $5! = 120$
(b) $(6!)(3!) = 4320$
(c) $6! + 3! = 726$
(d) $\dfrac{6!}{3!} = 120$
(e) $_nP_n = n!$
(f) $_nP_0 = 1$

3. $12!$

5. (a) $_{25}P_{13}$
(b) 0
(c) $(_{12}P_5)(_{20}P_8)$

7. $5! = 120$

Problem Set 5.3

1. (a) $_6C_3 = 20$
(b) $_6C_3 + _6C_4 = 35$
(c) $_nC_n = 1$
(d) $_nC_0 = 1$

3. $_{52}C_5$

5. (a) $_{12}C_6$
(b) $(_5C_4)(_7C_2) = 105$
(c) $(_5C_4)(_7C_2) + (_5C_5)(_7C_1) = 105 + 7 = 112$
(d) $(_7C_4)(_5C_2) = 350$

7. (a) $(a + b)^5 = a^5 + 5a^4b + 10a^3b^2 + 10a^2b^3 + 5ab^4 + b^5$
(b) $(2a - b)^4 = 16a^4 - 32a^3b + 24a^2b^2 - 8ab^3 + b^4$
(c) $(x - y)^3 = x^3 - 3x^2y + 3xy^2 - y^3$
(d) $35a^3r^4$
(e) $715g^9d^4$
(f) $20(0.9)^3(0.1)^3 = 0.01458$
(g) $3(0.99)^2(0.01) = 0.029403$

Problem Set 5.4

1.   110   DATA 11,3,0
        111   DATA 9,5,1
        112   DATA 12,4,0
        113   DATA 10,7,1
        114   DATA 11,7,1
        115   DATA 8,5,0
        RUN
        P(11,3)=990
        C(9,5)=126
        P(12,4)=11880
        C(10,7)=120
        C(11,7)=330
        P(8,5)=6720
        *READY

Problem Set 5.5

1. (a)

$$S = \begin{cases} (1,1), (1,2), (1,3), (1,4), (1,5), (1,6), \\ (2,1), (2,2), (2,3), (2,4), (2,5), (2,6), \\ (3,1), (3,2), (3,3), (3,4), (3,5), (3,6), \\ (4,1), (4,2), (4,3), (4,4), (4,5), (4,6), \\ (5,1), (5,2), (5,3), (5,4), (5,5), (5,6), \\ (6,1), (6,2), (6,3), (6,4), (6,5), (6,6) \end{cases}$$

The first coordinate gives outcome of first die, second of second die.
(b) Each sample point has the probability of 1/36.
(c) $E = \{(1,4), (2,3), (3,2), (4,1)\}$
    $F = \{(1,1), (1,2), (2,1), (3,1), (2,2), (1,3), (4,1), (3,2), (2,3), (1,4), (5,1), (4,2), (3,3), (2,4), (1,5), (6,1), (5,2), (4,3), (3,4), (2,5), (1,6)\}$
    $G = \{(1,6), (2,5), (3,4), (4,3), (5,2), (6,1)\}$

(d) $P(E) = \dfrac{4}{36} = \dfrac{1}{9}$

$P(F) = \dfrac{21}{36} = \dfrac{7}{12}$

$P(G) = \dfrac{6}{36} = \dfrac{1}{6}$

3. (a) $_{20}P_5 = 1,860,480$

(b) $\dfrac{_7C_2 \cdot {_8C_2} \cdot {_5C_1}(5!)}{_{20}P_5} = \dfrac{2940}{15504} = 0.1896$

(c) $\dfrac{_5C_5(5!)}{_{20}P_5} = \dfrac{1}{15504} = 0.0000644$

5. (a) $\dfrac{_4C_2 \cdot {_{48}C_1}}{_{52}C_3} = \dfrac{288}{22100} = 0.013$

(b) $\dfrac{_4C_0 \cdot {_{48}C_3}}{_{52}C_3} + \dfrac{_4C_1 \cdot {_{48}C_2}}{_{52}C_3} + \dfrac{_4C_2 \cdot {_{48}C_1}}{_{52}C_3}$

$= \dfrac{17296 + 4512 + 288}{22100} = \dfrac{22096}{22100} = 0.999$

or $1 - \dfrac{_4C_3}{_{52}C_3} = \dfrac{22096}{22100} = 0.999$

(c) $\dfrac{_{13}C_3}{_{52}C_3} = \dfrac{1716}{132600} = 0.013$

(d) $\dfrac{_{13}C_1 \cdot {_{13}C_1} \cdot {_{13}C_1}}{_{52}C_3} = \dfrac{2197}{22100} = 0.091$

7. (a) $p(e_5) = 0.1$
(b) $P(E) = 0.7$
(c) $P(F) = 0.5$
(d) $P(E \cup F) = 1$
(e) $P(E \cap F) = 0.2$
(f) $P(E') = 0.3$
(g) $P(F') = 0.5$

Problem Set 5.6

1. (a) $1 - {_6C_6}\left(\dfrac{9}{10}\right)^6\left(\dfrac{1}{10}\right)^0 = 1 - \left(\dfrac{9}{10}\right)^6 = 0.469$

(b) $_6C_1\left(\dfrac{9}{10}\right)^1\left(\dfrac{1}{10}\right)^5 = \dfrac{54}{10^6} = 0.000054$

3. $P(E \cup F) = 0.7$

Problem Set 5.7

1. (a) $P(E/F) = \dfrac{0.1}{0.2} = \dfrac{1}{2}$

(b) $P(F/E) = \dfrac{0.1}{0.5} = \dfrac{1}{5}$

(c) Yes (E and F are independent).

3. (a) $P(K/L) = \frac{1}{2}$
(b) $P(L/K) = \frac{1}{2}$
(c) No (L and K are not independent).

5. (a) $\dfrac{(0.25)(0.001)}{(0.1)(0.01) + (0.2)(0.01) + (0.15)(0.02) + (0.25)(0.001) + (0.30)(0.02)}$

$= \dfrac{0.00025}{0.01225} = 0.0204081 \approx 0.02$

(b) $\dfrac{(0.15)(0.02)}{0.01225} = \dfrac{0.003}{0.01225} \approx 0.245$

7. (a) $P(E \cap F) = 0.1$
(b) $P(E) = 0.25$

Problem Set 5.8

1. ${}_4C_4(0.8)^4(0.2)^0 = (0.8)^4 = 0.4096$

3. ${}_3C_2(0.99)^2(0.01) + {}_3C_3(0.99)^3(0.01)^0 = 0.029403 + 0.970299 = 0.999702$

5. $(0.001)^3 = 0.000000001$, or 10^{-9}

Problem Set 6.1

1. (a) 7.6
(b) 7
(c) 7
(d) 7
(e) 4.04
(f) 2.01

3. (a) Section 1: $\bar{X} = 75.4$, Md $= 75$, Mo $= 70$
Section 2: $\bar{X} = 74.8$, Md $= 77.5$, Mo does not exist.
(b) Section 1: $s^2 = 29.24$, $s = 5.41$, range $= 14$
Section 2: $s^2 = 178.36$, $s = 13.36$, range $= 43$

5.

Distribution A	Distribution B
$\bar{X} = 15.00$	$\bar{X} = 27.58$
$s = 7.53$	$s = 6.87$
Range $= 25.00$	Range $= 21.00$

7. (a) $\bar{X} = 14.91$; Md $= 13.00$; Mo $= 9.00$; Range $= 20.00$; $S = 7.05$
  (b) $\bar{X} = 14.09$; Md $= 14.00$; Mo $= 14.00$; Range $= 18.00$; $S = 5.61$
  (c) $\bar{X} = 37.68$; Md $= 37.00$; Mo $= 35.00$; Range $= 35.00$; $S = 9.73$

Problem Set 6.2

1.   66   DATA 10,75,70,82,81,68,70,70,75,81,82
         67   DATA 10,75,55,95,80,81,82,70,91,67,52
         RUN
         MEAN = 75.4 VARIANCE = 29.2406 ST. DEV. = 5.40746
         MEAN = 74.8 VARIANCE = 178.36 ST. DEV. = 13.3552
         *READY

3.   66   DATA 20,3.2,2.5,3.1,2.1,3.3,3.7,1.9,2.2,2.2,2.6,2.1,2.9
         67   DATA 2.8,3.6,3.0,2.0,3.5,2.2,2.6,3.1
         RUN
         MEAN = 2.73 VARIANCE = .308104 ST. DEV. = .555071
         *READY

Problem Set 6.3

1. (a) 0.1056
  (b) 0.0179
  (c) 0.8944
  (d) 0.9821
  (e) 0.4802
  (f) 0.0919
  (g) 0.1944
  (h) 0.5000
  (i) 0.9974
  (j) 0.0013

3. (a) 340 (to nearest integer)
  (b) 330.6 (331 to nearest integer)

5. (a) 0.1587
  (b) 0.7495

Problem Set 6.4

1. 0.0002 $(Z = -3.53)$

3. 0.3083 $(Z_1 \approx 0.50, Z_2 \approx 3.52)$

5. 0.9997 $(Z \approx 3.50)$

Problem Set 6.5

1.   150 DATA 200, .2, 20, 20, 1

3.   151 DATA 100, .01, 2, 4, 6

5.   152 DATA 1000, .001, 5, 5, 3

RUN

1.   FIND THE AREA TO THE LEFT OF Z = −3.53553

3.   FIND THE AREA BETWEEN Z = .502519 AND Z = 3.51763

5.   FIND THE AREA TO THE LEFT OF Z = 3.50175

Problem Set 6.6

90   DATA 27,64,76,62,60,65,65,74,70,55,61,78,87,51,30,64,80,84
91   DATA 73,46,58,37,48,91,70,70,33,65,70,10
92   DATA 21,90,67,85,67,65,75,82,78,84,70,98,74,48,90,61,78,95
93   DATA 70,66,100,70,70,10
100 END
RUN

X	Z	N
64	2.67082E-02	70.2671
76	.813382	78.1338
62	−.104404	68.9559
60	−.235516	67.6448
65	9.22644E-02	70.9226
65	9.22644E-02	70.9226
74	.68227	76.8227
70	.430045	74.2004
55	−.563297	64.367
61	−.16996	68.3004
78	.944494	79.4449
87	1.5345	85.345
51	−.825522	61.7448
30	−2.2022	47.978
64	2.67082E-02	70.2671
80	1.07561	80.7561
84	1.33783	83.3783
73	.616714	76.1671
46	−1.1533	58.467
58	−.366629	66.3337
37	−1.74331	52.5669
48	−1.02219	59.7781
91	1.79672	87.9672
70	.420045	74.2004
70	.420045	74.2004
33	−2.00553	49.9447
65	9.22644E-02	70.9226

X	Z	N
90	1.02272	80.2272
67	−.760575	62.3942
85	.635045	76.3504
67	−.760575	62.3942
65	−.915644	60.8436
75	−.140299	68.597
82	.402442	74.0244
78	9.23041E-02	70.923
84	.557511	75.5751
70	−.527972	64.7203
98	1.64299	86.4299
74	−.217834	67.8217
48	−2.23373	47.6627
90	1.02272	80.2272
61	−1.22578	57.7422
78	9.23041E-02	70.923
95	1.41039	84.1039
70	−.527972	64.7203
66	−.83811	61.6189
100	1.79806	87.9806
70	−.527972	64.7203
X	Z	N

LINE 10: END OF DATA
TIME 0.0 SECONDS

Problem Set G.1

1.
```
10  PRINT INT(−2.7),INT(3.891),INT(−2/9)
20  END
```

2.
```
10  FOR I=1 TO 3
20  PRINT INT(10*RND(8)+1)
30  NEXT I
40  END
```

3.
```
10  DIM N(6)
20  FOR I=1 TO 6
30  LET N(I)=INT(10*RND(8))
40  NEXT I
50  FOR J=6 TO 1 STEP −1
60  PRINT N(J);
70  NEXT J
80  END
```

5.
```
10  PRINT INT(28*RND(8)+27)
20  PRINT INT(500*RND(8)+1)
30  PRINT INT(31*RND(8)+60)
40  END
```

Problem Set G.2

1.
```
10  DIM A$(30)
20  PRINT "ENTER YOUR NAME IN QUOTES"
30  PRINT "FOLLOWED BY YOUR AGE"
40  INPUT A$,B
50  IF B> =21 THEN 70
60  GO TO 20
70  PRINT A$,B
80  GO TO 20
90  END
```

3. OUTPUT:

LOU	27
SUE	29
CLARA	51
BOB	62
ANNIE	97

4. Replace statement 50 by:
```
50  IF B> =65 THEN 20
55  IF B>29 THEN 70
```

5. OUTPUT:

A$ DOES NOT EQUAL B$
A$ DOES NOT EQUAL B$
A$ = B$ ABC⎫
A$ = B$ ABC⎭ repeated infinitely often

6. (a) Is improperly nested.